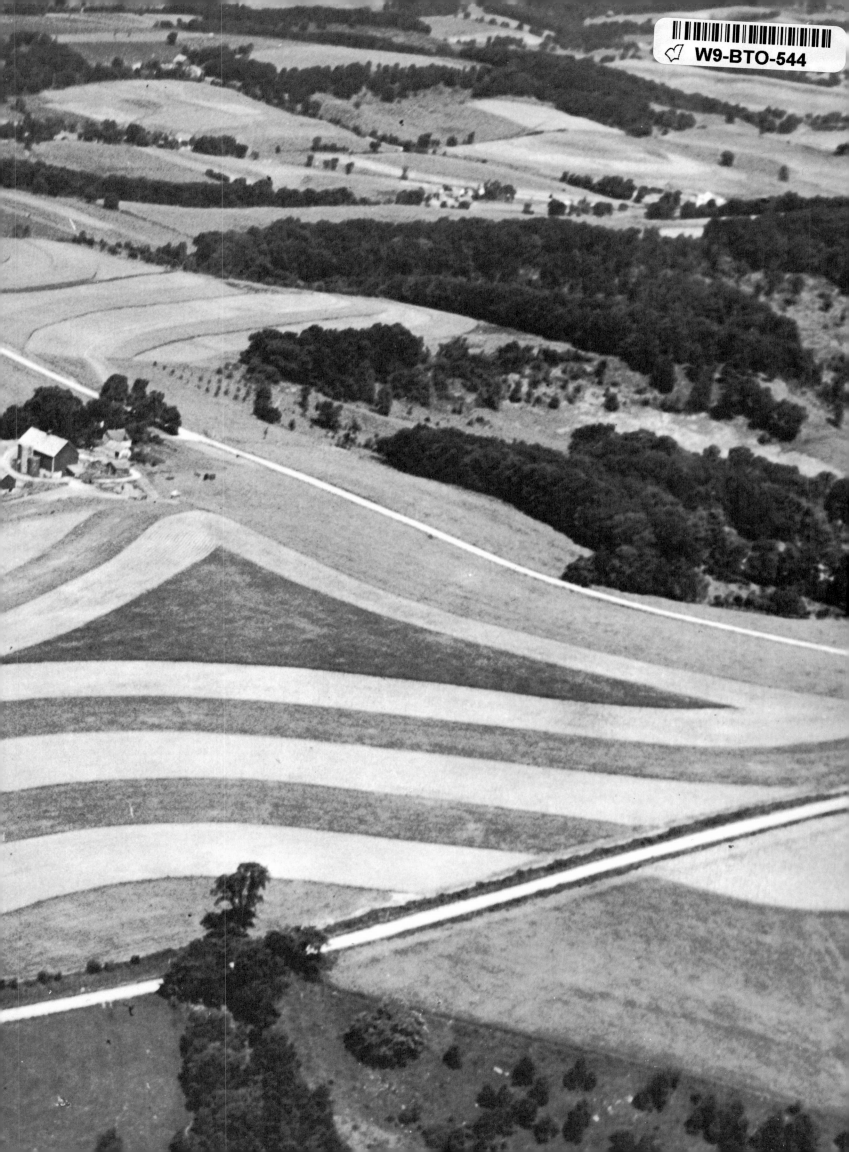

# The
# GOOD LIFE

*An intimate portrait*
*of life on the farms of America*

Edited by
## FREDERIC  B.  KNOOP
with Kirk Polking and the staff of The Farm Quarterly

# Foreword

*It takes more business skill, more scientific aware-ness and more patience than either God or the govern-ment usually allows, to be an American farmer today. But for many a harassed, city-bound executive, as well as the man whose life has always been the soil, the insistent dream is "a farm of my own."*

*To these men who feel that with all its frustra-tions, farming is still the one best way of life, this book is affectionately dedicated.*

*In our previous volume "The Good Old Days," we recalled life on the farm of fifty years ago.*

*Here, in "The Good Life," we show the farmers of America in the joys and struggles of farming today.*

# Contents

# Contents

In broad strokes of color, Spring brings her blossoms to a climax with whole hillsides of flowering fruit trees.

# The Signs of Spring

**W**HEN the spring sun warms the hillsides it is pleasant to sit down-wind from an orchard in bloom and breathe the laden air. The high-pitched hum of the bees as they go about their work of pollination is music to the farmer's ears, for it is a prediction of abundant harvests to come.

An orchard in flower is a bold gesture of nature. To see some of her shyer blossoms we must go into the deep woods. There, in spring, when wild flowers are at their best, you are surrounded by the sounds and smells of the earth coming back to life. If the day is still you can hear the dry leaves stir and rustle as the Jack-in-the-pulpit and the Dog Tooth Violet push their green shoots upward.

Only a few generations ago our country was all like this, a land of forests and swamps broken only by the treeless prairies. In the shade of the forests grew many beautiful wild flowers; in the swamps flourished bog-loving plants, among them some of our native orchids, cousins of the exotic greenhouse species.

The Moccasin Flower or Pink Lady's Slipper likes the acid soil of pine and oak woods. Just to be sure it will be seen, it hangs its flowers like jack-o-lanterns on graceful pikes.

When the Europeans arrived here they were amazed at the abundance and variety of our wild flowers. The English, in particular, sent over plant collectors to take back to their country specimens of our native plants which are now honored occupants of their gardens. Even today they are still developing some of our goldenrods and use them as accents in garden borders.

With the settling of our country came the need for fields and pastures to grow our grain and feed our cattle and horses. Our woodlands were pastured, destroying the wildflowers. Forests were cut down and swamps drained and filled. Farmland replaced wilderness and crops and livestock prospered. Wild plants disappeared because their woods and swamps had been destroyed. As towns and cities developed and population increased, more and more wild areas fell victim to the march of progress.

In recent years this encroachment upon our woodlands has alarmed those who like unspoiled nature. Today there are numerous organizations devoted to the preservation of our vanishing wildlife. Nature and wild flower sanctuaries have been established in many sections of the country.

Without any great effort, a farmer's wife can take under her protection a small piece of woodland, perhaps only a quarter of an acre, and bring to life the native wild flowers of her part of the country. If she chooses a spot near the edge of the woods which is near the house and can prevail upon her husband to fence it against the intrusion of cattle and hogs, she will have an excellent location for her wild garden. In fact, nature will have started it for her with the wild flowers that already grow there. Not only can she watch over these, but, keeping in mind the terrain of her woodlot, she can plant new species.

In general, woodland areas can be divided into two types, the first, open, dry, rocky woods and wooded hillsides; the second, cool, shaded, deep and damp woodland. Both types of terrain are liked by many species of flowering plants and shrubs. Woodlands of the first type are good locations for Rue Anemone, Wood Anemone, Hepatica, Spring Beauty, Early Saxifrage, Columbine, Foamflower, Yellow Violet, Lousewort, Dutchman's Breeches, Squirrel Corn, Pipsissewa, Spotted Wintergreen, Round-leaved Pyrola, Pink Lady's Slipper also known as the Moccasin Flower and Trailing Arbutus. The last two wild flowers are particularly fond of pine and oak woods where the Mountain Laurel grows.

Wild flowers which prefer the second type of woodland are Jack-in-the-Pulpit, Wild Geranium, Bellwort, Yellow Clintonia, Canada Mayflower, Indian Cucumber Root, Yellow Lady's Slipper, Partridge Berry, Wake Robin or Red Trillium, Showy Orchis, Wild Ginger, Red Baneberry, White Baneberry, Bloodroot, Fawn Lily or Dog Tooth Violet, Cut-leaved Toothwort, Crinkleroot or Two-leaved Toothwort, Herb Robert, Sweet White Violet, Wild Sarsaparilla, Bunchberry, Twinflower and Wintergreen. The last three favor evergreen woodlands in mountainous regions and are frequently found growing together.

These are the descriptive and colorful names our early settlers gave native plants. In the variety of blooms and leaves the plants are rugged individualists, too.

Sheltered by rocks from rough intruders, a farm woman's own private garden turns a flowery face to the spring sun.

Dutchman's breeches is a light and humorous touch of nature.

Columbine in its wild state brings a flaming area of color to shady spots.

A delicate patch of color in the midst of large, ornate leaves: the Wild Geranium.

Dog Tooth Violet likes the leaf-carpeted hillsides.

After the type of woodland terrain has been determined and a section of the woodlot chosen for the wild garden, it is a good idea to check the species already growing there against the list of those that could grow there. Rarely, if ever, does a limited stretch of woodland contain all the species of wildflowers possible to grow there. Nearly all the missing ones can be brought in from other parts of the woodlot or from a friend's property. Sometimes, due to road building or other construction, certain plants are marked for destruction. Saving these from the jaws of the bulldozer will increase the population of the wild garden and serve the interests of conservation as well.

Preparing the woodlot for a wild garden requires very little time and effort. No extensive clean-up of the ground is necessary. Some of the dead wood and underbrush can be removed, but the surface of the ground should not be disturbed by rake or hoe.

Dead leaves should remain on the ground where they are. They are the mulch or protection which nature gives to woodland plants. Eventually they rot and become the humus on which the plants depend for nourishment.

Plants which are to be moved from one location to another should be dug up with plenty of soil protecting the roots, packed in damp newspaper and kept moist. If they cannot be transplanted immediately, they should be placed in a cool, shady spot and watered. Replanting usually presents no difficulties if the hole is well watered before the plant is set in and the earth kept moist for several days until the plant is established in its new home.

If wild flowers are brought from a nursery they usually come as roots or bulbs, ready to put in the ground. October or November is probably the best time to bring in the newcomers for they will acclimate themselves to their new habitat over the winter and blossom at their appointed time the following spring. Planting depth for roots can be supplied by the nurseryman. Seeds should be sown and firmed down lightly. A burlap cover over the winter will protect them from extreme cold or heavy rains. This can be removed in April.

Once established, the wild garden will grow and become an ever-increasing source of pleasure. Each spring there will be the pleasure of welcoming nature's own wild blossoms.

# A Bill for Horace's Bull

ONE warm spring day we went out and bought ourselves four Jersey heifer calves, fawnlike little creatures with large, dreamy eyes and satin coats. They were aristocrats, descended from many generations of high-producing ancestors, and with them as a beginning we hoped to establish a pure-bred dairy herd.

During summer and fall they grazed the lower pasture. They drank from the tiny brook which meanders through the meadow, licked the big block of salt placed in one corner, lined up morning and night for their ration of grain, and they grew amazingly.

Fall merged into winter. Now their home was in the little stone barn, and in place of grass they ate clover hay from a big rack. Twice a day, no matter what the weather, we let them out. They would start at a walk down toward the brook, then suddenly break into a wild, eccentric gallop, tails raised, heads and rumps tossing. After their drink they would return slowly across the frozen ground, nosing at tufts of dead grass in a reminiscent sort of way.

The next spring they went out on pasture again, much larger now, and already losing their baby contours. They grew rapidly during May and June and July. Then we found that the grass in their pasture was getting very short. There wasn't room in the other pastures for them, so we went over to see our neighbor, Horace.

Horace has a large farm, mostly neglected pastures and broken-down barns and sagging gates. He's always just about to get the place spruced up, but something always comes along. So he puts it off. Yes, he told us, he had a nice pasture that he'd be willing to rent for the balance of the summer.

We looked it over; lush grass with a fair sprinkling of clover, two big oak trees for shade, a good brook. The fence, however, was down in half a dozen places. Horace said he didn't have time to repair it, but if we would do the work we could have the pasture for five dollars a month. It was high, but there wasn't any choice.

We fixed the fence; braced all the corner posts and strung new wire where needed, which was in a lot of places. When everything was in shipshape we led the heifers over. For fifty cents a week Horace agreed to feed them their grain, which we supplied. Every Sunday we walked over and looked at them. They certainly were making fine heifers.

When the first heavy frost arrived we brought them back to the barn, after paying Horace. We had found, not far off, an exceptionally fine Jersey bull, and had made arrangements to have the heifers bred in December. Then, the following fall, we would have four heifers giving milk and four more little calves to go on with. We hoped they would all be heifer calves, and be as good as their dams.

On election day Horace dropped around to see us. We figured he had a favorite candidate to recommend, a little late, to be sure, but that was his way. However, during the next half-hour his conversation covered a dozen subjects, none of them related to politics. We knew he wanted something and was working up to it, as they do in these parts. To come right to the point and bring up the business which had brought him over would have been a grave breach of manners in our neighborhood.

Horace covered the weather pretty thoroughly and skimmed through crop prospects. He mentioned the health of several ailing neighbors and finally got round to his bull. We had seen Horace's bull; at least that is what Horace called him. He looked like a bad caricature of Ferdinand; wicked little head with vicious red eyes and short, stubby

The dainty heifers were thankful for the steel-strand fence.

legs. His rump skidded off suddenly from the saddle like a ski run and he had a skinny chest and underneath was hung a great kettle of a belly.

"Yes, sir," said Horace, "he's some bull. He's got Holstein and Guernsey and Brown Swiss into him, and maybe some of this here Black Anguish."

As Horace closed his song of praise for his bull of many colors, he fished a paper out of his pocket.

"I just happen to remember I've got a little bill for you here." So that was it. Horace was up to his Yankee tricks again. "A bill? We paid you for the pasture rent, and for feeding the heifers. I've got the receipt here, and the cancelled check." Horace arranged his face in an embarrassed grin. "Oh, sure, that's all right; this is something different. You see, that bull of mine is a great jumper. He got so he could go right over the top of that barbed wire fence without touching it.

"I guess he bred all four of your heifers. Usually I charge a dollar apiece for breeding fees, but see-ing as how those heifers are something special I'll have to charge a little more; say six dollars for the lot. That be all right with you?"

We stood speechless. As we say around here, "Horace had knocked our props out from under." Our heifers would produce, some time around midsummer, mongrel calves, worth nothing except as veal. It would put our whole breeding program back a full year. And here was Horace handing me a paper on which he had scrawled, "Breeding 4 heffers . . . $6."

"Horace," I said, "I think you had better be getting home. I've just had some very bad news, and I'm pretty much upset. As for your bill, I'll take care of that right now." I slowly tore it into small pieces and tossed them into the grass. "You ought to know better than to try anything like that on me!"

Horace grinned uncertainly. "Well, can't blame a feller fer tryin', can you?"

Horace's bull wore a perpetual leer.

# Spring Weeds You Can Eat

WHEN your worries disappear—as though a mist had been lifted from the brain—and the warm air and sparkling sunshine show you the fallacy of work and the desirability of lying down on the new grass for a spell—a mess of greens is in order to celebrate the arrival of Spring. The greens will be there, for before men have discovered in their blood—quite apart from their calendars—that Spring has come, the plants have known it for some time and have sent up their tenderest, most succulent shoots and leaves and stalks.

Even before the snows have left the ground, the shiny green leaves of the winter cress have spread out like rays from a central crown and are ready to be gathered, cooked in two or three waters—for they are sometimes called *bitter cress,* and rightly so —and eaten as the first green food from the land. Dandelions and the common chickweed are ready for the pot almost as soon and together they make a good combination; the mild spinach-tasting chickweed blending with the more bitter dandelion. And then come a whole procession of the wild weeds that can be eaten, the marsh marigold and shepherd's purse, fireweed, penny cress, poke, and a whole host of the dock family—narrow dock, bitter dock, spinach dock, curled dock—and the leaves of the early blue violet and wake robin, and plants with such inedible names as skunk cabbage and bellwort.

In May and Summer come so many wild greens— plants like corn salad, stinging nettle, wild lettuce, ostrich fern and sow thistle, pepper grass, touch-me-not, lamb's quarters, scarlet pimpernel, and milk weed—that it is a wonder we bother to plant a garden at all. Being human and contrary, we chop these weeds out of our gardens and hunt for them in the fence-row and the wood lot and down by the creek.

One might even take a measure of revenge when gathering greens by eating the roots of the bothersome crab grass (which can be dried, ground, and used as flour) or the leaves of the wild onion or scotch thistle or stinging nettle, but green gathering is not a matter of spite or vengeance—the true lover of potherbs eats them because they are the most welcome food in the world at this time of the year. Once you have eaten a mess of greens prepared by a master cook such as Hattie Givens, you'll never let a Spring go by without thinning your blood with greens. They don't really thin the blood, of course. Quite the contrary, they bring to the blood the minerals and nourishment which the deep-rooted weeds have found in the lower soils. Mainly they have notified the inner man that it is Spring and he feels lighter, more buoyant—perhaps even thinner.

Hattie Givens is a large, friendly woman who comes by her knowledge of greens and how to cook them from her ancestors who learned the economy of potherbs in the old South. She is the kind of cook who can feed you forever on greens and a little smoked and salted hog jowl without tiring you. In the Spring she often puts on her wide-brimmed, black, summer hat and takes her nephew Rickie by the hand and wanders through the vacant lots and the fields and along the banks of the Licking River near her home in Kentucky hunting out black mustard and narrow dock (pronounced as though it were one word, narradock), and the other weeds which go into a mess of greens. Rickie industriously gathers blades of grass and leaves of trees and any other growing things within reach. Once when she asked him, "Rickie, what kind of greens you gathering?" he gave her a one-word answer, "Meat." Sometimes she visits a friend's farm for a green hunt. "This is Givens," she will say on the phone, "I have a little piece of jowl I was intending to bring out sometime you are home."

She has an enthusiastic though inaccurate memory as to birthdays and often sends a card or brings a small present to a startled child in mid-year and

"There's nothing like dandelion greens," agrees Rickie's friend, Jimmy McDonald. "I like 'em fresh-picked with hot sugar-vinegar poured on."

has been known to celebrate more than one birthday for the same child during the same year. She is as generous with her herb lore as she is with her birthday wishes. "In the first of Spring, dandelion, narradock, and black mustard comes the earliest and makes a good combination," she said as she sat on a camp stool for which she was dangerously large, culling through a basket of greens, throwing out some plants which were too tough and some poisonous peach leaves and grass stems (Rickie's contributions). "You mix them about even for each one. Later I like to get a mess of dandelions, narradock, shepherd's sprout, black mustard, and poke together and, if I can find water cress, I put in a very small amount because it's so bitter. My, my, you just can't eat much of it. And if you like greens with a little extra flavor, like I do, you put in a little piece of red pod pepper.

"When you go to cooking the greens," Mrs. Givens continued in her pleasant, soft voice as she stopped Rickie from dismembering a poke plant, "remember that the ones that are a little bitter, like poke, dandelion, wild onion, winter cress, skunk cabbage, or milk weed, should be washed good and then put in a pan and covered with boiling water to draw out the bitter. You boil them for just a minute and the water gets green; then you pour it off and put them in the cooking pot. Sometimes, if they are big plants, I scald them again before I put them in with the other greens.

"You cook them in water with bacon drippings or bacon or hog jowl with one pound of greens to a quart of water. If you use salt-cured bacon or jowl you don't need no salt, else-wise use a half-teaspoonful to the quart of water. Don't try to use butter in cooking them—it isn't a stout enough grease—and you don't need butter on them to eat if you've cooked them proper with jowl. Some folks put a little lemon on the greens, but I like vinegar better because it's more tart. Only cook the greens until they're tender; if you cook them too long, it takes away the flavor. If Rickie will stop helping me and let me get done here, I'll show you how it's done directly."

Among the greens which Mrs. Givens uses as stand-bys are poke, narrow dock, lamb's quarters, wild lettuce, black mustard, shepherd's purse, dandelion, wild cabbage, and water cress.

# How to tell eatin' weeds when you see them:

**POKE:** In late summer pokeweed stands eight to ten feet tall, branching like a tree from its heavy, woody stem. Its branches are usually covered with loose clusters of purple grapes which the birds love and which make a good wine. The ripe seeds can also be used to make ink. The leaves and stems are valueless at this time, but they do serve as good markers in the spring when you can spot the white skeletons of the  old plants and find the tender, green stalks pushing up from the old roots. These fat stalks with their leaves furled around them are best when gathered at around six to eight inches tall. Then they can be washed, scalded for a minute, and cooked whole. Later, when they grow a foot tall, the lower part of the stem is not used—just the leaves and the tip. When gathering poke don't try to cut it off below the ground level, the roots are bitter and, what is more, *poisonous*. Poke is most often eaten alone, like asparagus, though pleasanter, but it also goes well with other greens.

**NARROW-DOCK:** Even when gathered early, narrow dock has a coarser, tougher leaf than most of the other greens. In the spring the thick rosette of leaves seems to fight for space on lawns and in the fields. The leaves are short-stemmed with a blade three or four inches long which has a peculiar wavy margin—the plant is sometimes called curly dock because of the wavy leaves.

**LAMB'S QUARTER:** The Greeks called this plant Goosefoot because the pointed, toothed, pale bluish-green leaves, which are one to four inches long, resemble the footprint of a goose. The leaves and tip of the plant are gathered in early summer before the plant branches out. They cook down more than most greens so that you should gather about three times as much as you think you will need.

**WATER CRESS:** The crisp, tasty water cress should only be gathered by those who know the plant well since there are two important dangers present. Usually where you find water cress, you also find the deadly water hemlock which might possibly be confused with it. The second danger is contamination of the water. It is safest to wash the cress in chlorinated water to make sure that it is clean.

**WILD LETTUCE:** The deeply-indented leaves of the wild lettuce, which look a little like dandelion leaves, develop prickles when they grow older so they should be gathered before the plant reaches 15 or 18 inches high. This is one of the plants which should be put through one or two scalding waters to leach out the bitterness. Cold, cooked lettuce makes an excellent salad with mayonnaise as do poke and dandelion greens.

**BLACK MUSTARD:** Mustard plasters and hot-dog mustard are made from the seeds of this plant; its leaves make an excellent potherb. The plant is most easily recognized by its bright yellow flowers sprinkled over its branches and by the leaves which are long and slender near the flower heads and wide with deep-toothed indentations near the bottom of the plant. Its flowers are yellow, its leaves and stem are green, and its seeds are dark brown, which leaves its name a mystery.

**SHEPHERD'S PURSE:** The base leaves of the shepherd's purse look like an extremely vigorous dandelion plant. From the center of this crown of leaves grows a slender stalk a couple of feet high with leaves shaped something like thin arrowheads. The leaves at the base of the plant are the ones gathered for greens.

These are only the main greens used in cooking by Mrs. Givens and only a tiny fraction of the edible wild plants described in such authoritative books as *Edible Wild Plants of Eastern North America* by Fernald and Kinsey or *Edible Wild Plants* by Medsger. Here you can find lists of plants for soups and plants for flour, and for tea, and for starchy vegetables, and even for chewing gum. They also tell how to make the most out of such plants as milkweed whose shoots can be eaten as asparagus, the flowers as a green, and the immature pods as a boiled vegetable, and, oh yes, the sap can be dried and chewed as gum. And they give directions on converting the cat-tails that grow along the bank of the pond into a year-round food supply using the short thick shoots from the root stock as a salad and cooked vegetable in the autumn and win-

ter, the peeled young stems in the spring as something to nibble on, the flowering spikes before the pollen comes as a boiled vegetable eaten off the stem like a lolly-pop, and the pollen as a flour for making bread.

Once you get started finding edible greens you will not be limited by the book—only guided by what the Indians and others have found good and warned by the list of poisonous plants. Not listed, for example, is a plant which a Wisconsin pasture expert claims is delicious as a salad—ladino leaves. His cattle tuck away tons of it during the season and he and his family use a pound or two of the fresh leaves served alone with a French dressing or in a mixed green salad. "It is the greatest pasture crop for hogs, cattle, or man that I know about," he says as a testimonial. "I've eaten lots of it and I like it."

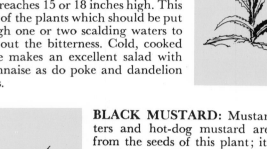

## How to make old-fashioned Dandelion Wine

Everyone who has ever been off the concrete slab of the city knows the dandelion; not too many, however, know how to convert it into a delicious, powerful amber wine. The leaves are eaten early in the spring before the yellow flowers come. When the plant blooms, it is wine making time. Mrs. Givens makes five-gallon lots of wine with the following recipe: "Pick a peck of dandelion blooms and put them into a five-gallon crock. Pour five pounds of sugar over them in four and a half gallons of boiling water. You let it cool right down to luke-warm so it won't kill the yeast and then add two cakes of yeast crumbled up. Stir the wine every day for fifteen days when it should be through working and then strain it through two cloth strainers. The wine is pale yellow. It is ready to be drunk or bottled for later."

## How to stay friendly with Uncle Sam while doing it

The Internal Revenue Service of the U. S. Treasury Department says: "In order to produce wine for family use, the head of the family must file Form 1541, 'Registration for Production of Wine for Family Use,' with the Assistant Regional Commissioner, Alcohol and Tobacco Tax, of the region in which the applicant resides.

"This registration is not continuing and a new form must be submitted each succeeding year during which it is desired to produce wine for family use, the year to be reckoned as commencing on July 1 and ending on June 30 following.

"Forms 1541 are available at the office of your nearest Assistant Regional Commissioner, or from the Internal Revenue Service, Washington 25, D.C."

The Internal Revenue Service also cautions producers that they must comply with any state requirements, since the legality of production of wine for family use varies from state to state.

# The Good Shepherd

"YES, SIR, that's right, I shear the ewes twice a year, in May and again in August. I know I'm not going to get much for me wool in August, but it's worth the effort the way shearing gets the ewes to settle." Those are the words of Harold Barber, the gnomelike English shepherd and head herdsman at the University of Kentucky Experiment Station. For more than thirty years, Barber has been showing Kentucky farmers how to take the guesswork out of the sheep business. His accent still smacks of his native English countryside, but his advice on sheep is distinctly for the sheep grower, wherever he may be.

His opinion on the value of shearing ewes twice a year came in answer to a question from a young Kentucky farmer, Bob Stanley. Stanley had been "foolin' around with sheep," as he put it, most of his life. His father always had a flock on the home-place. Just took them more or less for granted. They kept the place cleaned up, supplied a little income from wool and lamb, and that was it. Now, he wanted to do more with them.

Kentuckians are lucky that way. All they have to do is drop over to Lexington and they can talk over their sheep problems with two of the country's top experts on farm flocks—Barber, the little Englishman, and Richard Miller.

Miller took a trip to Australia and New Zealand a good many years back, saw the famous Canterbury lambs, and came back to Kentucky with The Idea that sparked the phenomenally successful Kentucky spring lamb program.

Working with Miller is Barber, whom associates and competitors alike refer to as the world's greatest shepherd. Bob Stanley came here for advice. Now he is getting it straight from the shoulder.

" 'Ow did we get on this business of shearing so soon?" Barber asks. "Let's go back and start at the beginning. You want to know 'ow to do a better job with your flock. Let me tell you just like I'd tell one of me boys here.

"You have sheep, so I don't have to tell you what to start with. To keep things straight, when you're just getting into it, work with not more than twenty-five or fifty ewes, a one or two-ram flock. Use purebred rams on crossbred Western ewes. For a commercial flock there's no point in using native ewes or in trying to save your ewe lambs for replacements."

"How do you select your ewes?" is Stanley's first question. Barber is ready with the answer. "Meself, I like the dark-faced, speckled-faced, or grey-faced ewe. They are good mothers, good milkers, very prolific and good shearers. Most of them are a Rambouillet-Hampshire cross. You'll get a lot of three-eights wool off them.

"I don't want a ewe that is stingy and shallow-bodied, but I don't want her too short coupled either. She has to have room to carry a pair of twins. She must have good length from shoulder to flank. And I don't want her wooled up in the head. A ewe with a clean face is a much better suckler than a ewe that's heavy wooled in the head. That's been my experience both with grades and purebreds."

Stanley was skeptical about how a wooled-up head could affect a ewe's milk supply, and he said so. Barber was quick with his answer. "I know every ewe in my flock like one of my family. I know every good suckler and I know every bad suckler and most all my bad sucklers are ewes that are heavy wooled in the head. 'Ow do I know? I can look at a lamb and see that bloom on him, that's 'ow I know.

"A ewe's leg must set well outside her, too, and she must be up on her pasterns so she can get around. Frank Goff, one of the best horse judges over in the old country, once told me, ' 'Arold, if you ever judge 'orses, let 'em walk. If they can walk good they can do something else.' That's the way it is with sheep, too."

### Picking the Ram

As Barber stops to light the stump of his cigar, Stanley asks, "What about the ram?"

"Purebred," replies Barber. He says that he has a personal preference for Southdowns and Hampshires. He likes the Southdown because it will get a quality lamb and the ewes have less trouble in lambing. He likes to use them on ewes that are having their first lambs, recommends using Hampshires later. The Hamps, in his opinion, get bigger, faster-gaining lambs that will hit the market a month to five weeks earlier. This cross, he explains, will have less quality, however, and the lambs won't hold their condition in the hot weather like the Southdown-cross lambs. Because of this, he creep feeds his Hampshire-sired lambs all the way through while he creep feeds his Southdown cross early and depends on pasture later. It is this kind of detail in raising stock that sets a man apart.

In selecting bucks, just as in picking his ewes, he puts a lot of emphasis on how they walk. "I want to see him stay together when he walks," is the way he puts it. "I don't want to see his shoulder blades working up and down. While I want length in the ewes, I want my rams short coupled. The packer buyer doesn't want a stringy lamb. He wants one that's coupled up. Jonas Weil, he was a packer buyer and a good one, said to me once, ' 'Arold, I like these lambs that grow sideways.' That's just the kind you want, the kind that fill out fast. When you're using long-bodied ewes it takes a short-coupled ram to make that kind.

"Then I want a ram that will handle, one that touches well. If I go to buy a ram from a man who has twenty-five or thirty for sale, I'll ask him, 'Have these rams all been raised the same? Have they all been fed the same?' Then I can close my eyes and touch those rams on the back and tell which one I want. I like that old rubbery touch. It's like when you put your hand on a basketball that isn't fully blown up. It'll spring right back at you.

"A ram should be short legged and his legs should be deep in his twist and thick in the leg. That's where your high-priced cuts are. And I want a short-necked ram. I don't like a necky sheep and the packer buyer don't like a necky lamb. Who buys neck meat?"

The Barber standard calls for a small head not wooled too heavily. His argument here is that the packer buyer cuts the head off and throws it away; also, the ewe has an easier time lambing a lamb with a small head. He is careful to point out that this is in regard to the ram selected for the commercial flock. For a purebred flock he favors the buck with a lot of strength and character in his head.

And he wants all these qualities wrapped up and put together in a ram with plenty of life about him. "I don't want no dead 'ead," he says. "I like the kind that when you go to ketch him here, he's over there, and when you go to ketch him there, he's here. They're fertile."

"I have too many barren ewes," Stanley says. "How can I get them to settle together?"

With a lift of his eyebrows, the grizzled little shepherd slips into a philosophical mood. "It's a funny thing about lambing down a bunch of ewes," he says. "I've been taking care of sheep since I was a kid in me teens. Give a bunch of ewes the same feed and the same treatment year after year and one year you'll have good luck and one year you'll

# Fooling a ewe into owning an orphan lamb

Ewes are stubborn about nursing any but their own lambs. This is how Barber makes the mother of a dead lamb accept an orphan. First, he skins the dead lamb.

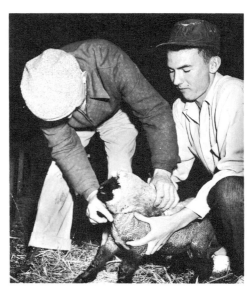

Then he slips the hide over the orphan, attaching it by bands of skin at the neck and ankles.

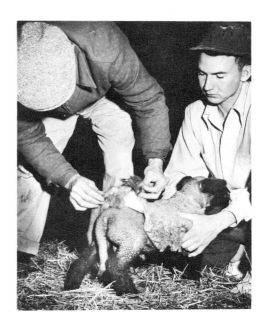

Fooled by the hide of Esau the ewe turns over her own lamb's birthright to the orphan, for three square meals a day.

have poor luck. Comparatively speaking, of course. A good shepherd is never going to have as much trouble.

"Take now last year. I had more ewes settle to the rams than ever before. I only had four barren ewes. This year I had practically the same bunch of ewes—ninety-two of 'em—and the same rams bred some of these ewes five times before they settled. I think the reason is, I didn't shear me ewes in August last season and the season before I did.

"I'd always advise a man to shear his ewes before he turns the bucks in. It's a big help in bunching up the lambing season.

"When to start breeding depends on whether a man can handle early lambs. Meself, I like to get me lambs in January and February so I can get them on the market before hot weather. In Indiana and Ohio I notice they get a lot of lambs in April. But I like 'em early. And most farmers down here can handle them early. They have tobacco barns with a stripping room where they can have a fire and hot water. Pick your lambing date, count backwards five months and that's when to start breeding."

"Is there anything else a man can do to bunch up?" Stanley asks, remembering the spread between his first and last lambs.

"Flushing the ewes will help to bring them all in heat in a short period," Barber answers. "Fresh, lush pasture about two weeks before breeding is fine for flushing ewes. We like bluegrass, but if you don't have it feed some grain, or plant rape and oats in May—nine pounds of rape and a bushel of oats per acre—that'll make good pasture by late summer. Flushing is an old sheepman's term, but all it means is to get the ewes gaining in flesh and condition."

If pasture is poor and a farmer has to feed grain, Barber advises straight corn, about a half pound a day starting about two weeks before breeding. The grain feeding should be stopped when the ewes start coming in heat. Barber believes a ewe should gain twenty-five or thirty pounds from the day she is bred to the day she lambs, but she should not get too fat. Too much fat causes hard lambing and she won't suckle well.

The ram needs attention at this time, too. They should have a late-summer shearing—"They'll work better," Barber says. Too much grain is as bad for the rams as for ewes. His rams get no corn. A quarter to a half pound a day of a mixture of three tubs of rolled oats, one tub of bran and a pailful of linseed oil meal is his favorite ram ration.

"And keep them cool," he warns. "Run 'em in a cool spot in the barn during the day, if you can, a spot where there's a little breeze stirring, and kick them out nights. Heat is hard on a ram. Ninety degrees will stop most of 'em cold.

"We test all our rams before we put them with the flock and we test them during the season, too. Some time back we bought a good ram up in Ohio. We tested him and he was a real live one when we put him with the ewes. Then a few weeks later it got pretty warm and we tested him again and he was blank! He wasn't worth 'ooray!'"

The rams at the experiment station are tested by examining a specimen of semen under a microscope to check the motility of the sperm. This is a quick and effective way of spotting an infertile buck; much better than letting a bunch of barren ewes tell the sad tale later at lambing time.

### Mark the Ewes

"I've always been told that a ram shouldn't be asked to handle more than twenty-five or thirty ewes; is that right?" asks Stanley.

"Yes," says Barber. "If I have a large flock and the place is fenced for it, I like to split my ewes into bunches of twenty-five and put a ram in with each bunch. A lot of fellows will put four rams with a hundred ewes, but if one or two of the rams aren't fertile that puts all the work on the others. A ewe goes fourteen to sixteen days between heat periods, so if you use a ram to every bunch of twenty-five ewes and switch them around every thirty days you're going to have a much better chance of catching any sterile rams.

"You want to pay particular attention to your ewes to see if they are settling properly. If you mark your rams under the brisket with marking powder mixed with oil and change the colors every fourteen to sixteen days, you'll be able to tell which of the ewes have been bred and which keep coming back to the buck. Those that have been bred will be stamped on the rump.

"A farmer should have some system for marking each ewe permanently when she's bred so he'll know at lambing time which are the forward ones. This business of looking over the flock and saying 'There's one with a big bag, I'll keep her up,' is no good. I know, I've done it meself. But you can't pay much attention to the bag on a ewe for when she's going to lamb. One ewe might have an udder with a lot of flesh on it and you'll think she's about ready;

another might have an udder without much flesh and her lamb will come before the other one's."

The Barber system works this way: The buck is turned into a bunch on a Monday, for example. At the end of the first week all the ewes that have been bred are marked with a red spot of branding fluid on the left shoulder. Those that are bred the second week get a spot on the near ribs; the mark for the third week is a spot on the near pin bone; the fourth week, on the off shoulder; the fifth week, on the off ribs; the sixth week on the off pin bone; the seventh week on the back of the neck; and the eighth week on the tip of the shoulder. Any of the early ewes that come back to the ram are respotted accordingly. Come lambing time it is then easy to pick out the ewes that are due and the whole flock doesn't have to be kept in the lambing barn at the same time.

### Lambing Time

"All right," says Stanley, "this brings us up to lambing time. How do I handle my flock then?"

"Well, of course, you'll have separated the bucks from the ewes long before then," continues Barber. "I usually take me bucks out in time to finish lambing in March. Then a month to five weeks before they expect any lambs, start feeding the ewes some grain. Start off with a quarter pound of whole corn and work up to a half pound just before lambing. Give them plenty of legume hay—alfalfa is the best.

"See that they have plenty of room—don't crowd them. That's mighty important. Don't crowd them at the hay rack or the grain troughs or through narrow doors or gateways. If you have your grain troughs down the middle of the barn have a rail above them so the ewes can't jump over them. Or have the grain troughs below the hay racks so the leaves won't be wasted.

"Give them plenty of good, clean water. Don't let any dirt get in it. They want it clean and if it has the least smell they won't drink it like they should.

"Make some lambing pens out of gates or panels. Have them about four feet six inches square. But don't put a ewe into one of these pens until she's lambed. Maybe we ought to call these mothering pens instead of lambing pens, because that's really what they're for, to keep the ewe and her lamb separate from the rest of the flock so she can mother him and keep him warm.

"Let her lamb in the barn, then put her and the lamb in the pen. If you put her in the pen before, she may have a lamb; then a twin comes. A pain hits her and she goes down on the first lamb and smothers it.

"Two or three days are enough to keep the ewe and lamb in the pen, depending on the strength of the lamb. Then you can turn them out with the flock. If there's a way to keep 'em separate I don't like to have my ewes and lambs running with the heavy ewes. The lambs are likely to jump up on the heavy ewes when they're lying down and that's hard on 'em."

"When a lamb is born always iodine his navel to prevent infection. When they get infection you might as well knock 'em in the head. It can clean a man out of the sheep business. Keeping your barn clean and using iodine on the navel right away, not hours later, will prevent it. I have my iodine in a big-mouth bottle, so I just pick up my lamb by the front legs and let his navel cord drop into the bottle.

"Sometimes a lamb is born that you'd think for sure is dead. Wipe the veil off his nose, blow down him, work his front legs, slap his ribs, pick him up by the hind legs and swing him. You'll usually get him going."

"What do you do with chilled lambs?" Stanley asks. "Take them in by the fire?"

"No," the shepherd replies. "I don't like to take a lamb to the fire. That's the way they get pneumonia. I use heat lamps. If you don't have electric in your barn and you have a lamb that's chilled, put three gunny sacks on the floor and wrap your lamb up in them. He won't smother. Put your hand in by his head and make an opening so he can get air. His breath will soon warm him up. Then take him out to the ewe and let him suck, or give him a little milk. After a little while take off one of the sacks; then after another little while take off another sack. Finally take off the last sack and cover him with it. It'll take a few hours to do this, but he'll usually be all right."

After a ewe has lambed, Barber sees to it that she gets a pail of clean water and he cuts down on her feed, at least for the first day. He sometimes cuts down on her feed for two or three days, depending on whether she had a single or twins, their condition, and whether or not she is a light or heavy milker. If, for example, she had a single and was a heavy milker, he would probably cut her to half feed—about a quarter pound of grain and all the hay she can eat—for the full three days. If she had twins or was a light milker he would adjust the ration accordingly. Whatever the situation, he gets

Two or three days in the creep pen are usually enough before the lamb is ready to run with the flock.

her back to full feed again after a few days and eventually he will get her up to a pound of corn a day.

The lambs are started on creep feed at two weeks. Barber recommends cracked corn. Crossbred lambs should gain about three-quarters of a pound a day with this to supplement their mother's milk.

Orphan lambs and wayward ewes that refuse to accept their lambs are as much a problem at the experiment station as anywhere else. Barber's guides in handling these situations have been shepherds' lore for generations. When he wants a ewe that has lost her lamb to adopt an orphan, he carefully skins the dead lamb and neatly fits the hide over the orphan, attaching it by bands of skin at the ankles and neck. If a ewe refuses to own one of a pair of twins, he resorts to the old trick of putting two lambs in a barrel and letting them lay on each other and crawl over each other until they have both lost their identity so far as scent is concerned. He puts them out to nurse about every hour and a half, putting out the rejected one first.

Barber is acquainted with such modern instruments as the elastrator and the Burdizzo clamps for docking and castrating, but he still prefers the chisel and jackknife. A man who performed the operation later in the season would probably find flies and maggots a drawback. Barber's lambs have forgotten

all about the ordeal, though, long before fly time. His lambs arrive early and he goes into action when they are two weeks old. "I always like to dock and castrate in the morning on a nice, bright day," he says. "The lambs will have a chance to walk around all day then and they won't get stiff.

"Meself, I always dock with a hot chisel. I don't like the rubber band. If I'm going to have me head cut off I don't want it to take two weeks. I think that's the way the lamb feels about it, too. And there's always a chance of tetanus from the rubber bands.

"You don't want to have the chisel quite red hot when your dock. If you hit the joint it'll go right through like butter. There are four blood vessels in the tail, two up and two down. Just touch those blood vessels with the corner of the iron to check the bleeding. Daub on a little pine tar and carbolic oil and that does it. Don't rub the mixture on because that might start bleeding.

"I use the old jackknife for castrating. Then I know it's done. Rubber bands aren't so bad here as there's not much danger of tetanus. If you want to use the rubber bands on the tail a good way to do it is to put the bands on for about two days, then cut the tail off and there will be no bleeding."

"Do you leave your lambs with the ewes right up to the time they go to market?" Stanley asked.

"Not if you want to get your ewes settled well when you go to breed them. I wean all my lambs the first of July, regardless of their age. This brings the ewes all up to breeding condition the same time. The morning after I wean the lambs I dose them for worms, then put them on clean pasture, usually rape and oats. To finish them out I like a red clover field. That's what makes them grow sideways. A little straight corn will help, too.

"My ewes I put on a bare pasture to dry them up. A heavy milking ewe I let go for about three days, then I ease her—I don't milk her out completely. I let her go three more days and ease her again and that's usually all she needs. I never have any udder trouble. The one thing with ewes is, don't ever let them get too fat."

The two students who are assigned to work with the old master came into the barn to start the evening feeding. The little shepherd allowed it was about time for him to be giving his charges a little personal attention, and Bob Stanley took his leave with a headful of ideas.

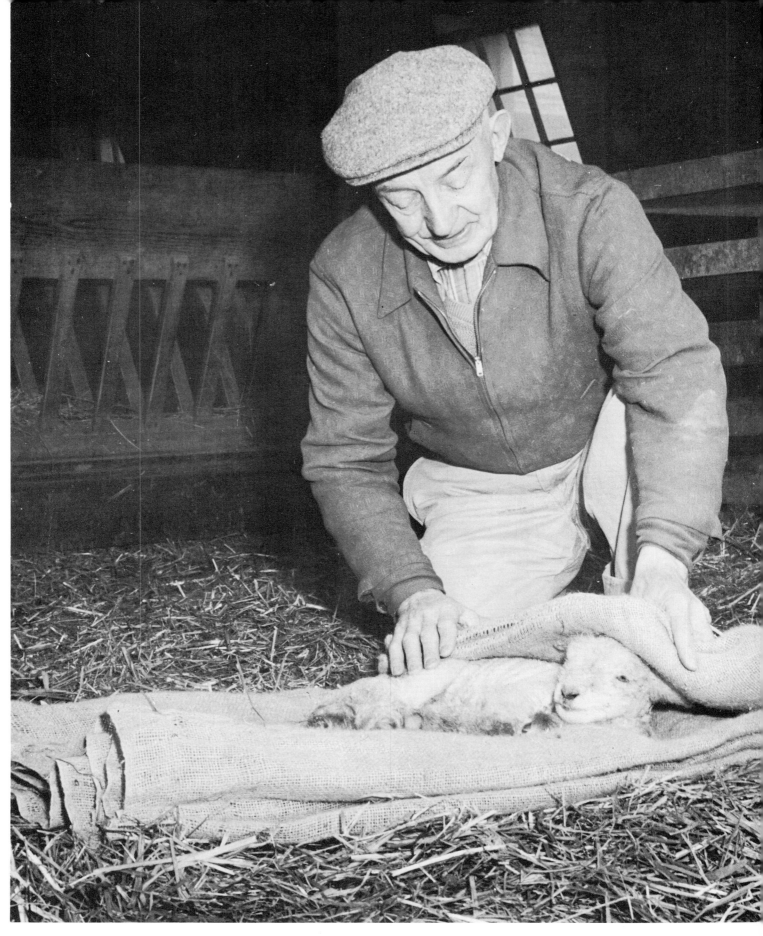

If you don't have a heat lamp, wrap a chilled lamb in three gunny sacks, with a little opening for air. His own breath will warm him up. Then take the sacks off one at a time and in a few hours he'll be on his own.

# The good life of the
# Gilfilens

NO ONE expected Ed and Jane Gilfilen to last more than one season on the farm. That was twelve years ago. Now there are five more little Gilfilens putting down roots in St. Martin, Ohio. To them, the family farm is still the best place to live.

St. Martin is too small to be called a village. There are two stores, a school, a church. From his window, Ed can see the school and the church beyond. The Gilfilens are small farmers. They are not small people. Measured in dollars, they are insignificant, but by the yardstick of happiness, they are to be envied. They work together; Sundays they kneel together. Theirs is a common goal, a sharing of responsibility, and quiet faith in themselves. When Ed steps out of his back door, he's in business. More likely than not, Jane and five little Gilfilens are right behind him.

Ed and Jane were married not long after he returned from a stretch in Korea with the army. Disaster sought them out early. Jane lost her mother, her only close relative, in a car accident. They lived in town then, spending weekends on the family farm, while Ed completed his last year at college. Each evening, after classes, he drove the 34 miles to the farm to tend a batch of 625 broilers in batteries. When the broilers reached two pounds, a fire destroyed them all. On a weekend trip to the farm, three months before her baby was due, another car crash left Jane with six broken ribs and a broken arm.

The farm, a run-down 63 acres of poverty grass, had been the home of Ed's grandparents. As a child, he had spent frequent summers there. The idea of trying to make a go of farming was not Jane's idea of how a man should apply a college education. But it was a home and if it made Ed happy, that's where she belonged, too. They loaded the truck with the furniture Jane's mother left them. The baby crib they took along has never been empty. Stevie followed Hank, then Terry and

To Ed and Jane Gilfilen, the family farm is still the best place to raise a family.

Peggy. Now ten-month-old Janey will soon have to surrender the crib to another Gilfilen, who is crowding the calendar. "It's our well water," says Jane. "It's even worked on a childless couple who visited us."

Shortly after they moved in, Jane urged Ed to get an estimate on having the place fixed up a bit. Maybe they could get a loan. They called in a carpenter. He looked things over. Then he 'lowed as how he was pretty busy. As he left, he pointed out that there was right smart work ahead.

That first year was an uphill fight. Their corn sickened to 30 bushels per acre. They lost half their soybeans because they couldn't get anyone to combine them on time. Their sows lost some of their pigs. A heifer drowned in an ice-coated pond. But somehow the cellar shelves were filled with canned goods from the garden. There was some good hay in the barn from sharing work in a neighbor's fields. The gilts grew fat on the nubbins gleaned from the cornfields.

There wasn't time in an 18-hour workday for the Gilfilens to feel sorry for themselves. It wasn't only the work; there was also the learning of how to do it. Even learning the simple things, like the easy way to lift a bale of hay, took patience. Patience you learned first. Ed learned to juggle the remodeling on his home with digging graves in the frozen ground for stillborn calves, the dormant sprays and the full-blossom sprays, and manure hauling. The blisters turned into callouses and the callouses tightened and set his hands.

The seasons blurred. Summer came on gradually, while the corn inched upward. Autumn faltered, was gone, came back again. The field work lulled, the machinery stopped and hands took over. Now a man could wire the barn, pipe water to the kitchen, cement the cracks in the well. But at County Fair time a farmer indulged himself and his family. That was a right.

Fall harvest began. Picking the corn and combining the beans stretched across weeks. The calves went to market; the check brought a few new clothes, boards for a farrowing shelter, a spreader. The washing machine would have to do another year.

January was like February, Monday like Tuesday, with the feeding, the shovelling, the hammering, the monotony, then a surge of new hope with the first calf and despair when its mother refused to let it nurse and broke its neck with one vicious jab of her hoof. More calves arrived and then a series of lambs, most of them greeting the world on raw nights at two in the morning. Winter edged along and the midnight checkup became routine. You scrunched to the barn, flashlight in hand, a misty chill outside, an ammonia mugginess in the cowshed. You took a final glance at the chicks under the brooder. Back in the house, you pulled the comforter over the youngest baby, who was already getting too big for the crib. The wind rattled the bedroom windows.

In the morning you awoke to find spring had slipped in unawares. You were back at the beginning, another year older, a little more firmly rooted.

The Gilfilens had no relatives to lend a hand. They had a few weekend work parties for friends out from the city, but the cooking took more time than if they had done the work themselves. There was discouragement and very little money, but life became a joy around the dinner table for, as every woman knows, food can fix a lot of things. It took only a couple of candles on the supper table to blot out the drudgery. It didn't cost anything to laugh. Jane told her friends, "A farm wife always knows where her husband is. Just listen for the sound of his tractor."

What farm life held for Ed Gilfilen, his wife failed to understand. Constantly at the mercy of the weather, he couldn't plan to buy anything when he couldn't count on anything for sure. Once a sow crushed her litter; again, he stood helplessly looking out the window while the hail ripped his corn crop to shreds.

Their second winter was endless. The mud was always with them; the green firewood hissed and fried and died in the kitchen stove; the water bucket wouldn't stay filled. Jane never got far beyond the back door.

Toward spring, something happened to Jane. Ed, off on a trip for planter parts, had asked her to keep an eye on the ewes. At mid-morning she remembered. In a cold March drizzle she waded through the mud to the barn. Just inside the door she found a newborn lamb, wet, neglected. An acrid fluid clung to him, smarting her hands. He smelled like crushed ragweed. His legs were rubber, his mouth smeared red and viscid, his nostrils bubbling mucous. His skin hung in wrinkles, the wool like a dirty dishrag. She stooped and held him against her. His heart beat with a furious pounding beneath his frail ribs. A glaze crept over his frightened eyes. He opened his jaws, clamped down on her finger and

with surprising strength held tight while his tiny body convulsed and thrashed. He was dead. Jane rose from her knees on the straw and felt a stirring of the unborn child within her. The ewes looked up at her with trusting eyes. These, too, needed a woman's tenderness and from now on she would give it to them.

The kitchen, the house, were no longer her boundaries. Her husband was not a worker who went off in the morning to a world from which she was excluded. The weevils in the grain bins, the rain at corn-tasselling time, became her concern as well. On the welfare of the livestock in the barns, the welfare of the family depended. The garden, the family cow, were security. Her youngest, still in a crawl, was as dependent on that cow as the calf, wobbling to the teat in its first effort to nurse. There was a lot a woman could do. An extra pig saved meant new clothes. The orphan lamb, warmed by the kitchen oven and bottle-fed, meant new drapes for the living room. Everything tied together; each leaned on the other.

To the children, the farm is joy and excitement. For Hank, turned six, throwing hay down to the cows is a part of his living and not a chore. A boy can take pride in the whiteness of the eggs he gathers. Stevie, four and a half, hastens to show how he holds a squealing pig while his father clips its needle teeth. There is a creek where cool mud oozes between a little girl's toes; and rabbit tracks to follow in the snow, and spider webs to trace in the granary. When summer work presses, they go with their mother to the fields with their father's lunch and there's a picnic under a tree at the end of a row. On winter nights, after the stock has been bedded down and supper is done, there's popcorn in front of the fireplace.

So much happens. The miracle of birth, a lamb giving its first trembling bleat, the pigs scrambling for a teat, the bursting of blossoms in the orchard; these are the things a child can see or hear or touch or smell. Death, too, they know. The bull killed by lightning, the drowned cow floating in the pond, are part of the pattern and the patterns within patterns of life and death; and neither holds fears for them. If you are old enough to wield a rake, you help cover the burial trench, and like father you don't look back.

For Jane, accepting the cycle of birth and death was not easy. Always she sensed that loneliness among animals in the birth and death process. They look at you in their helplessness, fearing you, yet

depending on you, while the herd stands stolidly by, untroubled. But try to catch an ewe or rope a calf and the others ward you off. The ram stands in your way, the bull squares his shoulders. But an animal in the throes of birth, or the agony of death, is shunned by its kind, and you can do what you wish, and they ignore you as well.

It isn't all work for the Gilfilens. One night a week Ed devotes to a local service organization. Time must be allotted the soil conservation meetings. The district soil man is a farmer's best friend.

Ed doesn't envy the city worker his leisure. "In town, what would we do with our leisure?" he asks. "Raise African violets? Or take the kids to a swimming pool to keep them off the streets? Once we took the kids to an airport to see the jets take off. But they couldn't take their eyes off a couple of horses in a nearby field. Here on the farm the pets they tend and play with now will be part of the herd in a year or so.

Seven big appetites on a one-man farm means everybody has to help, whether it's taking the crosscut saw to the cedars or gathering eggs to store in the cool, dark cellar.

"We don't turn the babies over to baby-sitters. When we visit, the kids are part of the party. We see a lot of the neighbors. Good neighbors are a blessing to a farmer.

"I couldn't stand being cooped up," Ed Gilfilen gives as his reason for farming. "Here I am with my own family twenty-four hours a day, with plenty of elbow room. I'm free, free to work myself to death if I want to, free from being a number on a punch-card, free to make my own decisions. It's the kind of freedom they call 'feeling easy in your harness.' No farm job lasts long enough to get tiresome. By the time the corn is laid by the wheat is ready. When you run your fingers through your own wheat in the bin, you forget the labor and the burn of fertilizer dust in the cuts on your hand.

"A man has to have faith. When you go out at sunrise on a May morning and the sod springs under foot and you hear the sparrows waking in the hedge, you get that faith; you know then that every calf and bird and tuft of clover are part of a thriving concern. You either feel it or you don't. If you don't feel peaceful inside when you're walking through the corn on a Sunday afternoon on your own land, you better move to town."

Work often becomes a kind of passion to a farmer. He doesn't feel right at the end of a summer day unless he's tired. There're the peeled knuckles from grubbing along the roadside and the water freezing on his cuffs at the stock tank in winter. There's a stretch of months when he has rubber boots on more hours than not and it seems like there never

31

Farm animals have a habit of being born during sudden spring storms or in the small hours of wintry nights. The coffee pot is a farmer's only companion.

and you slosh away the sweat and the tiredness at the yard pump. At the table you see the boys are getting bigger and that means more manpower coming along so you keep your eye on that extra acreage that you might someday be able to buy down the road. You know you'll never quit."

You don't find atheists in the country. You can't watch a field of wheat ripple and ripen without deep beliefs and without feeling that you're a small part of something pretty big and lasting. No man grows roses and cabbages for himself alone. You have to share to enjoy.

A farmer doesn't get sick leave or unemployment compensation. The work goes on. One year Ed Gilfilen cut his foot almost off on a scythe blade; another year he broke out with carbuncles. There hasn't been any vacation for the Gilfilens yet, except for Jane's annual spell in the maternity ward.

"According to Ed," says Jane, "my hospital visit always comes at planting or haying time. And always after a false alarm or two. The older boys think it takes three trips to the hospital to have a baby."

The Gilfilens income is going up. Ed says, "We grossed $5,165 last year, mostly from livestock, and we sold some wheat. Our net ran a shade over $2,000, plus our living. It would take double that to raise our kids in the city. Those figures don't tell the whole story. Our corn is up to 90 bushels an acre since we limed and fertilized the fields. We've got 11 sows with 110 pigs right now, along with 8 head of beef and 22 sheep. It's a small operation by cornbelt standards, but it's a beginning. Each year we knock a slice off the mortgage on the 52 adjoining acres we bought several years ago. The ladino grows thick in every field. We dug a new pond. We don't owe a cent on our equipment except for the welder I bought on time. All the terracing we need has been done. Most of the buildings have been repaired or remodeled. Our next job is to add three rooms to the house. Of course, Jane doesn't get many nylons. Still, we're all healthy. If I were to judge by the figures in my account book, I'd be pretty sick at heart most years. But we've had fun. We're pretty well on our feet. We've been happy."

was any dry ground under foot. There's the sudden April rain that drenches his skin and squinches through his shoes. In summer the straw scratches his arms and the chaff gets down his neck and raises a rash on his back. The salt sweat bites into the rawness under his belt in July. Any day can bring a crisis. A hopeful morning in May can turn into a tragedy with bloated cows stretched across the clover. There's the sinking feeling of watching a beef calf sell for $60 when it cost $80 to keep the cow over the year. "You want to give up right then," says Ed Gilfilen. "Or you say you'll quit next year. But you never quit. You go home to dinner

# Green Mountain Sap

**I**N Vermont there is a legend about the making of the first maple syrup. Once upon a time, before the coming of the white man, a squaw was cooking a mess of deer meat in sap from a "sweet water tree." Womanlike, she sat there and let the stuff cook down till it was syrup. The syrup tasted better than the venison. When her buck returned from his hunting he ate the whole pot of stew and was delighted. Wanting more, he went out, cut into the maple tree with his tomahawk, set in a spout of bark, collected the sap, and evaporated it by dropping hot stones in a kettle until the syrup thickened.

When sap ran it meant to the Indians, as it means to us, a renewal of the year, the beginning again. While the sap boiled there was dancing and feasting. The first batch of syrup off the fire was offered as a sacrifice to the Great Spirit in thanksgiving for bringing back the spring.

Then the white settlers, learning from the Indians, began to tap the trees. There was no white sugar in colonial times so the main portion of the maple crop was made into sugar. The sugar was made much the same as it is today—by boiling down the sap. At first the sap was not caught in buckets but in wooden troughs. There were no sugar houses in those days; the boiling was done in the open. A soap kettle was hung on a long pole with weights on either end and balanced on to a post so

Some tree-tappers bore the first hole on the south side of a tree because they say the sap starts there.

When the sap is running good, there's a constant stream from the spile. The sap gatherers go from tree to tree emptying the buckets of sap into their own pails. When these are full, they carry them to the "tommyhawk."

that the kettle could be swung on or off the fire. There were no tubs for storing the sap, so as it was gathered it was boiled. Green wood was used. Cutting down a tree as they needed it they boiled, night and day, out in the open. It snowed in the kettle; wind blew ashes and dust into it, and it boiled up black as pitch. But the blacker the syrup the better the early New Englander thought it tasted. Some of the old-timers today won't have "light and fancy" syrup on their buckwheat cakes. They like it black and strong.

Around the turn of the century, before the maple syrup caught the fancy of the luxury market, it was sold for about sixty-five cents a barrel, or was traded off for white sugar at the general store. Today it brings the farmer five to seven dollars a gallon. Even at this price, considering the amount of labor spent in the making, the farmer's profit is small. Still, if he didn't make a penny profit he'd sugar. He couldn't help it. It's in his blood.

To the Green Mountain people, when winter comes sugaring can't be far behind. Outdoors it's cold. The thermometer never goes above twenty and sometimes it drops 'way down, but it's a dry, clear cold that makes a fellow want to go out and work. The woods are bare, the trees steely grey against the mountains, spruces black against the snow. Suddenly there's a new warmth in the midday sun, and the snow goes soft in the hollows. A subtle sweet odor rises in the air, like the damp under maple bark. The Green Mountain farmer says this is the sap stirring in the maple roots. Winter is drawing its last frosty breath.

Then the sugar maker knows that he must watch for the signs in nature to tell him when to tap the trees. Those signs are handed down father to son through generations of men who have watched nature in the sugar lot.

*"Watch for the snow flea around the end of February. Three weeks after you see the first snow flea you can start tappin'."*

*"When the ice commences to crack and roar and the brook spews over, then it's time."*

*"And don't forget the wind. Three days to the southeast, and on the fourth, rain or shine, you can start."*

Sugar weather usually comes in early March when the temperature goes above 32 degrees and the nights are still frosty. On a warm day the sap will start with a rush, but don't worry if it slackens off. A light wind, warm spell, or a heavy freeze will check the flow, but with the return of normal weather the juice will run again.

Though sugarin' lasts only a few weeks the Green Mountain man has it on his mind and is working toward it the better part of the year. To many hill farms it's the main cash crop and the whole family helps out. The farmer works over the woods in the fall cleaning out the underbrush so that the maples will have plenty of light and air. A good maple farm has about 300 trees per acre.

Then too, clearing the forest in the fall gives the farmer a chance to gather the wood he'll need for the fires when the "evaporation" starts. He uses about a cord of wood to each fifteen gallons of syrup. He keeps his younger kids busy getting the sugar-house ship shape and the buckets painted. Some farmers use metal buckets to gather the syrup, but the Green Mountain farmer doesn't because his father and grandfather before him used wooden buckets. They say wooden buckets don't affect the flavor. They're not as efficient as metal buckets because they spring leaks and have to be watched continuously.

Some born-and-bred sugar farmers don't like bucket covers. They will tell you that the syrup sours quicker when it's covered during tapping. Those who belong to the bucket-cover school of thought will tell you that the cover keeps out the rain and the dirt. It's an even battle. They've been arguing about it for years and it's still a deadlock.

But they all agree that they must keep their buckets and tubs and tanks spotlessly clean. Every plank, shelf, spoon, and skimmer is scrubbed and disinfected. There must not be a speck of dust anywhere. If a chip or twig drops in the evaporator it will discolor the syrup, then you can't sell it as "fancy grade" for the top price.

Once the sugar house and equipment are in order the horses are opening up the snowdrifts and breaking tracks through the woods to make it easier to gather the sap. This sap gathering is a big job and takes a lot of willing hands. The farmer plans the whole campaign as if he were besieging a city.

The old timers have kept their horses for pulling the sap sleds but the younger generation has put the crawler tractor in harness. The chug of the Diesels and their oily fumes have caused a new

When the snow goes soft in the hollows and little pools gather in low spots on the sunny side of the barn, it's sap time.

"Tommyhawk" is a Green Mountain word for the low-slung bobsled used in sap gathering.

argument to spring up: "Those dang fumes floatin' through the woods give the syrup an off-flavor" complain some of the old timers, who have gone back to horses.

One day, when you weren't counting on it, the brook begins to flow and bubbles over the ice. That night you hear the angry roar of ice and in the morning the sun is smiling at you like it hasn't been away at all. It's sap weather. The signs are right. The boys pile the buckets on the sled and the team pulls off snorting clouds of steam. The dogs bark and run ahead into the bush. Man and beast feel a release from the prison of winter and long days around the kitchen listening to the women.

The tapper goes ahead with his tool kit slung over his shoulder. The tapping of trees is a serious business and the tapper knows it. He examines the bark for holes of other years for he is careful not to bore near an old hole. Some tappers bore the first hole on the south side of a tree because, they say, the sun starts the sap there first. Others prefer the north side because the sap runs longest on that side. This controversy has created another deadlock in sugaring technique. However, they all frown upon the fellow who doesn't use a clean bit. "Clogs up the hole," they'll mutter, "and you can't get a danged thing." The bit is usually three-eighths to a half inch in diameter, and if the warm spell holds, the hole can be reamed up to five-eighths of an inch, giving a better flow. The tapper drills in an upslant so the sap can run downhill out of the spout or spile. As he withdraws the bit you can see the sap ooze out of the hole and run down the bark, carrying with it the bits of shaving.

36

Though tapping a tree does no harm that the tree can't take care of and heal, careless tapping, too deep, too wide, or tapping twice in a season, can kill a tree, especially if the tree is young. Each hole tells its own story for all around it the cell wood has died where the tree has sealed off the wound and the bark is dry dust. If the tree were tapped here it would give no sap.

You'll see the fellow take great care in placing the spouts just inside the bark and outer layer. If they get too deep they'll be away from the free flow of syrup and the bucket will be half empty come morning.

Then he hangs the bucket on the hook under the spout, puts a lid on, and there you are. If the tree is a giant with a great trunk he'll drill several holes and hang two or three buckets, being careful not to have them too close to each other.

There are all sorts of spouts and sugar men argue over the merits of wood and metal the year 'round. Some prefer the metal spout and some want to whittle out their own. Wooden spouts sometimes break off when the bucket runs full, and old ones may sour the sap.

The boys work ahead, plowing through the snow, leaving a bucket under each tree. In steep places and near the tree trunk the snow "draws" them in, but there's a knack to wading on top of the snow. You have to walk "light" like you're walking on eggs or dancing, but some people never catch on and they sink in hip deep and wallow like hooked fish. People with heavy feet have to

learn to wear snow shoes.

Once the sap begins to flow the whole countryside is out in the sugar woods. Spotted along the mountain roads are the teams hitched to the tommyhawk, a Green Mountain word for sap sled. Sap gatherers are usually the kids of the family. Each has a gathering pail, and going from tree to tree they empty the buckets of sap into their own pails and when these are full they carry them to the tommyhawk. When the tommyhawk is full the team is headed to the sugar house which billows clouds of smoke and steam into the chill winter air.

The farmer's pride and joy is his sugaring house. In the Green Mountains it is usually an unpainted shed, weathered with the years, nestling against the side of a hill so that the sleds can be driven on the upper side and the sap poured into the large storage tanks with the blessing of gravity. On one end of the sugaring house is a room for wood for the evaporator and perhaps there's another little room at the other end for storage of the gear. The tanks are always on the north side of the house and on the outside so they will not be exposed to the heat of the fire, and they are on the shady side so as not to be warmed by the sun. The sap must be boiled as soon after it's gathered as possible, and meantime it must be kept cold, else bacteria will have a chance to develop in the sweet liquid and spoil the flavor. The roof is almost always of wood because the steam condenses on a metal roof and rust will drop down into the syrup and spoil it.

The capacity of sap to sour preys on the farmer's mind, and all modern practice tends to prevent it. A day in the sun is enough, or too long in the holding tanks. Like any sugar syrup, fermentation sets into sap and eventually leads to acetification — a process identical with the one that makes vinegar from sweet cider. In the old days Vermonters made a decent vinegar from maple sap, nothing to be preferred to a good throat-cutting cider vinegar, but a vinegar all the same, and handy. Once in a while a back-hill farmer who lives outside the apple country will set away some sap with vinegar in mind — but at all other times the syrup industry fights fermentation with both hands.

The arch is a long narrow furnace made of iron, stones and cement, or bricks. On it rests the evaporator or pan made of sheet metal or cast iron. It is about six inches deep and varies in size depending on the number of trees in the woods. The sap enters at one end, pouring in over the evaporator.

The younger generation has put the crawler tractor in harness.

37

As the water passes off as steam, the liquid at the farthest end from the entering point gets thicker and thicker and is finally drawn off at intervals as syrup. The "boiler" is an autocrat who rules the sugar house with an iron hand. He must watch the fire, skim off the foam and dust from the boiling sap, and watch the progress of the evaporation.

The sugar houses of the big commercial producers are light modern buildings, the interior much like a city factory with concrete floors, gleaming enamel, and all sorts of precision testing instruments. There is no oven. Instead the evaporation is handled by a system of controlled heat, produced by steam or gas or electricity. Gigantic drums line the walls ready to be filled with syrup and tending the evaporators is not one man "boiler" but a group of workers each with his individual job, and there's a foreman over all.

This assembly line system is efficient but not very romantic. But it is not for either reason that the Green Mountain farmer refuses to have any truck with it. Occasionally you will find a mountain man who has seen fit to copy the big producers' method of collecting the sap. Instead of catching the drops in buckets he uses a pipeline system. Wires are strung on trees and upon stakes in the ground the preceeding autumn and the tubing is suspended from this wiring. This prompt delivery of sap from tree to boiling tends toward improved quality because the sooner the sap is boiled the lighter the color and the finer the flavor. But as for "boiling" without a fire — the mountain man just doesn't believe maple syrup should be made that way. He likes the taste of the wood smoke so he goes along each season "boiling" the old fashioned way, the way he understands, and the way his forefathers have made maple syrup for almost two hundred years.

"Boiling" is not as simple a job as it appears. In every community there is a guild of professional boilers, men as smart as a whip and as neat as a woman. First the boiler lines up his tin containers along one wall. Into these he pours the syrup that goes directly to the regular customers. This trade list is a list of names handed down in the family for years. Beside these cans are large steel drums for the part of the crop shipped to dealers in the maple market. Nearby, where they'll be handy, he hangs the skimmers which are used to remove the impurities that come to the surface. A skimmer looks like a dust pan full of holes. Felt strainers through which the finished hot syrup will be passed to remove niter of sugar sand are shaped like a French beret and are about 10 inches in diameter at the top and about 14 inches deep. They are suspended in a milk can and the syrup is poured through them. A double layer of felt will do the trick too.

The boiler walks around the foaming evaporator constantly, his expert eye on the what is going on in the pan. As the sap boils down he turns the faucet and lets more in from the storage tank above. Now and then he opens the iron door of the oven and throws a log in. He dips here, stirs there, skims off impurities as they rise. To keep the flavor of the thin juice in the final syrup the evaporation must be done quickly and at as low a temperature as possible. The boiler takes care the sap at the bottom of the pan does not burn. Occasionally, when the foam threatens to boil over, he throws in a few drops of fresh cream from a handy cup and the foam subsides.

Boiling off seems to take endless time, but thirty barrels of sap must be boiled down to make one barrel of syrup. As boiling progresses, the boiler keeps his eye closely on the sap at the far end of the pan. As it darkens and boils in a thick cream the boiler makes his dramatic announcement: "Time to syrup off!" This cry brings the children running in from the woods and they all crowd around while the boiler tests first with a thermometer and then with a dipper. During the first days of sugaring, before the palate is dulled, sugaring off is an important holiday for the kids. If there's a fluffy snow on the ground they stow away unbelievable quantities of "sugar snow."

Of late the Green Mountain farmer has learned to use the sugar thermometer and hydrometer. You can see them in all the sugar houses, but here and there a sturdy old-timer scorns them for he is an expert in the time-honored method of "syruping-off." He knows exactly when it's time by the way the syrup "sheets" off the spoon as he holds it high in the air to inspect the ripe syrup, which is turning to the color of a golden sunset.

When the syrup "sheets" it is almost always at the proper density of eleven pounds to the gallon, specified by the government. If it is less it will not pass inspection and when stored it will ferment. Syrup that is heavier will pass inspection but when stored shows crystals at the bottom. Because he will lose money by selling this heavier syrup made with hit-and-miss methods, many a farmer has turned to the hydrometer and thermometer. An

The Boiler, virtuoso of the sugar house, is a man of weight in his community. He needs the neatness of a woman and a sharp eye for when the syrup "sheets" off the spoon.

approximate sea level temperature to work by is 219 degrees Fahrenheit — it is slightly lower in the mountains — which gives the syrup the required eleven pounds per gallon. Eleven pound syrup tested at a normal temperature of 60 degrees will show a hydrometer reading of 36 degrees.

Besides the boiling, many things must be watched for and tended to. If the sap is extra sweet, the operation will be speeded up because the season will be short. This isn't an unhappy turn of affairs because you get more syrup per barrel of sap under these conditions. The boiler knows, too, that a lot of sugar sand in the evaporator means the same thing. He must be careful not to let the sugar sand burn on the evaporator and he does this by "syruping off" first on one side and then the other. Each night he takes time to wash the evaporator of every trace of sand, which is largely malamate of lime, a harmless mineral found in maple sap.

Old sugar men have their own ideas about what makes flavor in syrup. They'll tell you that a tree facing south gives the best flavor with that nutty richness that rolls comfortably in your mouth. A heavy sweetness comes from the tree with roots in an underground spring. The weather helps too, of course. If the tree makes a good growth the summer before and has a healthy show of leaves, it will give a maximum of well-flavored syrup. If a winter storm tears off a branch the sap run will be light. Some say thaws sweeten sap, others that they sour it. Some farmers say cattle running in the sugar lot will improve the flavor of the syrup. Others say the trampling packs the ground and air can't get to the roots and the trees won't do

well. Science doesn't know the answer to these secrets of the sugar maple so the sugar people must find their own.

But some seasons the weather plays tag. The sun shines down hot so that you can smell the warmth. The snow goes soggy and in every direction you can hear water rushing. The first robins arrive and stand around, fat and sassy from a winter in Florida. "We'll be turnin' down the buckets now," they say. "When you wake up of a morning and the flies commence to buzz in the sunshine, even if you can smell the sap running you can just as leave take down your buckets because it's all over. The sap'll spoil before you get it in."

But it isn't over. Old lady nature is playing one of her practical jokes. Suddenly in the night it snows, sleet comes down, and the wind howls. The branches whip each other, bend under the heavy load of ice, and crash to the ground. On the next morning the sap starts oozing out of the wounded tree and the Green Mountain man's face shows how close his injured trees are to him.

Just as suddenly as the storm came on the sun comes out and the sap runs like mad. Then the boiler works on through the night, eating on the run. The family takes turn sleeping. Next morning you may wake up on an ice cap or a summer day. For in twenty-four hours the temperature can shoot up to eighty. Then all sugaring stops. The boys go around turning down the buckets, but the work of cleaning up waits until the family is rested.

The last Sunday of sugaring is the "sugaring

off party." The neighbors drive in toward late afternoon. But all that day the family has been sugaring off — making maple sugar and canning it hot from the evaporator.

"Sugaring off" in contrast to "Syruping off" means boiling the syrup longer at a higher temperature 'till it turns into sugar.

"Sugaring off" also means the conclusion of the season.

The "sugaring off" rig is a smaller pan set upon a small stone arch fired with intense heat. The pan is greased with some neutral fat, like lard or sweet oil, so the flavor won't get into the sugar. A much higher temperature is needed to make sugar than to make syrup and the boiling must be watched closely or else the sugar will burn to the bottom of the pan or foam up and boil over in a manner familiar to every housewife who has made cake frosting. Color and grain are affected by the amount of stirring it receives. For accuracy a thermometer is used to measure the density of the liquid and thus determine when it has "sugared." Two hundred and thirty-five degrees gives a soft sugar. Ten degrees higher gives a hard sugar. The sugar is poured into molds of many shapes and sizes and into small two-pound pails.

After the guests have arrived the children come down from the house laden with baskets of unsweetened doughnuts and sour pickles. Then they are sent out to find clean snow to pile on the plates. When the syrup is boiled down to a "wax" it is spooned and poured on the snow-piled plates and the guests set to with relish. This is a treat of the gods — the maple flavor is a dreamy mixture melting on your tongue.

"Eat up!" you are told. "Eat up on them pickles. You can't put down your share of sweets if you don't eat up on pickles."

The recipe for one of nature's most delicious confections—pour "waxy" syrup over clean snow. Grown-ups eat it with a spoon from plates, but for kids a snow bank and a twig is good enough. A bite of sour pickle points up the flavor.

# Witch Way to Water

OLDTIMERS in the Nebraska sandhills country south of Niobrara River still speak with awe of a gaunt Scotch-Irishman from Iowa who, though not a religious man, was a staunch disciple of the divining rod. "Old Moore," they remember, stood six feet six inches tall in his home-made socks, had hickory knots for muscles, and used his divining rod two ways—both successfully. One use for his pronged cherry twig was to detect underground water; the other was to aid his three sons in mastering the rudiments of propriety.

A neighbor chanced to be present one morning when Moore set out to locate water on the farm he had just purchased. Three bone-dry wells had already been sunk by former owners of the farm and the neighbors, long experienced in sandhill water problems, secretly felt sorry for the naive Iowan who believed he had only to wave a pronged stick over the parched earth to find water. One of Old Moore's sons, the runt of the family who measured six-feet-one, also thought it was nonsense and was indiscreet enough to say so.

For all his sixty-odd years and bristling white hair, Old Moore could move with the agility of an angry tomcat. In a twinkling he had the runt across his hip and the cherry rod was rolling dust out of his britches like smoke from a prairie fire. Old Moore then resumed his water-witching. Pausing at a spot a hundred paces from the barn, he drew a cross in the sand. "Here," he said, and walked away.

The three sons began to dig. Two days later the runt, plastered with mud, burst into the barn where Old Moore had swung his hammock between two cow stalls.

"We've struck water, dad!" the runt gasped.

The neighbors were amazed by the news but Old Moore, later known as the "Sandhill Water-witch," serenely moistened his thumb and flipped the page of his mail-order catalogue. "Naturally, son," he said. "Naturally."

To Old Moore and those like him, a mysterious, unquestionable affinity exists between the forked stick and underground water. But to others who have been disappointed by professional water-witches, or for whom the twig stubbornly refuses to perform, water-divining is pure superstition.

It is true that the divining rod, which dates back far beyond Biblical times, has been used for everything from a lie-detector to a wart-remover. The magic powers attributed to it in ancient times were so many and varied that "priests of divination" were as thick in every community as real estate salesmen today.

Cicero, familiar to but unloved by many a schoolboy, was no slouch as a soothsayer. Though he kept his work on a more dignified plane than most of his associates, he obviously knew the score. In his treatise on divination, Cicero needled his brother soothsayers with this remark: "I can't see how two augurs (men who interpret the rod's omens) can meet on the street and look each other in the face without laughing!"

At first glance, this admission that divining rods were merely props used by soothsayers on gullible clients seems to support the skeptic's argument that the forked stick is a hand-me-down for the same purpose. A little deeper burrowing into history, however, turns up a clinker in this proof. At some time during the course of centuries the divining rod divided into two separate shapes. The original rod, a straight shaft such as Moses used in obtaining water from the rock, and with which Aaron first turned the rivers of Egypt into blood, then into seething masses of frogs, has come down to us today in the form of the magician's wand.

The water-witches' divining rod, or forked stick, originated in the Harz Mountains of Germany where it was first used by prospectors to detect ore veins and later by peasants to locate underground water. Unlike the straight wand, the forked stick has been given serious investigation by many scientists both here and abroad. In the bibliography of the United States Geological Survey Bulletin 416, "The Divining Rod—A History of Water Witching," Arthur Ellis lists 582 books and pamphlets published on the subject since 1532. Curiously enough, geologists and physicists have always been wonderfully nimble in dodging the prime question about forked-twig divination: "Is it is, or is it ain't, a hoax?" Perhaps the closest approach to a direct answer lies in O. E. Meinzer's introductory to Bulletin 416. Says Mr. Meinzer: ". . . It is difficult to see how for practical purposes the entire matter (water-divination) could be more thoroughly discredited . . ."

Though they agree without qualification with this statement, twenty prominent university geologists recently answered a query about water-divination in such a manner as to reveal three significant facts. First, none of the geologists claimed knowledge of the effectiveness of the forked twig based upon personally conducted experiments. Second, more than half the geologists answered in the same vein as C. S. Gwynne of Iowa State College who said: "Although I place absolutely no stock in water-witching, I rarely try to dissuade others from their belief . . . Many things are not beyond the realm of possibility." Third, the geologists who flatly denounced water-witching as a fraud almost invariably added this enigmatic tag to their statements: "Please don't quote me."

What lies behind this mysterious turtlelike reluctance on the part of most scientists to stick their necks out? Why do they discredit the forked-twig, yet gingerly duck authorship of the assertion that all water-witches are charlatans?

From the very beginning, methods of divining for water have been almost identical with those used in hunting for ore. Just as a prospector may use a different kind of twig for each metal, the water-witch may choose a hazel fork for one locality and a cherry, beech, holly, or willow twig for other localities. Some prospectors and water-witches use the same fork year after year; others insist that the best results are obtained when a fork is cut from a bush close to where the divining work is to take place. A minority of modern diviners use metal forks and a few dare-devils have tried plastics, they say with poor results.

After selecting the proper twig, the diviner grasps one fork of the branch in each fist with his fingers turned upward so that the free end of the rod is higher than the level of his hands. He then wanders about at random until the twig suddenly begins to twist downward. It is said that this movement begins the instant the diviner's feet touch a spot beneath which there is water or minerals. As soon as the spot has been passed, the twig once again becomes immobile.

Most diviners agree that the amount of twisting done by a twig is in direct proportion to the size of an underground vein and its nearness to the surface. In proof of this they call attention to the scarred condition of the bark where their hands have gripped the forks during a strong pull. When asked by skeptics why the twig does not perform as well for one man as another, the believers explain that failure of a rod to writhe as though magnetized under the power of strong veins may be due to two things—either the operator is unskilled, or he may be possessed of impeding peculiarities which resist the forces of underground substances.

In all fairness, however, the preponderance of evidence against professional water-witches proves nothing except that divining rods can be used by incompetent operators and/or crooks. On the other side of the ledger, more than balancing the swindlers, are men of unquestionable character who use the divining rod solely to benefit their fellow men.

In the dustbowl country of Kansas and Oklahoma a few years ago a country preacher—a little bantam of a man in a frayed black suit and a black string tie—took up the divining-rod to locate wells for his stricken parishioners. Reverend Gossley's methods were simple and straight to the point. Accompanied by his congregation in wagons and buggies he once turned in at a waterless farm and stood bareheaded for a moment, watching the swirling dust eddies move restlessly across the fields. Finally he raised his arms and delivered a short prayer.

Rufus Courts, 78-year-old Brown County, Ohio farmer, prefers a weepy apple fork for his water-witching.

"Father in Heaven, we're standin' on Hirum Caldwell's farm today and You can see for Yourself the fix Hirum's in. His well is dry and he's haulin' water twenty miles from the Santa Fe tanks to keep his family and stock alive. Hirum's a deservin' man, God, and with Your gracious help we're gonna' get him a well. If You'll just show us where to dig, Father, we'll tend to the rest. Amen."

The prayer finished, Rev. Gossley began trudging back and forth, his black tie flapping in the hot wind while his thin face streaked with sweat and dust. In his gnarled fists was the divining rod; behind him trailed the silent, sober-faced farmers. Within the hour he had found a spot and the men started digging. They struck water at sundown.

On other occasions it was several hours before Reverend Gossley gave the command, and once the congregation followed him all one blistering afternoon and evening. Towards midnight he halted and prayed again, then took up the divining rod and almost immediately gave the order to dig.

Whether it was Reverend Gossley's prayers, the divining rod—or both—that produced results, is a matter of opinion. There are many who will swear by the Gospel that he found water where dry wells had been dug before. Sometimes the water was close to an abandoned well, sometimes it was half a mile from the farmhouse. But if ever there was an instance in which Reverend Gossley failed to find water, no one seems to remember it.

# Dry Land Spongers

THERE is no doubt whatever among dry land spongers that morel mushrooms, or "sponges" as they know them, are the food of the gods. A mortal can be no nearer paradise, they say, than when he sits down in front of a plate of morels sauteed in butter. Morels are not only the greatest of all nature's delicacies, they are a sort of opiate, too, for they make congenital liars out of honest men, steal them from their marital beds, and send them, with bowed heads, wandering into the forests and fields.

A morel addict never recovers. When the apple trees show their first faint blush of pink, the fever comes on. An addict becomes restless, and one morning he disappears. He is a man possessed during the few short weeks when the morels are in fruit. Like the lotus eater, he forgets home and loved ones, his business suffers, and he lies like Ananias. He ventures on the annual safari with hope, anticipation, and no little guile; he returns by devious routes from his secret hunting grounds, suspecting spies; he appears among his fellows briefly to tell tall tales of his harvest. No fisherman can hold a candle to him.

He banishes his wife from the kitchen and cooks his feast himself; he shares it reluctantly. This cult of sponge hunters is as old as man. The Neanderthal was not the first. There were those before him, more primitive, for the morel is a primitive form, one of the simpler plants and it hasn't changed much since the dawn of time. The morels or morchella, as the botanists call them, are found throughout the country—there are several species all of which differ so greatly from all other mushrooms that identification is simple and safe. Unlike the toadstool, the umbrella type of mushroom, all species are edible. You do not have to gamble your life away in choosing between the edible and poisonous species.

Two common and preferred species of morchella are the *esculenta* and *delicosa*. Typical of the entire group, they look like a piece of sponge resting on a creamy white stem. The stem is hollow, and the cap is usually conical or rounded; the over-all height is rarely more than seven inches. The color varies, depending on species, from a gray to buff or brown, and darkens with age.

The stem is rarely more than a third of the length of the entire mushroom except in a less desirable variety, the snake head, or *morchella semilibera*. In this variety, the stem is long and is topped by a small head shaped like a snake's. Its flavor is inferior. Both the stem and the body of all species are edible and are fairly equal in flavor.

The morel itself is the fruit or flower of the growth, by far the greatest bulk of which is below the surface. The flower or fruit emerges rather quickly when the conditions are right—some say they pop up in a moment and even emit an audible sound as they spring out of the earth. They dehydrate within two or three days. The fruit emits spores, as all fungi do. These spores are almost microscopic and may be carried away by the wind or on the feet and bodies of animals and birds. Squirrels are known to like morels and cache them for winter. They pass the live spores in their excrement.

The toadstool type of mushroom carries sudden death. It cannot be confused with the morel which looks like a hunk of sponge on a thick stem.

When the spore cell explodes, the spores are literally shot into the air. When they fall upon a suitable medium they may germinate and send forth in a single long filament to begin the multi-branched, underground structure of the fungus. The fruit body is formed, and by rapid cell production pushes above the surface of the ground. This is the sponge, or morel.

If every spore produced a morel the world would be up to its neck in mushrooms, and even the most gluttonous addict would have his fill. But only the rare spore germinates, and more rarely does the mycelium, the underground growth, find conditions sympathetic enough to develop and thrust its fruit above the surface of the ground. No one knows what these conditions are.

The common mushroom of commerce can be bought by the box or bag, or by the ton, for anyone with a damp basement can grow them with ease. It has been found relatively simple to produce the first stages of growth, the germination of the spore, under laboratory conditions. In a few cases, vestiges of fruiting bodies were produced, but even prayer failed to induce the fruit buds to develop. One researcher, Repin by name, claimed to have produced fruiting bodies in a cave in France in 1901. He said he placed cultures in flower pots, stored them in the cave, and nine years later reaped morels. His veracity has been questioned; anyway, members of the clan say, who wants to wait a nine-year cycle; certainly this can't be a lucrative enterprise.

Laymen among the morel hunters have had a try at growing them in captivity. A patient man, Orin Gessley, of Circleville, Ohio, tells of his frustrations and one small victory: "I've hunted sponges all my life," he says, "and I've tried to grow them for fifty years. Brought in soil from places where I found them, tried every known trick of soil analysis, fertilizer, and moisture. Nary a sponge did I get.

"My mother had better luck. She always dumped the cleanings from a mess of sponges outside the back door under an apple tree. The birds liked the pickings. One spring, about twenty-five years after she had started this custom, a puny morel popped up one morning under the apple tree.

"The only thing I learned in fifty years about how to grow morels was learned from this—that they reproduce in cycles—the spore must require a number of years of dormancy before producing a fruit. And I'm not too sure of this."

Morels are where you find them. And don't believe anything that a morel hunter tells you about that. Some will tell you that you find them only under hickory or ash trees. But the next one you find will be growing under an elm tree or up through a crack in the sidewalk on a busy street.

The morels appear in quantity in the cedar brakes of some of the southwestern states and are locally called Cedar Brake Fungi. Under such conditions a mass of debris persists year after year and attains a thickness of several inches. The shade of overhanging boughs produces and retains humus, thereby producing more favorable conditions for the growth of mushrooms than in unshaded spots. It is more a matter of degree and one cannot necessarily depend on a spot producing large crops over successive seasons. A spot that has produced well over a number of years suddenly becomes sterile, and a spot where none has ever been found just as suddenly begins to produce.

During cold, wet spring weather the well-drained southern and western slopes afford the best hunting. When it is hot and dry the northern or eastern slopes or the bottom lands are more likely spots. People who have kept accurate field records find little seasonal deviation regardless of weather.

The season is short. In most localities it lasts about

two and one-half weeks. This could vary depending on the number of species present in any one area. Their season parallels the northward progress of spring starting in February in the southern states, through May in the northern border states. At the higher elevations through the west they may be found in mid-June. Regardless of latitude or altitude, their development is determined by the capricious spring weather. The sound of warm spring rains on the roof is music to mycophagists.

Some of the most consistent and successful spongers prefer river and creek bottoms planted in alfalfa which have not been disturbed for several years, and are subject to flooding. Of course, it always helps to know which part of a particular field has produced mushrooms in past years. All other factors being equal, there appears to be an increase in numbers each year for three seasons after fields have been planted.

There are sections of the United States where morels are sufficiently numerous to attract hunters from considerable distances. One party described a morel hunting trip to the northern peninsula of Michigan. They returned with more than a bushel. One specimen was ten inches tall. Most of them were found on hummocks of humus in a coniferous forest where openings in the tree canopy permitted the sun to shine through. A goodly number of them were found on a sawdust pile of an abandoned sawmill.

Ask a successful sponger where he finds them and he'll give his arm a 180-degree sweep, look you in the eye, and tell you, "Out that-a-way."

The morel is not highly nutritious. It is mostly water, about 90 per cent, and has a rather heavy mineral content, some protein, and no starch. The taste and flavor is the thing, and who would want more? Attempts to describe the flavor of morels have met with less success than the efforts to grow them. Your question about flavor will usually be met by a generalization, "It's heavenly," or "It's better than anything you ever et," or just a simple look of ecstasy. In the south, they are known as Hickory Chickens, but their taste is neither like hickory nor chicken.

If any sponge hunter is ever so fortunate as to find more than he can eat at one time, he can keep them for a considerable time in a closed jar in the refrigerator. They can be dried, too, by exposure to a current of dry, warm air. Later, soaked in water, they can be prepared with little loss of flavor.

For canning they should be thoroughly cleaned and placed in boiling water for three minutes, then into jars and, with a level teaspoonful of salt, pressure cooked for 40 minutes or 3 hours of hot-water bath.

Freezing is the simplest of all. Slice the mushrooms in half, soak in salt water for ten minutes, rinse, drain, pack in containers, and dash them to the freezer.

They may be sauteed, boiled, baked, or made into soups, omelets, or sauces. The veteran sponger prefers them sauteed. Wash, soak in cold, weak salt water for fifteen minutes, slice the larger pieces down the middle, sprinkle lightly with flour, and fry slowly in an open skillet in butter. Season sparingly, for care must be taken not to impair the heavenly, delicate flavor. Take them straight—you won't want anything with them unless it might be a glass of ice-cold beer, or a filet.

A scholarly and thoughtful man once said of the morel: "The morel is truly the food of the gods. It is their exclusive food and it grows in the Elysian Fields in plenty; morels are rare among us mortals for the gods only reluctantly and rarely bestow their blessings on man. We must be content with the crumbs from the tables of the gods."

Morels are rare, and sponge hunters are secretive about where they find them. The same spot is good for years.

Tom Lasater is a straight-talking, controversial figure in cattle circles with a bagful of off-beat ideas that leave the conventional cattle breeder in a state of shock.

# The Innovator

THIS is a story about a man who became dissatisfied with the kind of cattle he was raising and developed his own breed. The story isn't so much about the new breed as it is about the unorthodox and original system of performance testing the breeder used to build his dream cattle.

The man is Tom Lasater. His 17,000-acre Colorado ranch sits astride Big Sandy Creek at Matheson, about 50 miles northeast of Colorado Springs. That puts him in the foothills of the Rockies where his cattle graze in a rarified atmosphere of some 5,500 feet. Way down at Falfurrias in the southern tip of Texas he has another ranch where the climate and altitude contrast sharply with the Colorado layout. This one he remote controls from the Colorado homestead. A dictating machine which records on a flat, easily mailable disc affords him an easy flow of directives and exchange of experiences with his Spanish-speaking Texas foreman.

In case you've never met Mr. Lasater we'll warn you to keep your guard up. Dressed in his Levis and boots, with a well-tanned face beaming out from under his Stetson, there's no mistaking the man's profession. In his mid-forties, he has the build of a sharply trained middle-weight boxer. He is a straight-talking, controversial figure in cattle circles with a bagful of off-beat ideas that leave the conventional cattle breeder in a state of shock. But success proves he's still far from needing a guardian.

The breed he originated is the Beefmaster—big, beefy cattle with the heavy, drooping ears of the Brahman and the Brahman hump in the males. They are the result of a cross of Brahman, Hereford and Shorthorn and come in all colors and mixtures of colors—red, black, white, yellow, brindle, roan, spotted—with red probably predominating. No effort has ever been made to select for color. Tom Lasater's father, the late Edward C. Lasater, ran 20,000 head of range cattle on his Falfurrias ranch and, in 1908, introduced Brahman bulls into his herd. He was once a pillar of the Jersey breed with his herd of 3,000 of the Channel Isle cattle. He also bred a strain of Herefords with red around the eyes. Tom's herd still shows evidence of this strain. Pigmentation around the eye, according to the Lasaters, and other experienced cattlemen, is a guarantee against cancer eye and pinkeye.

His herd is still small by range country standards. He has about 630 cows and heifers of which 350 are on the Colorado ranch. Dry weather and drastic culling make expansion slow.

The conformation of the Beefmasters, particularly the cows, is hard to describe. At first glance one is tempted to say they come in all shapes and sizes. But after riding around the Lasater ranges for awhile it becomes apparent they have several definite and important characteristics. They are big-bodied, long, of extreme heart girth, and with hindquarters that would delight the eye of the most discriminating packer buyer. Because of their infinite color pattern one can never look at a cow and say with complete assurance, "There stands a Beefmaster." But one who looks at a Lasater Beefmaster will seldom hesitate to say, "There stands a beef cow."

They have good udders, too; udders which are well designed to do the job at hand. And they are the most gentle cattle that ever chewed a cud.

The bulls are huge, long-bodied critters of all colors whose Brahman ancestry is immediately apparent in their hump, dewlap and sheath.

The most unique thing about the Beefmasters is that they are a recognized breed without herdbook or registry association. Tom Lasater cannot produce a pedigree or registration certificate for any individual in his entire herd. As a matter of fact, he can't even identify the sire of any of his animals since everything is range bred and there are no single sire herds on the ranch. That is all part of the Lasater philosophy of cattle breeding.

The goal Lasater set for the Beefmaster is efficient beef production. That's all. He doesn't give a hoot how pretty or how ugly his cattle look just so they produce beef. Individual pedigrees, says he, are for the birds—the vultures. They don't mean a thing. It's the total pedigree that counts; the herd in which every individual comes from stock with identical performance records. "Ninety-nine out of ninety-nine cowboys (cowboy is Lasater language for anyone in the cattle business) will always want to see the sire and dam of a bull calf before they

Docility is one item in Lasater's six-point standard in selecting for his Beefmaster breed. How much good beef he puts on the hoof for market is his only concern.

buy it," he says. "That's the worst thing they could do. That calf has got to stand on his own feet. His sire will represent only a small percent of the bull calf's calf crop and the same with his dam. Individual pedigrees are nothing because the blood washes out so fast."

Then he'll go on to point out the economics of breeding big, useful cattle: "The average cattleman," he says, "is overly influenced by selling price per pound. Actually it is price times weight times the size of the calf crop that gets the job done. Likewise, to produce weight it takes more than just depth of body or width of body. It takes depth times width times length times density.

"It is the weaning weight and the size of the calf crop per one hundred cows which are the key factors in the cattle business. In any given operation, if the annual cost of carrying a cow is eighty dollars, if the net weaned calf crop averages eighty per cent and the weaning weights average four hundred pounds, it follows that the cost of calf production will be twenty-five cents per pound.

"If this calf crop can be boosted to ninety per cent and the weaning weights to five hundred pounds, the calf production cost would be lowered to less than eighteen cents per pound.

"For the past five years we have averaged a net, weaned calf crop from all cows, including two year olds, of eighty-five per cent here at Matheson and eighty-nine per cent at Falfurrias. Both ranches have been through the worst drouth in history during this period and under these rough range conditions our calves will average six hundred pounds or better at eight months of age."

The man isn't exaggerating when he talks about the 600-pound weaning weights. That's exactly what his bull calves weighed at weaning Dec. 1, last year, at an average age of seven months. On July 1 of this drouth year, they averaged 994 pounds. Their only feed was two pounds of dehydrated alfalfa pellets a day from Dec. 15 to March 25 and six pounds of a grain protein pellet. During storms when they were unable to forage for themselves they were given some hay.

Lasater's all-time record on weaning weights was in the fall of 1948 when a three-year-old cow in a demonstration herd he had at Mason, Texas, turned off a 906-pound bull calf. The calf appropriately enough was named Don Elefante. The 17 bull calves from that particular demonstration herd averaged 668 pounds at eight months and the 27 heifers hit 563 pounds. None of these calves received any supplemental feed. The only winter feed their dams received was 2¾ pounds per day of 32 per cent protein range cubes for 70 days.

The program which produces this kind of cattle Lasater calls the caldron system of breeding, or the anti-pet system. And he guarantees that any breeder who has the courage and tenacity to follow it can have the herd of his dream in three generations of cattle, six years if he breeds his heifers as yearlings.

He makes no qualifications as to breed either. "Forget you ever heard of Beefmasters," he says, "you can do this with any breed you choose. You start by getting a bull from any ranch you want— say X Ranch. Look around, find the man who is turning out the kind of cattle you like, then get a bull from him. The important thing is in selecting the type of cattle that meets your standards regardless of the breed.

"Breed this bull to your cows—and again it makes no difference what breed they are, whether they are the same breed as the bull or not. Weigh and select the top heifers from these matings and breed them back to another bull from X Ranch. Select the top heifers again and repeat the process. After three crosses like this your herd will carry seven-eighths of the blood of the X Ranch and you will have your dream cattle. The judgment you have exercised in your culling and selecting will be much more important than the influence of the one-eighth original blood."

The system demands courage and tenacity. The caldron system is a very apt name. Lasater literally boils the culls out of his herd. He works with masses of genes, continually stirring the pot, selecting from the top those animals which meet his standards and ruthlessly culling everything else.

That's where the anti-pet idea comes in. There are no pets on the Lasater Ranch. Each individual must stand on its own feet. It gets no credit for being by an outstanding sire or out of an outstanding dam. The heifers are bred to calve at two. If they fail to drop and wean an early calf that year, or any subsequent year, out they go, with no exceptions.

"Any breeder who gives his cows a second chance just doesn't give himself an even break," is Lasater's way of looking at it. "True, we occasionally lose a good one this way," he says, "but we do get rid of *all* the lemons. You're not going to hurt yourself if you lose an outstanding one now and then so long as you keep the *average* of your herd at a high level;

but you can't afford to keep lemons."

All of which leads to another Lasater maxim: "No man can make any real progress in livestock breeding with high-priced stock. He just won't have the courage to knock a ten or twenty-thousand-dollar lemon in the head."

In Lasater's book there are no secrets, no mysticism in sound, progressive livestock breeding. The key is to limit your goal and keep your standards simple. If you want to breed beef, select for beef characteristics and nothing else.

"If you want to breed long-tailed cattle, that's easy enough," he says. "If you want red-colored cattle, that's easy too. But if you want long-tailed, red cattle that will make beef too, you're complicating the issue and it can't be done."

So to breed beef Tom Lasater has set up a six-point standard. He selects his cattle on the basis of disposition, fertility, weight, conformation, hardiness and milk production. No numerical value is placed on any of these standards. They are blended and when any one of them gets very far out of line it automatically becomes 100 per cent. For example, should a cow be just about perfect on the first five points but a poor milker, her days are numbered.

The Lasater Beefmasters have a disposition that seems to be the result of an outcross with a St. Bernard dog. Actually, that is how docile they are. Lasater attributes this to their Brahman blood. Docility, he contends, is an indication of intelligence, and Brahmans, for his money, are the smartest cattle that ever lived. Still, he admits this is a characteristic that can be found in any cattle, one that can be brought out by careful handling and selection. He breeds in the factor, then gives it every opportunity to assert itself. A stranger can go onto any Lasater range and the cattle will come right up and lick his face.

This is a "real cute characteristic" as Tom puts it, but it pays off. Quiet, relaxed cattle gain much faster than their tense, skittish brethren and it is a lot cheaper to handle them. Two cowboys and one of his older sons (13 and 11 years of age) are all the help he needs to work his herd.

Fertility is taken care of on the dam's side by culling. Every female two years old and up on the ranch has produced a calf every year or she wouldn't be there. A nine-year-old cow has produced eight calves, a twelve-year-old cow, eleven calves. And they must be dropped during a 42-day period in the spring. The bulls are turned in with the heifers and cows

the first of July for 63 days—three heat periods. The calves begin to arrive the following April 10 and any cow that drops her calf after May 22 is automatically culled. This eliminates the shy, slow breeders. It also insures a uniform calf crop for size and weight.

On the sire's side fertility is insured by the fact that the most fertile bulls sire the most calves. The yearling heifers are always kept separate from the older cows. Yearling bulls are run with them at the rate of one bull to ten heifers. Bulls are run with the cows two years old and up at the rate of one to twenty. Lasater has no way of knowing whether he has any infertile bulls in the herd. But he doesn't care. "If I have an infertile bull or a shy breeder," he says, "he doesn't hurt me a bit. All he costs is his keep. The fertile bulls breed the cows and this fertility is perpetuated in the calves.

"Can you imagine anyone trying to make a bull breed when he's shy or infertile, dosing him with hormones and all that kind of stuff? That's the kind of thing a man does when he starts fooling around with high-priced stock. He has a big investment and thinks he has to protect it that way. If a man is trying to make a living raising beef, fertility is priceless. Why would he want to perpetuate the genes of an infertile or shy animal?"

Weight, of course, is a major point in Lasater's selection program. All the bull calves are weighed individually at weaning and the bulls are weighed at least once a year as they go into service. Low gainers are eliminated.

The heifers are weighed in bunches at weaning and averages taken, and the yearling heifers are weighed at the beginning and at the end of the grass season. Lasater tops out 70 per cent of his heifers for replacements. Although individual weights are not kept in this department, small or pony-type heifers are culled by eye. Average weights are kept to make sure the herd is showing progress and culling is guided by the other five factors.

A recent visitor to the Lasater Ranch commented on what he felt was a "poor" head on one of the bulls. Lasater's reply was: "Out here we start judging cattle at the hindquarters and work forward. When we get to the front of the shoulders we stop looking. We don't care if they have a head or not. The only thing cattle need a head for is to take in food and water and emit a mating call. You can go to any packing house and buy all the 'good' heads you want for a dollar apiece."

That pretty well sums up the Lasater approach to conformation. If it will make beef—fine. If it won't—forget it. Those points which bear directly on dressing percentage and dressed beef grade are given prime consideration along with the points which make an animal a good rustler. A scientist once pointed out to Lasater that his Colorado ranges are the perfect grazing land, but that an animal must be equipped to get around on them like a buffalo or a horse. "We knew that all along," says Tom. "That's why we've always demanded that our cattle have a long, easy, swinging stride. A critter with a short, muscle-bound gait can't make it."

Lasater pays no attention to color or horns. Those are just distractions in his quest for beef characteristics; they have no correlation with beef-making ability. He admits that many breeders have been able to control color and at the same time produce outstanding cattle; but, he argues, they have sacrificed a high percentage of potentially good genes to get this color. The price is too high.

Many kibitzers have suggested that he try to breed the horns off his cattle. "Why complicate matters," he asks, "to do a job any farmer can do for twenty-five to fifty cents."

His reply to the popular enthusiasm for a "mellow, loose hide" is that he has never seen a steer whose hide didn't go all the way around him.

There is only one test for hardiness that will satisfy the Beefmaster's originator—survival of the fittest. In his herd there is no excuse for weakness. He defines hardiness as the animal's ability to maintain itself in a healthy, vigorous condition on the range without any assistance from man. The Lasater cattle are vaccinated against Black Leg, they are dehorned, they receive a little hay and some alfalfa pellets in the winter and that is about all the help they get. Any individual which needs treatment that is not herdwide in its application is culled. If a cow needs her hooves trimmed, if she needs assistance in calving, if she has to be milked out to prevent a caked udder, out she goes. If a bull develops sheath trouble he is dropped.

Result: A herd that is free from cancer eye, pinkeye, Bang's disease; cows with sound udders that provide a maximum of milk for their calves; healthy, vigorous bulls. The average production life of Lasater's cows is 14 years.

The feeding schedule was touched on above but it should be mentioned again as it is one of the tools in the development of hardiness. The cattle are expected to thrive under rough range conditions. In summer their only feed is the grazing they can rustle for themselves. Winter feed is 2 pounds per day of dehydrated alfalfa pellets with 12 per cent black-

Tom Lasater blended the genes of Brahman, Hereford and Shorthorn cattle to produce his own unique breed, the Beefmaster. "I don't care if they come out with purple polka-dots, as long as they make good beef," he says.

strap molasses added to the pellets. This 17 per cent protein feed they get for 100 days, from December 15 to March 25. Hay is fed only during storm conditions when the cattle can't get grass. Only the yearling bulls get supplemental protein—6 pounds of a grain protein pellet beginning at weaning and tapering off in the spring. At a price of $60 per ton for the alfalfa pellets it costs Lasater around $6 plus whatever hay she eats to winter a cow.

"We're in the milk business the same as any dairyman," is Lasater's comment on his herd's milk production. "Our cows must give enough milk to wean a big, husky calf. How much that is we don't know and neither does anyone else. Some people will try to tell you twenty-five pounds of milk a day is the optimum. We say twenty-five thousand pounds isn't too much if the cow and calf can handle it. The sky's the limit." Selection for milk production has been controlled by culling both the cows that failed to wean calves of qualifying weight or better and the cows that required milking at calving time.

Those are the Lasater standards and he sticks to them with grim tenacity. Any cow that drops a calf one hour after the 42-day period in the spring is a goner. If a cow loses a calf from any cause out she goes. Tom Lasater insists that it is only by this kind of absolutely ruthless culling that a man can make progress in cattle breeding. It is the only way to throw out every single lemon; the only way to continually raise the quality of the average of the herd.

Another Lasater rule is to make as few decisions as possible. "Let God decide" is one of his most frequent admonitions. "We didn't decide what kind of udders our cows should have," he says. "We selected for milk production and God put the udders on them."

After a man is completely steeped in a philosophy of breeding like this the actual culling and topping out of a herd—making them run the gauntlet, as Lasater calls it—is practically automatic.

"You don't want to waste your time fooling around with the outstanding individuals," he warns. "They're nice to look at and all that but the place where you have to put your time and judgment to work is on the border line. It's just like a man going through a forest looking for trees of a certain dimension. Those that are well above or below that size he never gives a second look. The border line cases demand his time.

"So at weaning time when we are topping out our heifers we make a rough cut first, top and bottom. Then a top heifer in the cull pen or a cull heifer in the top pen will stick out like a sore thumb. Then we mill through the pens looking for minor points, maybe clicking in ankles and hocks indicating a tendency toward double-jointedness and an inability to carry weight. We're all the time watching for skittishness and signs of a nervous disposition.

"We know all the calves come from fertile stock since we have already eliminated all those dropped after the forty-second day of calving; we've checked them all on weight; we've given them the once over for conformation; we know that if they and their sires and dams hadn't passed the test for hardiness they wouldn't be here; and we can get a line on their dam's milk production from the calf's size and condition. First thing you know our topping is finished."

Calving time is the main culling point for the cows. That is when those that fail to drop a calf or calve after the 42-day period put themselves on the check-out list. Then some more are culled in the fall for having raised a poor calf.

The bull gauntlet starts at about two and a half months. Obviously, poor calves are castrated at that age. This year 53 bull calves were saved and 71 castrated on the first go-round. Eleven more were cut in September and an additional selection was made at weaning time. The yearling bulls are weighed and a final selection made before they go into service and they are weighed and topped out every year thereafter.

The entire Lasater operation is keyed to the production of breeding stock under rough range conditions. The steers and cull heifer calves go to market right off the cows at weaning time. Nine or ten yearling bulls go into the herd along with ninety to one hundred heifers. Bull calves from the top 30 per cent of the crop are offered to the public for breeding purposes.

The Lasater program is performance testing carried to the extreme. He admits that in a program in which the majority of the decisions are left to nature, numbers are a man's best friend. Yet he is convinced that even the man with only a 20-cow herd can lift his stock far above the average and make continual progress if he will only limit his goal, cull ruthlessly —and let nature make most of the decisions.

"One of the country's larger breeders unintentionally paid us the finest compliment we've ever received," he says. "This breeder told a friend, 'Nature has done for Tom Lasater what he refused to do for himself.'"

Lasater's cattle are gentle; these walked right up and tried to lick the photographer.

# Feeling for Turtles

A Green River turtle hunter tells his experiences in his own words

ALTHOUGH this method of catching the hard-shelled snapping turtle may not appeal to most folks, others will not hunt them any other way. The snapping turtle is nocturnal in its habits, they are voracious, they will eat most anything that comes their way; it is said that snappers never feed except under water. It is strictly carnivorous. Many young ducks and mushrats fall prey to the sharp jaws of the snapper.

When daylight comes the turtle will retreat to some dark place such as the bank holes of mushrats, overhanging banks under tree roots, along the banks under-driftwood piles, old submerged logs; they frequent sluggish waterways, ponds and lakes more so than they do swift rocky streams. The best time to feel for turtles is on nice warm days from daylight to noon, as the turtle will most likely be headed in during the first part of the day; they

turn and will be headed out; then they are most likely to bite the feeler's hand.

Feeling for turtles should never be undertaken in an area where the cottonmouth moccasin is found as they frequent the same places as do the turtles. The harmless water snake is very frequently found when feeling under the banks of creeks. They will sometimes give you a very nasty bite but are in no way dangerous. It is always wise to identify any snake that should by any chance bite you. I never worry about them as I am also a snake collector and come by some nice specimens while feeling for turtles.

My experience with turtles is that they will bite under water the same as they will above water. I have never been bitten badly although I know feelers who have been terribly bitten; a large snapper can and will take a finger off with his sharp mandi-

56

bills. One should always take a buddy with him so he will have some one to help him if he should get into trouble; a first-aid kit and a good sharp knife should always be carried with the turtle feeler. I always keep my hand closed into a fist; in this way it is difficult for the turtle to get a hold on the fingers. Many times I have had them bite my hand when they strike.

I always wear only trunks and tennis shoes when feeling for turtles. I wade along the banks and feel as far as I can reach back in all the mushrat holes and overhanging banks. There are times when mushrats will attack your hand; they can give you bad bites. I feel around in all tree roots and drift piles and old logs; when a turtle is found I feel around the shell until I find the deep notches in the shell over the tail, then I get hold of the tail and out they come. If they are very large I use a gaff hook on them. If a turtle should bite you they will sometimes release their hold in a short time if you push their head back in the shell with the gaff hook, otherwise you will have to cut them loose or wait a long time; then there are some that may not let go at all.

I never keep a turtle under six inches. Some may weigh fifty pounds or more; they are dangerous ones and get very nasty when gaffed and are hard to handle. It is wise to keep your hands away from their feet as they have long sharp claws and can cut you to the bone and cause a bad wound. I don't know of snappers clamping on you with the shell; their shell is not hinged like that of the box turtle. Therefore there is no danger of being clamped on by the shell.

Turtles may be sold to a great many places in the larger cities, fire departments, lodges, American Legions, sporting clubs, restaurants, hotels, markets where sea foods are sold. Good singles are bought by the individual who does not want more than one. Any amount of turtles can be kept indefinitely in pens made of heavy wire netting; ten-foot square will take care of twenty-five or thirty turtles very nicely. The pen must be built in water deep enough so that the turtles can completely submerge, as turtles cannot eat if not submerged. Most any kind of meat will do to feed them; some place should be provided so they can get into the dark during daylight. They can then be sold as you get your orders; small ads in local papers will usually sell all you can get. Most everyone lives within a hundred miles of large cities and should not have any trouble selling all they can catch.

I sell most all I catch live weight for forty cents a pound. I do not have to dress very many; sometimes buyers want them dressed. Here is how I dress them. I first get them to take hold of a pair of pliers, then I pull their heads out as far as I can and cut them off close to the head. I then hang them up and let them bleed for a couple of hours. I then scald them until the dark skin slides off easily, leaving the skin a creamy white. Then I cut the feet off with a pair of snips, then the bottom plate is cut loose from the upper shell and removed, the entrails are then taken out, leaving only the meat and shell to be separated, which is easily cut out. The loin cannot be taken out, so I cut the spine and the two loin strips out with a cleaver; the skin may or may not be taken off. Personally I never take the skin off as it retains all of the flavor in cooking. All scent glands are removed as is the fat which has a strong taste. I deliver live turtles with the car; they may be put in gunny sacks or left loose in the back of the car. For dressed turtles I have an army food container with six food compartments with clamp-on lids and space for fifty pounds cracked ice. This will keep the meat in good shape a long time. I get up to eighty cents a pound for them dressed.

# My own favorite turtle dishes:

### Roasted Turtle on the Shell

*Dress turtle as instructed, only leave bottom plate attached on one side, remove entrails, wash good two or three times, stuff with dressing, sew on bottom shell and roast until well done. Dressing may be any kind the individual may desire. A few strips of bacon may be laid over the bottom plate to keep it from roasting too dry.*

### Fried Turtle

*Take pieces of turtle, dry them, dip into egg batter, roll in cracker meal or corn meal, season to taste, and fry in very hot deep fat.*

### Turtle Soup

*Brown 1 lb. ground turtle meat in 1 tablespoon shortening. Add small (12 oz.) bottle catsup, two onions chopped fine, 4 hardboiled eggs chopped or sliced, ½ lemon sliced, two quarts water, three tablespoons browned flour (place flour in a shallow pan in a slow 300° oven and turn frequently until well-browned) and 1 tablespoon pickling spices in a bag. Add salt, pepper, Worcestershire sauce and lemon juice to taste. Simmer for two hours. Remove spice bag before serving. This makes a potful big enough for a family of four.*

### Baked Turtle

*Take the desired amount of turtle, place in roaster, place strips of bacon over turtle, add a couple of bay leaves, a cup of apple cider, ½ teaspoon salt, ⅛ teaspoon cinnamon, 1/16 teaspoon each cloves and nutmeg. Start your oven at 325 degrees F. or slow. Put meat on rack in roasting pan (if you are without proper rack, set meat on lid of shortening can with holes punched in it), lay bacon strips and bay leaf on top, season with salt and pepper, heat the apple cider and add the spices; every fifteen minutes baste turtle with this tantalizing mixture and see what a flavor it gives the turtle; bake till turtle is tender.*

# The Swimming Hole

"YOU can't go swimmin' for an hour after dinner, or you'll get the cramps. So's you might as well chop some stove wood." That's the final word from Aunt Martha as the screen door slams. For awhile there is the intermittent sound of chopping from behind the summer-kitchen, then silence, then a boy's voice at the kitchen door: "Is it two o'clock yet, Aunt Martha?" As the last few minutes drag past there is only the low hum of boys' voices, punctuated by loud "I betcha's." "I betcha' I'll be the first one in! . . . I betcha' I can stay under the longest." Finally the screen door squeaks open and Aunt Martha gives the word, "Now you can go." The first quarter mile is taken at a run; then panting the boys slow down to a trot. The closer they get to the swimming hole the hotter the stones become. Then there's the clover field to cross, cool and moist to the bare feet. Far in the west there are towering thunderheads, motionless in their majesty.

The heavy, sweet breeze from the black locusts in bloom across the creek is spiced with a trace of mint. Only the clank of Uncle George's mowing machine following the wandering creek meadow breaks the spell of the growing, vibrating world. The last few yards are done at a sprint and clothes are shed on the run. A stinging splash of a "bellywhacker" is the start of an afternoon of splashing, diving and baking in the sun that is never matched on exclusive beaches or in tiled pools. Here you can know the cooling softness of water along your full naked length. Here you can be half porpoise and half boy. It's good fun to tie your best friend's clothes in knots and hide them in the bushes, even if you know that he will do the same to yours. This is the old swimming hole. This is the kind of a summer day that country boys carry in their memory always; when they think of summer, these smells and sounds and feels come rushing back.

60

# Summer Romance

ALL of a sudden it hit you! You saw her standing in the sun with the clean wind tossing her hair . . . and the girl in the yellow sunbonnet who cried at your schoolboy taunts was gone. Instead, there stood a woman, slim and sweet and smiling, with dreams in her eyes that two could share. There was a touch of magic in that summer. Somehow, the senses were sharpened. Every bird, every cricket sounded a fanfare for your sweetheart. In the fragrant evenings, there were meetings in the orchard and by the spring-house where the honeysuckle climbs. There were trips to town, and long goodnights. The white clematis on the porch was luminous by moonlight, and the lightning-bugs winked in the distant meadow. There were richer summers in the years together, but none held the magic of the first.

Berle Mercer and his family left Nebraska to stake a homestead in Alaska. The government has given him a 20-year lease to see if he can profitably raise these Highlander beef cattle for Alaskan consumers.

# The NEW Pioneers

STATEHOOD for Alaska has opened vast new and unclaimed acreage within the United States. The new State poses an inevitable question to a restless people with a tradition of moving into new country: What does it take to make a go of farming there?

Berle Mercer and his wife, Claire, know some of the answers from recent and vivid experience, having completed their first year and a half in the territory. At least, they know how to start a cattle ranch on the edge of the arctic circle.

They have brought a herd of cattle through the 40-below-zero winter on the open range without disastrous losses. They have lived through the weeks of gloomy darkness of midwinter and the mosquito-infested days without night in summer. They have reveled in the wonders of their wild acres of tundra, forest, crag, and mountain meadow at the foot of North America's highest peak.

To keep them solvent, Claire worked in a government office in Fairbanks during the winter—commuting weekly on a train that regularly locked horns with bull moose on the track. Berle cared for their three children and for his herd of cattle in

weather that will freeze spit before it hits the snow. Through it all they have learned how to ranch in this new and strange country. Each of them had one thing it takes to make a go of a ranch or a marriage, the affection and unquestioning support of the other.

The Mercers, in the very vanguard of what promises to be a new Alaska "gold rush," certainly could never have fit happily into the more settled ways of modern American farming. In spirit and temperament they are pioneers, individualists whose lives have been colored by a desire to get away from the rigid pattern of stateside life and be themselves. This state of mind no doubt has been encouraged by the fact that genetically they do not follow the usual pattern—both are identical twins. Their marriage made the headlines when in a double ceremony Berle married Claire and Berle's twin brother, Merle, married Claire's twin sister, Clarice.

As identical twins invariably do, both miss their twins back in the home state of Nebraska. There as kids the two brothers had sat on the corral fence and talked out their dreams of what they would do when they married and started out on their own.

Both agreed they wanted to be cattlemen, like their father, and both agreed Nebraska was too small for them.

The brothers met their future wives at a convention of the International Twins Association in Omaha thirteen years ago. Courtship was carried on mostly by mail. They were married in October, 1950, in Mount Vernon, New York, the home of Claire and Clarice. The two couples went to live on the home ranch, near Thedford, where the boys continued working.

Soon after their honeymoon the four of them were sitting again on the corral fence. "We're going to Alaska," Berle said. "We'll lease land and take up some animals and be ready to feed people who'll go there for the oil and the mines. It's crowded here—too many people. Claire and I want elbow room. Besides, if you haven't an 'in' here, you're out."

So the Berle Mercers went to Alaska. In May 1952 they reluctantly parted from their twins and drove a 1946 Dodge Power Wagon, loaded with personal things, up the Alcan Highway to Nanana, a small town about 90 miles north of their present location, which is almost the geographic center of the state. They planned to acquire a lease on grazing land and bring up a small herd of buffalo which Berle had bought from a government herd in South Dakota. Buffalo, he reasoned, would do just fine in Alaska. They would take the winters in stride, scrounge for themselves on the native grasses, and fight off the wolves and mosquitoes. A market could be found in the slaughterhouses which supply meat for the Indians and Eskimos.

But they were frustrated from the start. They found that the importation of buffalo is forbidden —Alaska closes the door on wild animals, and buffalo are wild animals, according to the book in Washington. Then government red tape held up the lease. Further complicating their problems was the arrival in November of their first child. Short of cash and with no lease in sight for the foreseeable future, they reluctantly returned to Nebraska in February, 1953.

But their dream was not tarnished—they would regroup and replan. They knew now what Alaska demanded, and they knew what they wanted and how to get it. They had passed through the Mt. McKinley National Park on their way to Nanana and had seen the wild grasses hip-high in the mountain valleys. Old Alaska hands told them this area

This is the Alaskan frontier of Berle Mercer. The redtop native grass feeds his cattle well, but he carries the rifle for emergencies and the incessant mosquito plagues both man and beast.

is the best cattle country in the territory—the winter winds sweep the deep snow from the pastures and here the chinooks come early. Berle applied for a lease in the McKinley reserve and late in 1956 signed for 290,400 acres. This leased land surrounded a place he had heard about in Anchorage, a hunting lodge, with other farm buildings and 158 acres of deeded land within sight of Mt. McKinley. And the lodge and land were for sale.

Another lucky break for the Mercers came when a rancher near Thedford heard of Berle's plan to develop a breed of cattle for Alaska. In the neighbor's opinion Mercer seemed to be just the sort of fellow to make a go of an Alaska venture. He offered to grubstake him and agreed to buy and ship an assorted lot of crosses as soon as the Mercers were located and in operation. Berle's father became a

second backer when he loaned them $20,000 to purchase a hunting lodge and its 158 acres.

So again, in February, 1957, Berle loaded the personal belongings of the family in a newer Power Wagon and plowed and slid up the Alcan Highway to Anchorage and on to Healy, 200 miles to the north. Two miles from Healy he unloaded the wagon at the lodge, started a fire in the kitchen stove, and went to work. He crossed off the days until Claire and the children—three boys by this time—would join him, by air, in April. The cattle came a little later, in June.

The cattle for the big experiment were purchased from Baxter Berry of the XX Ranch, Belvedere, South Dakota. There were 54 of them, 11 purebred Scotch Highlanders and 43 crosses, Highlander-Longhorn, Highlander-Hereford, and Highlander-

Shorthorn. They left Belvedere by truck on May 26, 1957, were taken up the Alcan Highway, and loaded on railway cars at Fairbanks for the final leg of the trip. They arrived in good condition at Lignite on June 3 and were immediately turned on range. There were 4 bulls, 10 cows, 9 steers and the remainder young heifers. Berle brought up 14 of his own cattle from the Nebraska ranch in the early summer. These included two milk cows.

Almost everything happened to the cattle that summer and winter, most of it bad, and much of it unexpected. The herd split up and a pair apparently started back for their native Scotland, for they were reported by a train crew late that winter holed up miles to the north.

The biggest loss, totally unexpected, came from the railroad. "That track seemed to have a fatal fascination for the cattle," Mercer said. "Only two trains a day, but it seemed there was always one of my cattle on the tracks."

A check made in the spring showed that 15 were killed on the tracks. The railroad was indirectly the cause of one other casualty. Soon after the arrival two of the purebreds calved. One of the calves wandered too near a section gang and when last seen was being chased by two Eskimo workers, who regard anything with four legs, covered with fur or hair, as fair game.

Those near the corral were fed baled native hay and one pound of cake a day. In mid-January some of them developed scabby patches due to lack of vitamins. This condition cleared up when they were given an oat-vetch-pea mixture. Those that were on range fared better, having access to wild cranberry and other native plants, which supplied the vitamins. "If I could have fed them on the oat-vetch-pea hay all winter," says Mercer, "I don't believe we would have had any losses." None of the animals were under cover during the winter.

When the spring chinooks came and the snow melted and the native redtop sprang up like magic in the mountain meadows, Mercer counted his winter losses and added up the totals of what he had learned about running cattle in Alaska. The purebred Highlanders came through far better than any of the crosses. The Highlander-Longhorn were second best, the other crosses a poor third. He stretched barbed wire to keep his cattle off the tracks, and put up as much oat-pea-vetch hay as he could lay his hands on. He knew that the Highland cattle could take the worst of the Alaskan winter and thrive; he knew that his fears of losses to bear and wolves were groundless, and that when an Eskimo section crew was working near, he had best ride herd.

At the end of his first year, 15 had been lost on the tracks, 14 had winter killed, 9 were butchered and sold, 2 were unaccounted for. He received a second shipment of 50 purebred Highlanders in August. "These are the cattle for Alaska," he says. "I'll stick to the breed.

"There's one other very important thing I've learned about raising cattle in Alaska," he adds. "They'll eat four times as much hay at 40 degrees below zero as they will at zero. It takes a lot of fuel to combat the 40-below cold. I put up 90 tons of hay last summer—this year I'll double that."

Mercer's steers put on two pounds a day on the high-protein Alaska wild redtop. The redtop is high in protein, but the first frost kills it completely and the protein shrinks almost to zero. It does make good hay if cured properly. A younger brother came up from Nebraska to help out in the haymaking. The weather was in their favor—practically 24 hours of daylight and little rain at this time of year.

Much of the 290,400 acres in the lease is worthless for grazing—mountain, tundra, and bush. However, conveniently near the corral is 3,000 acres of valley where the top soil is four feet deep and rich in calcium and phosphorus. The bush can be burned or bulldozed off, nitrogen added, and a bumper crop of oats, vetch and peas harvested. Mercer figures that the range within easy reach has a potential of 3,000 head of cattle, fed entirely from the pastures and meadows.

The Mercers live in a five-room frame house, log faced, pleasant and homelike, among trees with a fine view of valley and mountain. Mt. McKinley broods in the distance like a guardian God of the endless miles of forest and stream and mountain. A spring-fed stream runs near the house—in midsummer it is cold, and always clear and sparkling.

There are two barns, a log corral, a bunkhouse, a "cache" screened and tight against varmints and used as a deepfreeze for game and other meat, an aluminum hay shed put up recently, and assorted sheds and outbuildings—one used as a shop, another as a garage.

Included in the purchase price of the place were the furnishings of the house and assorted farm machines and tools, including an arc welder, a very necessary piece of equipment in this isolated spot. The farm machinery is heavy on the haymaking side —two mowers, two rakes, wagons, a baler, plow, disk, and a big Allis-Chalmers tractor with a fitted track for the snow and the boggy meadows. The

In the log corral, the Mercer family watch Berle rope and throw one of the Scotch Highlander cattle for treatment.
On the opposite page, the Mercers' ordinarily tractable cow leaves Berle holding the bucket in the middle of milking.

Mercers brought three horses and two mules with them from the States, and quite useful they are—gasoline is 53 cents a gallon. One of the mules took sick last winter and died. The other four animals are in good shape. Their two milk cows are Shorthorn-Scotch Highland crosses, good for both milk and beef.

They have a telephone—a call from Nebraska reaches them in minutes—and electricity from a home generator sufficient for light, appliances, and a washing machine. Fuel for heating and cooking is wood or coal, which is quite cheap there. Radio reception from Alaska stations is good. The Mercers have no TV.

The nearest neighbor is about a mile away at Lignite, a whistle stop on the Fairbanks-Anchorage railway, where there are a few families. Healy, two miles away over a dirt road, is the metropolis of the area; 200 souls support a church, a movie, and a general store where one can buy most everything that can be carried away in a shopping bag. There is no school. The Mercers plan to tutor their own children, now five, three and two, with the aid of a correspondence course.

"One of the blessings of statehood, we hope, will be convenient schools," said Mrs. Mercer. "Neither one of us knows much about teaching and I don't know how we could find the time. We'll just have to cross that bridge when we come to it."

During their first year the cash sometimes ran thin, but they squeaked through. Berle explained, "We didn't want to go heavier in debt, so Claire went into Fairbanks and got a Civil Service job. She came home on weekends and kept me and the boys in line. We couldn't have come through that winter without her salary."

Claire rode the 350-mile round trip on the government-owned, single-track Alaskan Railroad. On Monday mornings at 5:10 she flagged the train with a lantern at Lignite. Then she sat in an old coach, ignoring the too-expensive dining car, until reaching the end of the line and her secretarial job.

With the snow thrown up in high banks along the track, the trip could be delayed, very often because a bull moose would prefer the packed snow between the rails to the drifts on either side where he was easy game for the wolves. For 10 to 15 miles the moose would run ahead of the train until, exasperated, he would turn, lower his head, paw the ground, and charge. Two thousand pounds of moose would jolt the train, halted by the wary engineer. The bull would rebound, eyes glazed, and fall in his

tracks with a broken neck. The Indian crew would then emerge, bleed him, and hoist the fresh meat into the baggage car.

The Mercers have a kitchen garden which supplies them with fine vegetables during the season. "You plant a seed up here," says Berle, "and it pops out of the ground; you can almost see it growing." Cabbage, beans, lettuce and such, mature in half the time it takes in the States, due to the long daylight and the abundant moisture and fertile soil. There are from 85 to 100 frost-free days and one can read a newspaper at midnight during two months of this period.

Recreation for the Mercers is largely home-made—a rare movie in Healy, a picnic along a mountain stream. Hunting and fishing are of the kind sportsmen dream about. "Trout fishing is so good you don't have to lie about it," says Berle. "We have plenty of deer and bear and you can always get a grouse or ptarmigan a few steps away from the house."

There is a bug in the ointment. "This would be the perfect place, for me, if it weren't for the mosquitoes," Berle said. "The first year we were here we couldn't go outside without a head net and gloves from early spring to summer. They came in black clouds and were big and bloodthirsty. We were all a mass of bumps. This year they haven't been so bad. The children have played outside in shorts."

At times mosquitoes are a menace to livestock. "Cattle won't graze when they're fighting mosquitoes," says Berle, "and after a while they accumulate so much poison they lose weight. I've had to carry a switch to drive them away from my horse's face—they would choke him if I didn't. One reason the Highlanders fared better than the other cattle was their long hair gave them pretty good protection against mosquitoes as well as the cold."

The problem of combating the sub-zero temperatures was not as great as the Mercers had anticipated. "Forty degrees below zero isn't so bad if you know how to dress for it," Berle said. "You don't dare stick your tongue out and you've got to be careful about your ears and feet and hands.

"The cattle, if they have a windbreak, do very

Mercer, with his youngest son (right), flags the Fairbanks-Anchorage train. The train crew handles such errands as ordering spare parts or fetching medicine.

well. We had a case or two of frozen hocks among the cross breeds, but the Highlanders know how to protect themselves. They were better off than we were in the water department—we often had to melt ice, but the Highlanders ate snow.''

Mercer carries a rifle in a saddle holster wherever he rides. "You never know when you'll find an injured or sick animal you have to finish off. If you should get hurt yourself, or lose your horse a rifle is the best thing to have with you. And I'm always on the lookout for predators—they may not harm me but the less of them the less danger to livestock, especially the calves I hope we'll soon be having.

"We think we've licked the two big problems, the winter darkness and the isolation, of living in Alaska," Berle says. "We don't see the sun for five weeks in winter—it never even peeps over the mountains to the south. During the darkness we take all the time we can doing the chores, we read a good deal, listen to the radio, write long letters home.

"I don't mind the isolation—a Nebraska ranch seasons you to that. But Claire, who worked in a busy office before we were married, might have had a few bad months if she'd had time to think about it. This would be a sad place if you didn't like the people around you. We all love each other here and while we're isolated, we've never been lonely. We do miss our kin and we miss most of all neighbors with similar interests. I would like to talk over common problems with neighbors—that would be helpful because we've had no experience to follow here."

Mercer will have 20 years, the term of his lease, to round out his experiment. He is required to run 50 cattle the first year of the lease, 150 the third year, and 500 the fifth year. Lease costs are reasonable—the first three years will cost him a total of $400; after that, 60 cents per animal unit per year. He can grow anything, but he cannot sell anything off the land except as beef. A recent law revises the homestead regulations—no homesteads can be taken out on leased land. He cannot purchase land within the lease, and cannot homestead himself.

Alaska produces only about 5 per cent of the food it consumes. In that field lies the big opportunity, but climate is the limiting factor. Those who know say that only in beef can the state be self-sustaining. That is why Berle Mercer should be judged as a wise and far-sighted farmer, willing to risk the hardships of a pioneer life to prove that there is a good living to be made in cattle in Alaska.

These letters, written by the Mercers to the editor after this story was completed, show their personalities, better than anything we can say.

*Dear Sir:*

*I desire to have a few things more mentioned to help make a true rounded-out story:*

*My wife, Claire, worked from in early November, 1957, until July 3, 1958, as a Civil Service worker in Fairbanks, Alaska, to give us needed operating money for the ranch here, and groceries. If it had not been for her working I don't know how we would have ever managed and of course this was of great importance to all of us and a great hardship for her. The most of the time she went to Fairbanks on Monday mornings, leaving here about 5:10 a.m., and came home about 11:50 p.m. Friday nights. With her spending the weeks in town it left very little time on weekends to accomplish the household tasks for a full week at a time. It also meant that she was deprived of spending very much time with the children. So you see she has suffered more and contributed more to the success this past year than anyone else and many people up here and stateside know that so it would not look or sound good for it to be written around me for everyone would then think I was a story grabber and the credit would be going where least deserved.*

*It is really wonderful having Claire home again for now we can get back into the swing of things, for things just haven't clicked right with her being gone. It did interfere a little with my work, tending three small sons during winter and spring and trying to accomplish great things out of doors.*

Berle E. Mercer

Lignite, Alaska

*Dear Sir:*

*I would like to add a few words about the letter Berle Mercer wrote you today:*

*I feel my role as family supporter has been greatly exaggerated and I do not deserve all the credit my wonderful husband has given me.*

*When it became evident last fall that we would need additional income, we tried to figure out the best plan all around. If Berle had taken a job, most of the ranch work would have had to be neglected, and our whole operation would have suffered. By my taking a job, our cattle received the attention they deserved and the most necessary work was accomplished. Of course, having the additional care of three small children and the house, Berle was greatly hampered from getting everything done that he would have liked to. But I think he deserves much more credit than anyone, for taking such wonderful care of the boys during the weeks, with the cooking to do, much of the laundry, keeping the house constantly warm—and all the outdoor chores and work besides, which included checking on the cattle every day, whether it was 40 below zero or not.*

*There is no doubt that this arrangement was a hardship on all of us, and we are all delighted that it is over. But I do want to emphasize that Berle is the one who has kept us going. We are, all of us, working hard at this together, and I look upon my past job in Fairbanks as no more than doing my share to succeed here.*

*Just wanted you to know how I felt—no one is more courageous or generous than my husband, or deserves more praise!*

Claire L. Mercer

Lignite, Alaska

# Pickling Time

"MOST people know, just naturally, what's good for them," said Mrs. James B. Nichols of Newtown, Connecticut, as she looked up from peeling a brittle, deep-green cucumber. "Why, I remember my Grandmother always used to have either cucumber pickles or little sweet ones on the table for breakfast every morning. One fall she wasn't feeling so well and Mother told the Doctor she thought Grandma shouldn't eat pickles for breakfast. The Doctor's answer was short and to-the-point, 'If she has had pickles for breakfast these 92 years, then taking them away won't help.' "

Highway Six, between Danbury and Newtown, Connecticut, now cuts through the Nichols' farm, fairly close to the beautiful, big white frame homestead that's been in the family over 200 years. Over the farm home tower huge maple trees. The view from the high hilltop takes you far down the Hoosatonic River valley.

"Cucumber pickles," says Mrs. Nichols as her eyes sparkle, "Yes, indeed; I recall the crocks and crocks and jars and jars of pickles put up every year, when I was a girl at home. There were eight children in our family, and one or two aunts living with us always, and never less than two hired men. It paid to put up lots of everything, with that big family.

"We raised bushels of cucumbers, and did we like them! Had them for breakfast in season. And, oh, the pickles!" continued Mrs. Nichols, "I'll give

you some of our favorite recipes. Three of them were Grandmother's, and the fourth came from the minister's wife in Roxbury, where I went to church as a girl.

"I was hardly more than a girl when I met Mr. Nichols—just 17. Father thought I was too young to marry and sent me to Wheaton Seminary. Then when I married at 18, and came here to Newtown to live, Mother made a cookbook for me of the family recipes. I did the same thing for my own two girls, who both now live in Hawaii. I still put up plenty of pickles every summer. We think they add the spice you need with a meal. I learned to like pickles early in life and was taught cucumbers, fresh or pickled, were good for you."

Science today verifies the soundness of Mrs. Nichols' respect for the cucumber and pickle. At Michigan State College, Dr. F. W. Fabian, Research Professor of Bacteriology, with Dr. C. A. Hoppert, Professor of Biochemistry, conducted three years of study into the matter. Analyses of fresh cucumbers, and the different kinds of pickles made from them, were obtained to determine their value in the human diet. Pickles from every section of the United States were collected and studied.

Not only do they have health-giving and body-building Vitamins A, $B_1$ and $B_2$, and a very considerable amount of the anti-scurvy C Vitamin, they furnish some essential minerals, including a notable number of milligrams of iron.

No wonder ancient mariners, as well as Caesar and his legions, considered pickles a "must" for health on sea voyages or long campaigns. And Cleopatra believed them essential for beauty's sake. Queen Elizabeth prized them as a delicacy, and so, too, did the Sixteenth Century Dutch, leading fine food fanciers of the then Western World.

In our own country, George Washington and John Adams are on record for their appreciation of pickles. Thomas Jefferson wrote, "On a hot day in Virginia, I know of nothing more comforting than a fine, spiced pickle, brought up troutlike, from the sparkling depths of that aromatic jar below stairs in Aunt Sally's cellar."

No one knows when pickles were added to the human diet, but their popularity has persisted and today is growing rapidly, a classic example of the sometimes instinctive good judgment in diet. Here in the United States pickle eating is on the increase.

Time was when the chief importance of the pickle patch was to contribute to the good living of the

# 'Mmmm Pickle Recipes

*Quick Dill Pickles.* Wash small cucumbers and pack in quart jars. Place two stalks of dill with flowers in each jar, one at the bottom and one on top.

Bring to a boil:

1 quart vinegar
2 quarts water
1 cup salt

While boiling hard fill jar to overflowing and seal.

*Olive Oil Sour Pickles (brine cured).* Slice together:

100 small cucumbers
25 tiny onions

Cover with salt and let stand three hours, then drain.

Put down in a large crock with:

1 cup olive oil
4 tablespoons celery seed
4 quarts cold vinegar
2 cups mustard seed, white or black

Ready after a week, but improve with aging.

*Quick Sweet Pickles.* 7 pounds cucumbers. These should be yellow-ripe and cut in sticks.

Simmer in salted water 5 minutes and drain.

Make syrup of:

3 pounds sugar
1 pint vinegar
4 sticks cinnamon
6 whole cloves

Put cucumbers in syrup and boil just until tender, but firm. Fill jars with the cucumber sticks, cover with the syrup and seal.

"For pickling whole," advises Mrs. Nichols, "I use the White-spine, Straight or Chinese (China Long) cucumbers when small. They sell well at our roadside stand, for slicing, and are good producers. I use any of the three for the sweet pickle sticks, when yellow-ripe."

The four basic types of pickles suit a variety of tastes: overnight pickles, sweet gherkins, sours and jumbo dills.

grower and his family. Now it has vined-out into a big cash crop.

There are just four basic pickle types—dills, sours, sweets and quick or overnight—from which the countless pickle variations are derived. Three main dill types are made. The Genuine dill is produced by putting fresh-picked whole cucumbers into a brine flavored with dill and spices, and cured by natural fermentation. They are made both at home and commercially. Processed dill pickles are started in strong brine and finished later in dill solution. Overnight dills have their fermentation stopped after a few days by being put into cold storage, or by sealing jars immediately.

Sour pickles are made from cucumbers that have been cured in brine and later packed in vinegar liquor flavored with pickling spices. Whole, sliced, or in mixes with brine-cured vegetables, the varieties

of sour pickles are almost as numerous as the pickle makers.

Sweet pickles, the third basic type, are sometimes sour pickles from which the vinegar has been drained. Then they are finished in sweet, spicy liquor, the strength of the syrup being gradually increased. For finest flavor they are aged. Homemade sweet pickles are generally of the fourth type, quick or overnight.

Quick pickles include dill, sweet or sour flavors, and undergo no long brine-curing or fermentation. Easy to do, they're popular for home pickling, and when rightly made are delicious and keep well. Commercial quick pickles are often called "Quickles."

Since home pickling need not be tedious, most farm wives like to put up their own pickles. Mrs. Nichols' four New England recipes, followed with exactness, will yield prize pickles of fine flavor and crispness.

76

# Cooperation in Plum Valley

WHEN the first settlers came to Plum Valley in 1850 there were forests of oak on the hillsides, and along the creek that snaked through the Valley were thickets of wild plum trees. In autumn the children gathered the fallen plums from the banks of the creek and pulled them out of its pools with long sticks. They shared the wild fruit with the Winnebago Indians, but there was enough for all.

The red jam that the pioneer housewives made from the plums was often served with a dinner of wild duck or turkey. By the end of the first winter the creek and the fields above it were named for the fruit and called "Plum Valley."

The oaks of the Valley made the joists and framing timbers for the big barns, and the slopes they had covered were cleared for corn. By the turn of the century the creek had changed its course, for silt was washing down from the hillsides. The wild plum trees were gone and the fields stood bare at the mercy of drenching rains and winter thaws.

Ten years ago the farmers of the Valley began to worry.

The road across the bottom land on Bill Dreischmeier's farm had washed out in a flash flood. A section of the county road had to be raised because the creek was silting up and overflowing. When workmen were changing a culvert near the foot of the Valley they dug into a section of rail fence that had been buried by silt carried from farms up the Valley.

When Plum Creek flooded the Valley, Charles Schroeder said, "We lost four inches of top soil from a corn field that was just prepared, and brush washing down the creek ruined 60 rods of fencing."

When these farmers decided to take group action on their erosion troubles their first problem was to slow down the speed of the water that ran across their fields. They knew that the faster running water moves the more soil it can carry. By employing conservation practices throughout the Valley they could keep much of this water on their fields long enough for it to filter into the soil. The rest they could direct into grass drainage ditches where it could do little damage. The plan could succeed only when each of the farmers did his share in holding the water back, and providing safe grass-protected waterways.

The change started one night in February when 46 of the farmers from all over the Valley gathered at the Plum Valley schoolhouse to found an organization that was something new in soil conservation work for their community. Here the farmers in one small watershed have grouped together in an effort to conserve the resources of the whole Valley.

They had seen how one farmer can have a complete conservation plan yet suffer from the effects of erosion when silt from farms up the Valley wash down and cover fields below. One farmer can employ contour farming, terracing, diversion ditches, renovate his pasture land, tile his wet land, and

When work is slack, Plum Valley farmers gather on their cooperative experimental plots. Eight test strips on 3½ acres of sloping land each have a siltation basin and a measuring stick to tell the story of what rain does to the strip.

This 10-acre field, now a good producer, was once abandoned by Joe Barbour because of gullies. Plum Valley's conservation project gave the field contours and a new grip on life.

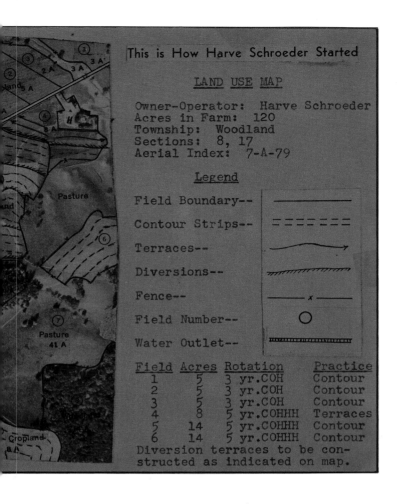

This is How Harve Schroeder Started

LAND USE MAP

Owner-Operator: Harve Schroeder
Acres in Farm: 120
Township: Woodland
Sections: 8, 17
Aerial Index: 7-A-79

Legend

| | |
|---|---|
| Field Boundary-- | ——————— |
| Contour Strips-- | = = = = = = = |
| Terraces-- | ‿‿‿→ |
| Diversions-- | //////////////→ |
| Fence-- | —— x —— |
| Field Number-- | ◯ |
| Water Outlet-- | ▬▬▬▬▬▬▬▬ |

| Field | Acres | Rotation | Practice |
|---|---|---|---|
| 1 | 5 | 3 yr.COH | Contour |
| 2 | 5 | 3 yr.COH | Contour |
| 3 | 5 | 3 yr.COH | Contour |
| 4 | 8 | 5 yr.COHHH | Terraces |
| 5 | 14 | 5 yr.COHHH | Contour |
| 6 | 14 | 5 yr.COHHH | Contour |

Diversion terraces to be constructed as indicated on map.

fence his woods, yet without the help of his neighbors do little toward making his community a better place in which to live. They felt that a conservation program to be effective must include more than one farm.

Plum Valley is in the northwest corner of Sauk County, Wisconsin, 75 miles north of Madison. It extends over into Juneau and Vernon counties. Most of the people in the Valley do their trading in Wonewoc, which is two miles from Plum Valley, and go there on Sundays to the German Lutheran Church.

From the headwaters of Plum Creek, where Joe Goodman has his farm, to the foot of the Valley where the creek joins the Baraboo River the Valley is about six miles long. The average width of the Valley is two and a quarter miles. It includes 9,660 acres of hilly land. There is some fairly level bottom land like that on the Otto Schmidt farm at the foot of the Valley, but his is the exception, for most of the land that drains its water into Plum Creek is steep and easily eroded. The top soil is shallow soil that the farmers had to do something about saving or eventually abandon.

This is dairying community and most of the

milk from its Holstein and Guernsey herds goes to the butter-processing plant at Wonewoc. The owners know that they must keep these animals in feed but have begun to realize that they can substitute grass crops for corn. Everywhere in the Valley farmers are talking about grass silage and as time goes on more of them will store their grass crops this way. It fits into their new farm conservation plans that usually require five-year rotations.

The plan to organize the farmers was conceived in the mind of Perry Carroll, the local farm planner for the Soil Conservation Service. He had been visiting the Valley regularly since he took over his job in Sauk County, and every time he traveled through those hills he could see more plainly the need for conservation action. He persuaded a few of the farmers to change over to contour farming; but most of them stuck to the old plan. One farmer said, "Perry had been coming out this way for years. He would leave some literature and in the evening when we got inside and took our shoes off we'd read it, but that was about as far as it would go. Then one time at a meeting he told us he thought it was about time to get started on soil conservation organization."

Forty-six farmers and their families attended the first meeting. Word had already reached the farms throughout the Valley. News travels fast on a party line. The farmers knew why they were gathering and wasted little time in setting up a long-range conservation program. They finished the meeting with enough ideas to keep them busy for several months. Their new by-laws stated that any farmer in the Valley could become a member of the association but that during the first year of membership he had to start using some conservation practices on his land.

The membership fee was set at one dollar a year and the fee included a whole farm. They appointed Emil Backeburg, who specializes in Guernseys and contours, temporary president and a couple of months later his neighbor Walter Larson was voted into office for the first year.

Conservation farming has meant a change in the farmer's work. In some cases the whole farm system had to be reorganized and the land farmed in entirely different fashion. It happened this way on the Schroeder farm.

Harve Schroeder is no longer young. He has three children, one of them grown and living away. He has owned his farm for thirty years. A few years ago he began to realize that there had to be some changes made if he continued to farm his steep hillsides. With the help of Carroll he drew up a complete farm plan and in one year has changed his whole program to conform. Now that he has a good start Harve says, "The only thing that makes me want to kick myself is that I didn't start farming this way twenty-five years ago."

He bought his farm right after the first World War. There are 120 acres in one strip from the creek back across the hills. Most of the land is fit only for pasture, and the fields that can be cultivated should be in long rotations that include from two to four years of grass and hay crops. He wants to work into six-year rotations as soon as he can. This will be a year of corn, a year of small grain, probably oats, and four years of hay.

All of his crop land except fifteen acres of bottom land along Plum Creek is steep enough that it must be either contour strip cropped or terraced. The contours and diversion ditches were laid out in the fall, and the next spring Harve changed as much of his land over as he could find time for. The neighbors say that he tried to do three years' work in one but that he's getting along with it.

It was a January thaw the following winter that made him fully conscious of the need for contours in his fields. "I had that piece behind the house all plowed up for spring planting," he said. "I'd put a lot of good lime and manure on it, too, then the thaw came. The water ran off that hillside and left a big gully every rod clear across the field. All the water ran down between the barn and the house. During that thaw it was so deep that I couldn't get to the barn wearing four-buckle overshoes without getting my feet wet. It just made me sick, and there I had to look at that field until seeding time. I told my wife, 'that's enough. I'm going to contour these fields.'"

He is no longer bothered with water running between the barn and house. The field is being farmed in strips that are on the contour. It is a long slope and two strips above the house is an 800-foot diversion ditch to carry run-off water from the field rather than let it chase on down the slope. On long slopes the Soil Conservation Service suggests a diversion ditch every fourth strip. When Schroeder has completed his readjustment from ordinary farming his farm will have five diversions.

Mrs. Schroeder helped plant 1500 pine seedlings on a gullied slope that is too steep to pasture. This will protect the land from future gulleying and eventually provide timber for farm use.

There are forty-one acres of pasture that will be permanent pasture as soon as Schroeder finishes working on it. He renovated fourteen acres last spring and this is now the best pasture on his farm. He worked it up with a "quack grass digger" which is a spring tooth harrow on wheels, and seeded it with a grass and legume mixture. After he had it dug up he seeded oats. In each bushel was mixed 8 to 9 pounds of brome grass. While the seedbed was still fresh he planted his pasture which included: 6-8 pounds of alfalfa, 4 pounds of red clover, and about one-half pound of ladino. Before he dug up the surface he gave the field between 200 and 400 pounds of a complete fertilizer per acre.

The middle of that same summer the field was ready to pasture. He divided it into three plots with single wire electric fences and rotated the cattle from one area to the other. Under this plan he has pasture even during the hot weeks in the middle of the summer.

The pasture that he renovated last spring is one of his steepest fields. Emil Backeberg said, "That's the field Harve fell out of a couple of times. Harve doesn't have a run-off problem on that field. The rain just hits it and falls off." There is one spot in it where he couldn't work his old narrow-gauge tractor on the contour, but had to get around above the steep place, head down-hill, set the brakes, and slide.

Schroeder's farm isn't completely changed over yet but it is well under way. He has plans to terrace one field and tile a piece of bottom land. He also wants to fence off his woodlots to complete his conservation plan.

It is hard to find a Plum Valley farmer who will deny the value of conservation farming. Most of them are convinced and sooner or later will apply soil and water-saving practices to their land.

When Perry Carroll started the Plum Valley Soil Conservation Association, he exposed himself to criticism from the other Soil Conservation Service men in his region. Their objection was that the Plum Valley organization was really an association within an association, for there was already a soil conservation district organized in Sauk County. The whole difference, however, hinged on the fact that here was a group of farmers getting together on their own rather than depending on government agencies to carry out the program.

It took one year to change the face of Plum Valley from erosion-ready hillsides to these gently-contoured farms.

# The Friendly Meal

SUPPER always seemed to be the friendliest farm meal. Certainly in the 80's it was the most pleasant hour of the day for an orphan boy heading into his teens.

Around lighting-up time, I would make for the kitchen with its pleasant odor of dried apples that dangled on long strings above Grandma's high-backed "Home Comfort" range. Earlier in the day I had watched her Vermont-proud, straight back as she swivelled from under her "broad shelf"—that wide surface housewives dedicated to cooking uses—to a barrel of buckwheat flour, measuring it out by the scoopful, preparatory to bread making.

The scent of Grandma's bread dough baking in the elevated oven at the rear of her wood-burning range had presently drifted beyond the comfortable old kitchen, an enticing aroma to young nostrils. Buckwheat, rye, graham, all were common flours of my Vermont boyhood.

Such griddle cakes as Grandma could whisk up from India wheat taken from our own acres direct to Parson's grist mill, put through his huller, ground coarsely, and returned to us in the form of flour rich with yet-to-be-discovered vitamins! Spread those cakes rim to rim with fresh country butter, right out of the butter molds with their pineapple and leaf patterns, spill some of Uncle David's pale maple syrup over a smoking pile, and you had an epicure's dream on the tines of your fork.

Supper was a simple affair. The dining room of my grandfather's weathered frame home was non-existent. All meals, prefaced by a sincere blessing, were eaten in the kitchen at a long table which easily seated ten. It was supper which found us most relaxed. No rush for after-breakfast chores, no feeling of the work ahead, which hung over dinner and urged us back to the fields.

My small tasks were nearly all done at eventide. I had carried in short chunks of split white-skinned birch until they rose in a high, even pile from the big woodbox next to our stove. I had helped Uncle lug in some pails of milk to pour in the shining staircase of four, six, and ten-quart tin pans on our milk room shelves. In my search for eggs I had braved the sound and fury of the setting hens, and these I had placed carefully on the mound in Grandma's blue-rimmed earthen bowl. What custards they would make, once Grandma broke a dozen eggs into her mixing bowl! What cookies, golden with the yellow of uncounted yolks!

If summer lay upon the hills, I would have spent my day running over green slopes; catching unwary grasshoppers; eating the comb filched from a bumblebee's nest; swimming with some barefoot crony; driving Uncle's small herd to and from their sloping pastures; loitering at the old barway where the brakes rose almost to my waist in order to gather a handful of blackberries. If snow whitened those same hills, I'd be looking for a denned-up woodchuck or sledding down long, glistening slopes, to come home with crimson cheeks and a lumberjack's appetite. When I swung up the low bank before the homestead lot, I looked forward with a twelve year old's open delight to a big meal. No formal dinner has since brought me the same glow of satisfaction.

'Soon as I pushed open the kitchen door, two

To a country boy at the end of a summer's day, supper at grandma's was always the friendliest farm meal.

Confidences shared with Caesar were sure to go no further.

house cats leaped after me. Indian pudding? Must be *that* I smelled. I could even hear the faintest sizzle in the pudding's center, on taking a hasty peek into the oven to reassure myself. Or potato soup, thick, full of grated onion, topped off with a fast-spreading blob of butter when it reached the table in a generous all-white covered tureen. With this were served puffy split crackers, known rightfully to us, since they were made in a neighbor town, as "St. Johnsbury" crackers.

Possibly pound sweets, baked until their swelled sides burst and the mixture of sugar spices in the cored interior had formed a jelly-like substance which would be enriched by a splosh of thick cream. Or apple sauce from the Mackintoshes, winesaps, transparents and red Astrakans growing in Uncle David's orchards. He was an easy mark for every nursery salesman who drove his buggy into the farmyard and always bought some new variety for the upper or lower orchard.

There might be salt pork and baked potatoes, the pork, after being cut in neat squares, floured and browned to a crisp; the potatoes mealy and white as their jackets were parted. Baked beans? Say, take some of Grandma's yellow eyes flavored with molasses from the big brown jug in the buttery, given a long, unhurried baking in her chubby bean pot.

Another Vermont favorite was baked peas. The dried peas would be soaked overnight in water drawn from our well.

Then, after a cautious parboiling with a fleck of soda in the water, these would be removed from the stove at a strategic moment and placed in a covered blue baking crock with a wire bale handle. Maple sugar would be added, and a moistening of water; by some a final pinch of ginger would be sprinkled over the concoction. Add great squares of fresh pork and there you have it.

When Uncle Frank, who had a large apiary, stopped by for supper with us, he often came bearing a comb of fresh bees' honey. This made a tasty side dish to be served in a deep saucer. You ate bees' honey as a luxury—not freely, as in the case of maple syrup.

On occasion, I was the provider of a supper dish. Persistently, except for the diversion of momentarily snaring a spring azure butterfly or a gay clouded sulphur—I had picked tiny wild strawberries from open fields close to home. On receiving these, Grandma shook them into a brown-flowered Ironware berry dish, carefully picking

out the grass and weed seeds. High bush blueberries were also a supper favorite as they bobbed about in saucers abrim with heavy cream. Later in the summer came raspberries and blackberries.

In deep summer we sat down before lighting-up time. But in northern Vermont that period in the summer was always far too short. Most of the year the last meal of the day was eaten under the soft glow from kerosene lamps. The stove, if its grating stood open, offered a separate flicker of fire, that danced in my Grandmother's gold-rimmed spectacles. Both house cats dozed lightly in their basket. The big kitchen rocker still swayed gently where my Aunt had just shoved it aside at the call to table.

Beyond, in "the new barn," built some 20 years ago, the cows' soft, contented moos echoed back and forth, while all the farm creatures settled down for the night. My uncle's little Morgan mare whinnied engagingly. Thrushes sang their their resonant vesper song.

At first we ate briskly and silently, as farm families do, content with the knowledge that a second, even a third helping was wholly in order. Presently inconsequential bits of news were exchanged. I told of some exciting adventure which only made my elders smile indulgently. A sense of completeness settled upon those round the plain spruce table with its dark finish. Another day was reaching its peaceful close.

Grandma, still following the fashion of her girlhood, had turned her tea from the cup into the big saucer from which she sipped it. Uncle David, resting his weary feet for the first time since breakfast, tilted his oval-backed chair against the wall. Our hired man unloosed the drawstring of his cambric tobacco pouch and twisted his pipe around to fill it with Hard-a-Port cut plug. Aunt Nancy Howard smiling, smirking to herself, relived an evening with an old beau of sixty summers back.

Below the porch, and beyond the south pasture, stretched row on row of purple-shadowed mountains. Deep farm quiet lay upon the countryside. Save for faint sounds from farms a half mile distant, this stillness went unbroken. Daylight dwindled away. We sat encircled now by friendly beams from our unshaded lamps. Tomorrow would be another today—unless, perhaps, we were working in some far field, then Grandma might blow the old dinner horn to summon us from our tasks. This was a rare instance, my inner man being all the dinner horn *I* required.

Endless spring rains in that Bad Year kept farmers off the land. Day after day, Louis Bromfield and his manager, Bob Huge, gazed silently out at the cold, soggy fields of Malabar Farm.

# The BAD YEAR

THE rains began, cold and dreary, at the beginning of the month of April and day after day they continued through April, through May into June. Meanwhile, the fields grew wetter and wetter, until at last the hillsides themselves began to weep, the water oozing out of their sides down the slopes onto the lower ground. In the flat country to the west of us the fields became lakes of water, sometimes almost unbroken for miles across the level rich fields.

In our country, oats, if one is to have a good crop, should be planted as early as possible, for winter oats, seeded in the autumn, rarely weather the rigors of the northern winter and a farmer cannot afford to gamble on them. Oats planted in March have the best chances of success. Planted after the middle of April the chances of vigor and yield are lessened. Planted after the middle of May the yield is cut in half or if hot, dry weather comes on, the results may be utter failure. This year planting in March was out of the question for the fields were still frozen and covered with snow. The usual "false spring" which allowed us to put in early oats did not come at all, and then the rains began, falling day after day, in showers some days, in drenching downpours on others. And always it was cold, so cold that even the wild flowers and the morels (those first delicious woodsy fungi that grow in the deep forests under ash trees or in old and dying orchards) were confused. A sudden burst of sunlight brought some of them into flower and fruition only to meet disaster on cold, frosty, moonlit nights. The delicate, tiny Dutchman's breeches all met a frosty death while in full flower and the trilliums turned up stunted, brown-fringed petals toward the gray skies instead of the usual luxuriant blossoms that sometimes covered whole acres of our deep woodlands in drifts of white. The bluegrass, water-soaked and cold, languished instead of growing and kept the restless cattle (who knew better than we do when spring should be at hand) prisoners in the barns and soggy barnyards. They mooed and cried out in their restlessness, the sound of their mournful voices drifting far across the woods and hills.

And slowly, throughout all our country, the complaints of the farmers, impatient to get into their fields and worried over the cold, soggy fields, began to raise into a wail.

Charley Schrack, standing in the doorway of the barn, watching the fields drenched by gray rains,

*The Spring of 1947 was one of the wettest in all history. Corn and oats were planted late and sometimes not at all; hay was ruined. Farmers ordinarily take the seasonal vagaries of the weather in stride, but in forty-seven many said, "Nothing could be as bad as this!" Few gave up; their natural stubbornness and resiliency conquered even the weather; crops were planted and harvested. How this was done on Malabar Farm was told by Louis Bromfield in his book,* Malabar Farm. *This chapter,* The Bad Year, *is reprinted by the permission of the publishers, Harper & Brothers, New York.*

said, "I can't remember anything like it in fifty years." Lots of farmers talk that way, when drought or floods by persistent rain begin to spell disaster, but this time it seemed to me that Charley was right, for it rained when it seemed impossible. Rain seemed to fall in cold, frosty weather out of skies that were comparatively free of clouds. It was as if the heavens were a gigantic showerbath with a small irresponsible child playing with the chain which released the water.

And Nanny said, "I'm beginning to wonder if the atomic bomb didn't have something to do with all this rain. Maybe the scientists had better stop discovering things before they destroy us altogether. It begins to make you believe in the story of the Tower of Babel. Man can become too pretentious."

And the next morning I read in the papers that government agencies had warned planes to keep below the level of twelve thousand feet since the atomic cloud from the Bikini tests was passing for the third time around the earth and had just reached us again. That night and for two days, it rained without ceasing.

At Malabar and among the hills of our neighbors we were better off than the flat country people, for the water did not stand in lakes on our hills of glacial gravel loam. The worst we had to face were the seepage spots and "wet weather springs" which appeared here and there, sometimes at the very top of a hill. These we could plow around, leaving them water-logged and fallow, for another and better year. Our soil was loose and open and you could work it wet without too much damage if there was enough organic material mixed with it. And we had the advantage of mechanization—that when there was a break in the weather we could get into the fields and with tractor lights burning, work on shifts all through the night.

And that was what we did during that awful spring and so somehow we got ninety acres of oats into the ground, some of it in land which had been rough plowed through Bob's foresight the autumn before and was all ready for discing, fitting, and drilling. We got in our oats in one of those two-day breaks when, if the sun did not shine, the rain at least did not fall. Then the rain broke again and the cold persisted and in three or four days the oats were through the ground in a pale, misty shimmer of lettuce green across the wet, brown fields. And our hearts and stomachs felt better and our pride rose, because we had in the ground probably more oats than any farmer from the Appalachians to the Great Divide. On our loose, well-drained soil, oats did not mind the cold nor the rain. It was the kind of weather from which it benefited in the early stages. We were having March weather at least a month after March had passed.

There is in every good farmer a curious, overwhelming, almost malicious pride common to the human race but especially well-developed in the cultivator. It is born of satisfaction in being "smarter" than his neighbor, in having his acres look greener, in getting his crops in earlier, in having fields where the hay or the pasture is heavier. And conversely, there is in every good farmer a kind of perverse satisfaction in the discovery that his neighbors' fields look poorly. The sight of a poor crop in someone else's field somehow cheers the farmer whose own fields are lush and green.

That is why a good farmer grows short-tempered and desperate when the weather turns against him. With each day of drought, of flooding rain, he becomes more frustrated and savage, because the weather alone he cannot lick altogether either by machines or muscle or long hours in the field.

And so farmers everywhere that spring grew ill-tempered and angry. They did not wail. It is only the poor farmer who wails or looks for scapegoats or excuses for his own failures of energy or intelligence.

Still it did not stop raining. Time for planting oats receded into the distant unchangeable past and time for corn plowing came along, and still it rained and stayed cold. It was the year when Al Jolson's old song, "April Showers" had a great revival and every juke-box and every radio program was blaring forth a ditty which insisted that it was raining violets.

It was a song that sounded very sour to the farmer that spring. The violets, which grew on banks like weeds in our county, were small, shriveled and frostbitten. There were no warm showers. There were only flooding downpours, day after day as May slipped past toward June and Ellen said, "They ought to change that song to April Showers that bring the flowers that bloom in July."

Countless farmers abandoned all hope of planting oats. They talked of other crops and of putting all their land into corn. Corn planting time came along and still it rained. Here and there in our hill country one could see farmers dripping wet on their tractors, turning over sod ground for corn planting. Sod ground, especially in soil like that of our country, can be plowed fairly safely when it is still too wet because the roots and vegetation help to keep the ground open, aerated and keep it from packing. We too plowed sod in the rain and turned under acres of rank sweet clover on the loose, alluvial soil of the farm we rent from the Muskingum Conservancy District. We dared not even put a tractor wheel on the small acreage of water-logged clay.

But even after the ground was plowed it was too wet to fit for planting. Day after day went by, each rain bringing us nearer to the last date at which corn could be planted and have any chance of maturing before the average frost date of October fourth. Then the rain stopped for a couple of days and again we worked night and day until all but ten acres of corn were in the ground. By our own standards at Malabar, we were three weeks late but with luck that corn, changed at the last moment to a quick-ripening, short-season hybrid, would mature if the frost held off.

We were thankful that we had all our corn in save for ten acres of clay which we could not touch because it was as wet and sticky as glue. So we planned to put that into buckwheat, let it serve the bees and then plow it into the soil for the benefits it would give us the following year. "At any rate," said Bob, "it will look pretty, and it's better than leaving the ground bare or to grow up in weeds."

And again, smugly and pridefully, we settled back aware that we had probably more corn in the ground than any of the farmers west of us all the way into the corn-country where the fields were still more like the carp ponds of Austria and Czechoslovakia than the fertile fields of the mid-western bread-basket country. But still it rained and remained cold, and we began to worry over whether the seed would rot in the ground. Then for three days the rain suddenly stopped and capriciously the weather changed from cold to oppressively hot with a hot, baking sun and a new peril developed—that even with all the organic material we had pumped into the soil for years and the fresh crop of sweet clover turned under, the soil was so wet that the hot sun might bake the surface and prevent the tender, germinating corn from piercing the surface. So on the third day I climbed aboard the tractor, attached the rotary hoe and drove it full speed back and forth across the surface of the cornfield because the faster you drive it, the more efficiently it works, breaking up the surface and throwing the tiny weed seedlings and bits of crumbling earth high into the air.

Driving at full tractor speed, I felt good. The sun was shining. The alluvial gravel loam was dry enough for the rotary hoe to work efficiently. The Conservancy farm lay alongside the big artificial lake formed by one of the dams of the Muskingum Flood Prevention Project. The lake beneath the clear skies and hot sun was a brilliant blue. The distant wooded hills were tropically green and lush from all the rain. The birds, mute during the weeks of downpour, chorused from every tree, bush and hedgerow and from the marshy land along the lake came the sound of splashing caused by the thrashing about of the big carp engaged in an orgy of reproduction. And in my heart was that gnawing old farmer's pride that we had outwitted even the weather. It was one of those fine days which is recompense for weeks of bad weather.

At sundown I drove happily home and ran the rotary hoe briskly over the plantation of beans, peas and sweet corn. And then at supper time, as the shadows began to fall across the valley and the lush forest, there came a sinister note of warning. Out of the symphony of birds singing and the music of the frogs in the ponds below the house, there emerged a note which fell on the ears and assaulted my senses as violently as a shrill fife playing loudly and discordantly in the midst of a great orchestra. It was the cry of the tree frogs calling for rain. It came from all sides, the same monotonous, trilled note which in time of drought can be the most lovely instrument in the whole symphony of nature.

I said, "Listen to those damned tree frogs! Haven't they had enough? I'd like to go out and strangle every one of them!" And from across the big table I heard a loud chuckle from Anne.

When I asked, "What's so funny?" she said, "Just the picture of you going around the farm strangling every tree frog with your bare hands."

Tree frogs do not, as legend has it, "call for rain." On the contrary, they call when the atmospheric conditions foretell rain. They are not suppliants; they are prophets. I looked out the window and against the brilliant sunset, big, dark, unmistakably wet clouds were piling up at the end of the valley. I couldn't believe it could rain again.

That evening everybody on the farm was feeling good and on such evenings the men and the kids on the place are likely to gravitate to the lower farm. It was a kind of public forum in the center of the thousand acres and when the rain is falling people gather in the machine shop where Kenneth is kept

Sudden floods swept away bridges and houses and drowned livestock if you could not get to them first.

busy during bad weather repairing machinery or ingeniously making machines which we can't buy because they are in short supply or don't exist. On fine evenings we seem to gather there spontaneously just to talk or enjoy the evening or sometimes to go fishing in the pond that lies below the shop.

We all went home at last, still feeling good. Two things were certain—that we were ahead of most farmers and that no matter how hard it rained we had lost and were losing none of our precious soil. It stayed where it was meant to stay, held in place by thick pasture and hay sod or the protecting sodded strip which prevented it ever getting away from us.

Tired from the all-day jolting ride on the rotary hoe, I fell into that deep sleep that comes only after physical labor in the open air, the kind of sleep which you can *feel* yourself enjoying with an almost voluptuous pleasure. Even the dogs were tired from the long day in the field and forgot their snack in

their eagerness to go to bed. They fell asleep in their chairs even before I found myself lying with eyes closed and the book I was reading fallen aside. I awakened long enough to turn out the lights and fell into that warm, pleasant oblivious sleep which must be like the reward of death to very old people who have led long, full and happy lives.

I slept "like a log" until about two in the morning when a prodigious clap of thunder which rocked the whole house awakened me. The thunder was bad enough but there was another sound even worse. It was the sound of rain on the roof, a sound which in the dry, hot days of August comes like a celestial benediction. Now it sounded like a curse from Hell for not only was it the sound of unwanted rain but of ropes and buckets and torrents of it, the sound of Niagaras, of unwanted water streaming from gutters and spouts which could not carry it off fast enough. And above and through the sound of the rain on the roof came another sound of water even more menacing—that of the spring brook which ran through the garden below the house.

It was a sound I had not heard in seven years, since first we controlled run-off water on the hills and pastures above. Now, after all these years, the clear little creek was roaring again. It meant not only that it was raining hard and that the water-soaked land could drink up not one more raindrop, but that this was flood and perhaps disaster. I rose and went to the door, and Prince, who sleeps on the foot of my bed, jumped up and went with me. There I heard another sound, even more ominous—the roar of Switzer's Creek a quarter of a mile away which had been clear and well-behaved, never going out of its banks since farmers upstream had begun taking proper care of their fields. Now it was roaring again. It could only mean flood.

With a feeling of helplessness I went back to bed, to lie there sleepless and worrying over the fact that all the work I had done with the rotary hoe was useless since these torrents of water would pack the earth harder than ever; worrying over the cattle, the calves, the horses in the bottom fields. I knew from the roar of Switzer's Creek that this time it was not merely rain but a cloudburst of the proportions that sweep away bridges and houses and drown livestock in the fields. I slept a little more, fitfully, and each time I awakened I heard the unwanted hateful rains streaming down and the increasing roar of the streams.

At daylight I went to the door and looked out over the valley. Part of the lower pasture was flooded but the livestock was safe on high ground, drenched and grazing peacefully in the downpour. Through the middle of the flooded field ran the swift, muddy current carrying with it whole fences, trees, rubbish, bits of hog pens and even a brand new milk can bobbing along on its way from some spring house upstream to the reservoir lake below.

It rained until nine o'clock in the morning when suddenly the awful downpour ceased and everyone on the farm—men, women and children—streamed out of the houses toward the bridge over Switzer's Creek. There was the kind of excitement among us which comes perhaps as a recompense to people in the face of destruction and disaster, a kind of exhilaration which brings all people, whatever their temperaments or differences of character, together on a common level.

The first concern of the men was the new flood-gate that Bob and Kenneth and Jesse had constructed only a day or two before to separate the bottom pastures. It hung from a heavy piece of steel pipe between two concrete buttresses of the township bridge, made thus so that when the water rose it would swing out and float. To build it had taken a great deal of time and hard work.

The gate was still there, swinging out almost flat on the surface of the rushing water. Now and then a log or a whole tree swept swiftly beneath it without lodging it or tearing it loose. It was a good piece of engineering. Everybody was proud of it.

Then, with all the dogs, the men crowded into the jeep to inspect the rest of the farm. The wheat fields so green and lush even the day before, were beaten down in spots as if a giant had flung great pails of water against the wheat. In the wild swamp and woodland we call the Jungle, the water poured through the trees high above the banks. Here and there a log or a tree had become lodged, collected a bundle of flotsam and jetsam and the diverted waters had cut out a whole new channel. We stood there on a high bank, silent, watching the flood, awed yet somehow exhilarated by the terrific, unpredictable, incalculable power of rushing water.

And last of all we set out for the Conservancy farm on the edge of Pleasant Hill Lake built years ago to check just such floods as this. We went with forebodings for we knew that the dam would be kept closed to hold back the water and protect the helpless people in the towns downstream along the Muskingum River all the way to the Ohio and perhaps even down the Mississippi to the Gulf of Mexico. As we neared the Conservancy farm the forebodings grew for the rising waters of the lake had already covered the lower road. There had never been such a flood before in all our experience so we could not know what that high water meant to the fields of which we had been so proud because our oats were all above ground and flourishing and our corn planted even in the midst of the weeks-old rain.

Cautiously, I felt my way with the jeep through high water. We just made it and as we came out the other side on the high ground we found what the water on the road meant. It meant that our pride, the oat fields on the Conservancy farm, lay under four to six feet of muddy water. In the shallow water near the banks we could see the rippling wakes left by the big carp as they moved in to take advantage of the plowed muddy oats field which they found ideal for spawning. For a long time we stood there watching the water-traced movements of the big, invisible carp.

Then Kenneth said, "I guess we might as well make something out of this mess. I think if you all make a drive we might corner some of these big carp." So the men and the boys down to George Cook, who is nine, took off their pants and waded out in their shorts into the cold water making a chain to trap the carp in shallow water. Even the dogs joined in. As if they understood the game they moved forward in a line with the men and boys trying to drive the carp into the shallows. Only Bobby, who was four and might have found the water over his head, stook on the bank and shouted advice as one big carp after another turned swiftly and darted between us, sometimes even between one's legs.

It wasn't any good. Every carp escaped but somehow the game raised our spirits. We all decided that probably the water would be released quickly from the dam and the oats field would be left free of it again before the crop and the beautiful stand of sweet clover sowed in it would suffer damage.

That afternoon the air cooled and the bright sun came out and two days later the gravelly cornfield was dry enough to repeat the whole process with the rotary hoe, all the long hours of rough tractor riding at top speed, to break up the crust all over again and let the young seedlings through. While I worked back and forth across a big sixty-acre field, the air turned muggy and hot once more and the wind shifted a little to the south which is always a bad sign. I kept listening above the rumble of the tractor for the sound of train whistles. In our county when one hears the B. & O., it means rain. In midsummer one prays for the B. & O. For once I wanted to hear a Pennsylvania whistle. Presently, as I was finishing the job with the rotary hoe, I heard a whistle. It came from a B. & O. freight train pulling up the long grade to Butler and never have I heard it more clearly!

At twilight I rode the tractor the two miles back to the house. The setting sun disappeared beneath clouds and as I rode the drive up to the Big House, great solitary drops of rain began to fall. Before I got into the house the drops began to come down by the trillions, in torrents. I thought, trying to deceive myself, "Very likely it's only a big thunderstorm and will quickly be over." The water in the reservoir had already gone down about two feet in two days, leaving part of our oats field bare in time to save it.

If we had another heavy rain it would mean, with the lake level above flood stage, that instead of the young oats plants being released before they drowned, the whole field would be flooded again and perhaps the cornfield that lay above it.

I was wrong. The rain was no thunderstorm. It was the same kind of flooding rain that had come down two nights earlier. Indeed it was worse, if possible. Eight o'clock came and nine and ten and still it poured. The little brook in the garden began to roar and then from the valley came the louder roar of Switzer's Creek.

I went to bed to read, thinking I could take my mind off what could only be disaster. But it wasn't any good. I tried reading novels, agricultural editorials, magazines, but through all the print and ideas, good and bad, came the devilish sound of torrents of water pouring off the roofs and the rising roar of the little brook. And at last when my eyes grew tired and I began to feel drowsy, I heard the ring of the telephone. I knew it was someone on the farm ringing because the sound is different when the ring is made by cranking the phone handles instead of pushing a button in the central office. I thought, "This is it. Something bad has happened on the farm!"

Bob's voice answered me. He was calling from his house below not far from the creek. He said, "I think we've got a job. The horses in the bottom are scared. They're running up and down crying out. One of them tried to get across the creek and is marooned on the island. We've got to look after them and the cattle."

I asked, "Is it worse down by the bridge?" And his voice came back, "Brother, you ain't seen nothing."

I dressed, gloomily, worrying about the animals and especially the horses. Cows and steers are generally phlegmatic. They either take things calmly or go completely wild, but horses, and especially saddle horses, get frightened, like people, and for me the horses, like dogs, are people. I took only one of the dogs with me. I chose Prince because Prince owns me—I don't own Prince—and he is the steadiest of them all save old Gina who has always been wise and calm. But Gina was too old and plump for wild adventure. Too many dogs might only make confusion. And besides they were likely to follow me into the water if I had to go there and be carried away in the flood. Prince was a good swimmer and he would obey me and not get panicky. So Prince, delighted and excited, jumped to the seat of the jeep.

One wet morning we found this knob-eyed neighbor on the windowsill trying to escape another cloudburst.

Bob met me at the bridge, water streaming from his hat and jacket. He had an electric torch and with that and the lights of the jeep I saw quickly enough that I hadn't seen anything until now. The water was so high that it was seeping through the wooden floor of the bridge and sliding past beneath with a terrifying speed. A whole log struck the edge of the bridge and made it shudder and then slipped under the water out of sight in a second. In the earlier flood there had been backwaters and whirlpools beneath the bridge where rubbish gathered but now there was nothing but rushing water going past so fast that I felt a sudden dizziness and instinctively stepped back from the edge.

He told me about the panic of the horses. "I heard them all the way up at the house."

I said, "Get in. We'll take the jeep out in the field and use the lights." He didn't think we could make

it with the Jeep but I knew better than he did what it could do.

He said, "I'll get my car, leave it on the road and put all the lights on the field and join you."

While he got his car I opened the pasture gate and drove through. Even the high ground was running with water and wherever there was a depression the water stood in deep pools. I put the Jeep into four-wheel drive in low gear and she did what she was supposed to do. She plowed through mud and water until the lights penetrated a little distance into the mist and driving rain, enough for me to see that only a rim of bluegrass remained above the flood. The lights picked up two things, both white, the white spots on the Holstein cows which had gone to the high ground and were either grazing or laying down and the white blaze on the forehead of Tex, my own mare, as she came toward me splash-

93

ing through two feet of water.

Tex is a beautiful Kentucky mare, chestnut with a white blaze, and the proudest and most spirited of horses. She rules the others and it is impossible to catch any of the others in the field until you have first captured Tex. The other horses follow her with docility. But she is not too easy to catch and likes to play a game of enticing you near to her and then suddenly kicking her heels and rushing off. But in the flooded field she wasn't behaving that way and now ran straight toward the lights of the Jeep followed by another horse. As I got down she came up close and whinnied. There were no antics now. She was afraid and wanted to be taken care of. Then the lights of Bob's car were turned into the field and I saw that the other horse was Tony, Hope's horse, young and strong, who is by nature a clown. But tonight he wasn't clowning. He too whinnied when I spoke to him

I recognized Tony with a sinking heart because I knew that the missing horse marooned on the island in the flood was Old Red. Either of the others were strong and spirited and could have taken care of themselves even in the terrible current that was running, but Old Red was old and tired. He was a little deaf and nearly blind. He was the one you felt sorry for.

Old Red had brought up the little children until they had learned to ride well enough to handle the younger, more spirited horses. If they fell off he would stand until they picked themselves up and climbed back on. He never got flustered or showed off and reared like Tex and never clowned as Tony did. He was twenty-one years old when we bought him, because he was calm and docile. He was just a horse, never a high-spirited queen like the thoroughbred Tex nor a wild, impish polo pony like Tony. Sometime in his youth when perhaps he had been a carriage horse on some farm, he had been abused for on his shoulder he bore the scars of old galls from a collar. He wasn't a clever horse or a spirited horse or a beautiful one. He was always just a kind, patient, old slob. And now, at thirty years of age with his joints stiffened and his teeth mostly gone, he was marooned on an island in the midst of a roaring flood such as the county had not seen in half a century. I wished it had been one of the others.

As I took hold of Tex's halter, for the first time without her giving an indignant toss of the head, Bob came up out of the darkness and rain and mist with the light. He was carrying a long rope.

"I thought," he said, "we might need this to get over to the island to get the horse off."

I told him the missing horse was Old Red and that I'd better take the other two to the barn before they turned completely panicky and uncatchable.

Tex led easily enough. She wanted the dry safety of the barn and Tony followed as always at her heels. Prince, despite the fact that, like all Boxers, he hates getting wet, trudged along beside us, his ears down and his stub of a tail pressed low in an effort to get it between his legs. Bob went off through the water to check on the cattle on the high ground. On the way back the roar of the flood seemed to grow steadily louder. After the two horses were safely in the barn, I discovered on my return to the field that the water was still rising.

I waded into the water and was joined presently by Bob, but as the water rose deeper and deeper above our ankles and knees, it was clear that we were never going to make the island.

Then out of the mist, the willows of the island emerged, but there was no island. There was only swift-flowing water covered with leaves, bits of sod and branches. And then out of the mist catching the light from the cars appeared a ghostly Old Red. He was walking up and down, whinnying loud enough to be heard above the sound of the water.

I called out to him and he stopped, looked toward me and then started in my direction but as soon as he reached deeper water he turned back to the island and the shallow water.

There wasn't any way to get to him. The water had risen so high that on the whole of the farm there wasn't a rope long enough to permit us to reach the island, and even with a rope tied about your waist, there wouldn't be much hope of getting through the torrent. Knowing horses, I knew that even if you made it, there was small chance of getting a horse in a panic to follow you.

I shouted to him again and again and each time the old horse started toward me and each time when he got into deep water he turned back to the island.

Meanwhile both Bob and I were drenched. The water ran inside our jackets and down our bodies. Prince, miserable in the dampness, crouched beside me. At last I gave up.

"There's nothing to do," I said, "but hope that he'll stay there and that the water won't get much higher."

And so we turned away with a sickening feeling through the rain and water, leaving the old horse

When there was a break in the weather, farmers got into the fields and, with tractor
lights burning, worked on shifts all through the night.

where he was. The other horses were in the barn
and the cattle all safe on high ground. There wasn't
anything to do but go home. We had hot coffee at
Bob's house and as I said good night to Bob, he said,
"Maybe I opened my big mouth too soon—saying
we hadn't anything to worry about." I laughed but
I knew what he meant—that probably sunrise would
find most of our corn and oats deep under the water
of the big lake.

By the time I got back to the bridge the planks
were under water and before I drove across it I got
down to make sure that the planks were still there
and the bridge safe. You could not make sure but I
got back into the Jeep and took a chance. I speeded
up the Jeep and made a dash for it. The water flew
high on both sides so that together with the pouring

rain and the rushing water it seemed for a moment
that all of us, Prince, myself and the Jeep were
caught in a raging torrent of water. The planks
were still there and we made it.

At home Prince and I dried ourselves off and
joined Mary for hot soup and a snack with all the
dogs, who treated the wet and miserable Prince with
such resentment for having been the chosen one on
the expedition that a fight developed between him
and his brother, Baby. Then I went to bed after
taking two sleeping pills so that I would not waken
in the still early hours of the morning and hear the
terrible rain and think of Old Red alone on the
island in the rising flood.

It was nearly eight when I wakened and the rain
had stopped. The old orchard on the hill above my

95

room was streaked with early morning sunlight and the red sandstone rock looked brighter and the trees lusher and more green than I had ever seen them. But in the back of my mind there was a sore spot which could not be healed until I went to the pasture. I had to know what had happened to Old Red.

It must have stopped raining some time during the night for the water had gone down and the surface of the island, littered with branches and trees and old boards, was now above the flood. But among the willows there was no sign of Old Red. I felt suddenly sick and in a last hope I thought, "Perhaps he is all right after all. Perhaps he's just around the corner of the slope." And I went back to the far end of the house and looked out, and there behind the slope, peacefully munching bluegrass with the few teeth he had left was Old Red, behaving as if nothing had happened.

After breakfast Kenneth and I climbed into the Jeep with the dogs and set out for the Conservancy farm. We already knew the worst for from the Bailey Hill we could see the lake—an enormously enlarged lake covering twice its usual area with clumps of trees here and there barely visible above the water. This time we couldn't get through the lower road at all. Not only was the road under ten feet of water but Charley Tom's pasture was under ten feet of water also. The bridge structure was out of sight.

So, turning around, we took the only other course of reaching the Conservancy farm; we took to a rutted abandoned old lane and the open, soggy fields and somehow we made it. As we came over the crest of a slope we saw the full extent of the disaster. All the oat fields and half the corn land was covered by water and here and there in low spots in the field there were great ponds of water as big as small lakes.

We sat for a time in silence looking at the wreckage. It wasn't only the money loss, but the loss of the long hours of work and care we had all put into those fields.

Then Kenneth said, "There's a new milk can bobbing on the edge of the current. We might as well salvage something."

So together we set to work to get that solitary milk can out of the swirling torrent. It was not easy but by the use of long tree branches and poles we maneuvered the floating milk can to a point where, wading in up to his hips, Kenneth salvaged it. He fastened it to the back of the Jeep and we climbed in and set out for home. There wouldn't be any recompense in cash for the damage done by the

waters of the lake; we rented the whole farm from the state with the gamble that some day there might be just such a flood. And anyway money is poor recompense to a good farmer; he wants his crops and the satisfaction that goes with raising them.

For three weeks most of the Conservancy farm remained under from five to twenty feet of impounded water, kept there to prevent its menace from being added to the already disastrous floods on the Mississippi. When the water went down at last not one living thing remained but only the desolation of logs and fence posts and driftwood scattered across the barren fields. Even the trees were killed along with the blackberries and elderberries that filled the hedgerows. We had not only lost our crops, but we had to clear the fields of this desolation. What little corn or oats remained on dry ground was growing but looked pale and yellowish in the water-soaked ground.

And elsewhere on the upper farm more rich wheat was beaten to the earth to mildew and smother the specious seedings. The bluegrass behaved in the water-soaked earth exactly as it did in time of drought. It grew tough and went to seed early and it was possible to clip it only on the high ground. Everywhere else in the fields, the power mower bogged down and had to be pulled out.

Good farmers are by nature, optimistic; otherwise the uncontrollable vagaries of Nature—the floods, the droughts, the plagues of locusts—would long ago have discouraged them and the world would have been left starving. We were no different from other farmers—we hoped that the great flood marked the end of the persistent intolerable rains.

We were wrong. June passed into July and still the rain continued, not simply showers or simple rains but cloudbursts coming sometimes twice a day. Even the fish ponds fed from tight sod-covered land and springs overflowed their barriers and big trout and bass escaped into Clear Fork and the lake below. Came time to fill the silos with grass silage and we began cutting and hauling but quickly found that every tractor had to carry a log chain so that we could pull each other out of the mud, a minor disaster which happened ten or fifteen times a day. Twice the big John Deere dug itself into the mud up to its belly and a string of four lighter tractors, chained together, could not drag it out. In the end with four-by-fours chained to its giant wheels it succeeded in lifting itself out of the mud.

Not until July did Switzer's creek throw aside the ravages of rain and settle back into its normal path.

Somehow the silos got filled with the lush, heavy alfalfa, brome grass and ladino, but even the grass was so filled with moisture that it had to be wilted a long time before it could be safely put away. Weeds grew in the corn and more wheat was beaten down in the fields of which we had been so proud. The oats which remained grew more and more lushly and all but the tough, stiff-stemmed new Clinton variety were beaten to the ground while weeds began to grow up through them.

Then the weather turned warm but the rains continued and at night when the air cooled the whole valley was blanketed in heavy white mists which appeared at sundown, rising in smoke-like writhing veils above the trees. For days the valley seemed more like Sumatra or Java than midsummer Ohio country. Rust appeared for the first time in

our experience on the ripening wheat and mildew on the leaves and fruit of the fruit trees. Some of the grapevines began to die back from the tops, a sign that their water-logged roots could no longer stand the lack of oxygen and the wetness of the earth. Three times the vegetable garden was replanted and three times drowned out, sometimes standing for days under four inches of water.

Then came a brief respite which in itself was very nearly a disaster. There was no rain but in its place there was a brilliant, burning sun accompanied by hot winds which burned the moisture out of the top soil but not out of the subsoil where the water still soaked the roots of all vegetation. It baked a crust over open ground and burned the over-lush leaves of the crops. At night the moisture still rose from the soaked ground in heavy blankets

of fog. It was as if now it was the earth rather than the sky which was raining.

Somehow we managed to combine the wheat, although we lost from five to fifteen bushels per acre of wheat literally beaten into the earth by the torrents of water. Except for thirty acres of good oats on the highest ground, the crop was ruined. In the heads there were no grains at all but only chaff. And from over the rest of the Middle West there rose a cry that drought was ruining the corn crop just at the crucial moment of tasselling and pollenization. Because there had been so much rain the corn had set shallow roots on the surface of the soil and now suddenly that surface had been burned, baked and hardened.

But in our valley even the short, vicious heat was only a delusion. As it came time to make hay and chop and bale straw the rains began again, not simple rains but the old cloudbursts. Ragweed grew higher and higher in the standing straw and the hay, partly dry and then soaked, rotted in the fields.

Weeds everywhere grew like the fierce tropical growth that overwhelms settlements and plantations in a few weeks in the Tropics when the battle against them is relaxed for a season. The whole farm, usually so neatly and proudly kept, acquired a disheveled, unkempt, half-tropical appearance.

And so it went, on and on, through the end of July and then August and well into September. There was no hay-making season at all, even for the second cutting and when there was a day or two of sunshine the hay, dried during the day, became water-soaked again each night from the heavy, damp fogs which settled each night in the valley. At last we took in hay which was still damp. Some of it moulded, some of it heated and turned brown and a little came through as the good green hay which we always made in a summer that was even vaguely reasonable.

Only the pastures and the new seedings gave us any pleasure or satisfaction, for they were lush and green but even this was small compensation for all

"Gradually the season began to recede into the past. It was becoming the 'old season.'
It was time now to plow and fit for wheat, to clip the bluegrass pastures and the weeds
for the last time in the evil year of nineteen forty-seven."

the lost labor and seed and fertilizer and the depression which arose from the sight of wet hay and weed-choked cornfields. The buckwheat planted later on wet ground produced a bumper crop but few farmers take pride in lowly buckwheat and the season was so wet that the bees could not even work the blossoms.

And then presently in the beginning of September the rains stopped and miraculously two weeks of hot weather day and night set in, and suddenly the corn, after dawdling along all of the summer, began to show signs of ripening and making a crop. The soil began to dry out for wheat plowing and that miraculous resiliency which preserves farmers against utter and paralyzing despair began to assert itself.

Gradually the season began to recede into the past. It was becoming the "old season." It was time now to plow and fit for wheat, to clip the bluegrass pastures and the weeds for the last time in the evil

year of nineteen forty-seven. With the turning of the first furrow the pride which was humbled began to rise again. The fields were full of moisture and the plowing was easy. The earth turned over behind the plow, dark and crumbling, and you smelled already the wheat harvest of the coming season which you knew would be the greatest harvest we had ever known. The lime trucks began moving across the remaining worn-out high pastures raising visions of deep thick clover. In the desolated oat fields of the Conservancy farm and on the poor strips of the Bailey Place the sweet clover stood deep and rank. The new season had begun.

And then came the warm, clear weather of October, brilliant with the deep green of the new springing rye and wheat and the burning colors of the forest. From brilliant blue skies the sun shone all day long while the work for the new season went on its way and all hearts sang.

Steam engines get in your blood. Walter Crouse, right, and his helper, Bill Ficken, give "Louise," a 36-year-old Case, an annual workout to keep alive an ancient art.

# "She's sort of an antique"

WALTER fell in love with her some 15 years ago, when he first saw her. She had a few rust spots here and there. Her paint was scaling. She was in need of an overhaul. But in Walter's vision, every pound of iron and steel and brass in her was precious metal.

Walter Crouse is a steam-engine man. He has stoked the fires and watched the gauges and handled the throttle on a dozen different steam engines around Boone, Iowa. Now his joy and his work are centered around Louise, his latest and finest engine. He named her after Mrs. Crouse and some say it is hard to determine on which he lavishes more love.

For ten years he pleaded, cajoled and bargained with her previous owner, an old-timer from Ottumwa, Iowa. Five years ago he won out, and for $750 she was his to take apart and to polish and, best of all, to set into motion, eleven tons of meshing, chugging, reciprocating motion.

Louise had cost her first proud owner $2500, a tidy sum 36 years ago. She was built to last. Her boiler plate is heavy and her pistons of the best steel. She has size, but not massive size. She gives the impression of lean and sinewy power, a streamlining created long before the word was invented. Louise was the product of caressing hands, and since her debut more caressing hands have preserved her polished brass, her black iron and her trim of green and brick-red.

She was sort of an antique even from the day she came, spick-and-span, out of the Racine works of the J. I. Case Company. That was in 1925. When she was complete, a new era had already taken over, an era of gasoline. She ushered out an age of steam with her first whistle blast. The smaller, power-compact gasoline engine was opening up the way for the combines. The combines, their reels chomping into the standing wheat, swept across the plains, pushing the sheaf-dotted fields, the threshing dinners and the harvest goings-on into a memory.

Whenever there's a parade in Boone County, Iowa, Walter Crouse and Louise are there, too, drowning out the bands. He put rubber treads on her high steel wheels so he could drive her on the paving. "One Sunday," says Walter, "my boy took her for a joyride through town and I thought he'd get pinched, but he wasn't."

Louise is more than an engine man's hobby. Each summer she gets a workout. The past season Crouse threshed about 350 acres of oats. "This is a cattle-feeding country," he says. "Farmers like the threshed straw. Makes much softer and more absorbent bedding."

If you happen by while he's threshing, Walter will gladly show you Louise's metallic and ear-splitting charms. "I'm mighty proud to have you here while she's running," he'll say.

"I started out when I was just a kid, about 15 years old. Hauled water at first. Believe it was in 1914. I worked for an old man who owned a threshing rig. His engineman was always drunk. One day the boss said to me: 'I'm going to run that guy off. Walter, do you think you can run the engine?' I said I'd sure like to try and he told me to go ahead. He just let me alone, never bothered me and I got along just fine. I had the time of my life.

"We got through the rest of the wheat, then the oats and a little buckwheat. Those times the rig was started up along about dog days and you never got home until around Hallowe'en. We never had any real trouble that season, but I got my come-uppance that winter. We stack-threshed in the fall. Stack runs could wait 'til October or November. Then like most steam rings, we ran a sawmill in the winter. I learned a lesson I never forgot. You have to be on your toes all the time when you're handling fire and steam and power. We were hooked up to the saw and I was at the controls. I started her up and I didn't look down for a second. When I did, there was an old guy aholding on to the saw and it just happened that I had reversed the engine or I'd have split him in two. As it was, he was just thrown away from the saw."

When Walter threshes, Bill Ficken goes along, too. Bill is past seventy. "He's an old Dutchman," says Walter. "Can't keep him from blowing the whistle. Just deefens you. Have to keep telling him to blow her just a little, not open her up. He knows every bolt on her, just as I do. Louise's been all gone over. Inspected by the state boiler inspector. She's in A-1 shape. Better shape than Bill is, I guess. He's kind of crippled up but he springs to life when the steam gets up and the engine starts to spit. You can see his face glow. He goes along more for the good time than for the pay. He had a stroke once, but

being with the engine seems to restore him to health. He's an old thresherman like me and nothing gets him madder than for some one to toss a tree branch in the separator. When the machine is hurting, you feel the hurt inside, too."

Walter wasn't satisfied with only a whistle. He wanted a bell also. "I have about a hundred dollars in that bell," he says. "Got it from a junkman who was a tough one to deal with. An old railroad man. He knew a good bell when he saw one. That bell came from an old woodburning locomotive. Listen to that tone!"

Men like Walter Crouse don't consider themselves just engineers. Their engines, used for shredding, sawmilling or any other purpose requiring stationary power, are, of course, nearest their hearts, but they like to think of themselves primarily as threshermen. Threshermen have always been a proud and respected lot, men of calibre who in their heyday had their own national brotherhood, their professional magazines, conventions and strict requirements for membership. To them, and to most farmers of their day, steam engines meant threshing and threshing was a labor of love.

It took 20 to 25 men to do a good job of threshing. In the field 6 to 8 pitched bundles, 8 teamsters on bundle wagons was usual, with 2 to 4 men on the grain boxes, plus men in the mow or at the stack. The feeder stood on the separator platform, the

Smoke belches, soot and cinders get into your eyes, the chaff makes your back itch. It's hot and you sweat, but you love every minute of it. Opposite: This medium-size wrench was part of the original tractor tool kit.

fireman tended the boiler and the engineer ran the show. A "water-monkey" kept his team busy hauling water for the boiler. Often a boy tended the wetted burlap-covered water jug in the field.

Preparations began early. Women were busy in the kitchen days ahead. A jag of coal had to be gotten from town, for each farmer supplied the coal for his own run. The hogs got their minerals from the left-over lumps. The threshing rig—engine drawing separator, team drawing water tank—often pulled in for a setting late at night and the engine crew, too far from home for horseback travel, would put up in the hayloft. At 4 a.m. they turned out to stoke the boiler fire. One long toot on the whistle meant steam was up and "she" was ready to roll. By 7 the first bundle wagon jolted into the lot from the fields and another farm-owner, scanning the sky, felt more assured that his harvest would beat the weather.

The sun grew hot and the sweat ran. Smoke belched, soot dropped, fumes smarted the eyes. The straw spewed from the pipe snout, working into shoes, down itching backs. Swirling chaff filled nose and mouth. Over all was noise, the flapping belts, the droning separator, the clanking, hissing engine.

Competition and practical joking among the crew made short work of the morning. Your innards told you it was dinner time before the 11 o'clock whistle sounded. On the back porch, all the family's soap and combs and feed-sack towels were waiting beside the wash pans lined up on benches. A washboiler full of coffee steamed on the oil stove in the laundry lean-to. At the table, the trenchermen dug into the heaping platters, the oldsters cornered the high talk, eyeing the five kinds of pie, and the womenfolk kept up a steady parade to the kitchen, content with their fate of a leisurely second table after the men returned to the threshing. The threshing dinner was a farm wife's hour in the sun; before many days everyone in the area would know what kind of table she had set. A man could be invited into the best threshing rings on his wife's reputation as a cook.

After dinner the noise and confusion began again. The wheat got drier and changing the grain boxes kept the teamsters hopping. When the cows came mooing up to the fence, waiting to be milked, it was time to throw the throttle. The sudden silence felt odd in your eardrums. There wasn't much time before dark to oil up and to clean the gummed dust and the thistledown from the sides of the engine. That was a day measured by light to see and work by, not by clock or writ.

# The

When horsepower was a matter of bone and muscle rather than steel and gasoline, great-granddad was mighty proud of his mare that could brush along the road, leaving all challengers in her dust. Many an impromptu race was occasioned by a trip to town; likewise, many a trip to town was simply the excuse for a good, hot dash.

Inevitably, time came to be the leading contender in these events; racing was transferred to the track and a special registry established for animals that could trot or pace a mile in 2:30 or better. Thus the name Standardbred was given to a horse that could go a mile in what was referred to as standard time. Today the standard is 2:20 and the magic number of the sport is 2:00; the two-minute mile being considered the gauge of perfection.

The Standardbred horse of today is a highly bred animal that traces his pedigree back through generation after generation of forebears who through the years have reduced that first 2:30 record (actu-

# *Standardbred*

ally, it was 2:29½) taken by the gray mare, Lady Suffolk, in 1845, to the present trotting record of 1:55¼, held by Greyhound, and Adios Butler's pacing record of 1:54³/₅.

Standardbreds are both trotters and pacers. The Standardbred horse is raced in harness hitched to a light two-wheeled sulky. His action is very smooth, having little of the vertical motion of the galloping horse or runner. Trotting is a two-beat, diagonal gait in which the left foreleg works in unison with the right hind, the right fore with the left hind. In pacing, which is a lateral gait, the two left legs work together and the two right legs work together, causing a kind of rolling action from side to side as the animal moves forward. For this action they have been nicknamed wigglers or side winders.

Most people think of horse breeding these days as merely a pastime for the wealthy. That's not the case with the Murrays, William and William B., a father and son team. Their 460-acre Bonnie Brae

Farms, just south of Wellington, Ohio, produces just one cash crop—horses—and they've made an outstanding success of it. In this age of machines, many might scoff at the idea of raising horses for profit, yet the Murrays last year grossed around $150 per acre from their 460 acres, only half of which is in cropland. The elder Murray, in his ninetieth year, did practically all the baling on the farm, putting up thousands of bales of hay and straw. And the Murray hay has topped all competition at the local county fair for years.

Bonnie Brae's income is from three sources: breeding fees, boarding fees, and the sale of yearlings. The farm stands four stallions. Each of these is bred to 30 to 50 mares during the course of the breeding season. Only about 30 of the mares are owned or leased by the Murrays; the rest are the property of other owners.

Of the four studs, The Widower, now 26 years old, is the Murrays' favorite. They got him for $8,300 from Dr. D. B. Rice of Britton, South Dakota in 1948. In 1959, The Widower led all living sires in the number of standard record pacers. Eight of his get have beaten the two-minute mark.

The mares on Bonnie Brae Farms are a high-class lot, too, though as always in the livestock field, they are lacking in the glamour that attaches to the studs. Four of the mares have produced two-minute performers. One of the favorites among the Murray mares, though not one of the best producers, is Lily Direct, by Billy Direct. This little black lady has a personality that just can't be denied. "We bought her at the Harrisburg Sale in the fall of 'fifty," Bill will tell you. "She was a good, honest little race mare who had campaigned for four years in the stable of Brooks & Drew up in Maine and had taken a record of 2:08⁴/₅. We went to $3,300 to get her and her groom was so heartbroken when she was sold, he was crying when he turned her over to me.

"He asked me if I'd let him come to see her. I said certainly; and do you know, for years he came from his home somewhere in New York State just to see Lily Direct. He was an old man, too. He didn't care much about anything else on the place—just wanted to see his mare."

Just as the cattle ranch turns out stockers and feeders, the feedlot produces beef steers and the sheepman sells lambs and wool, the product of the horse farm is its yearlings, the race horses of tomorrow. In the horse business the yearlings are usually sold at the big public sales held in the summer and fall. The big Kentucky trotting horse nurseries like Walnut Hall, Castleton and Poplar Hill sell at Tattersalls in Lexington; a good many of the Indiana farms go to the Indianapolis Speed Sale; the huge Hanover Shoe Farm in Pennsylvania sells at Harrisburg. The Bonnie Brae youngsters are sold along with the offerings of other top Ohio farms at the Delaware sale of the "Stars of Tomorrow" conducted by the Ohio Breeders Sales Company late in September every year. For the past few years they have been averaging around $3,000 per head.

Bill Murray is president of the sales company. Selling race horses, he says, is a snap compared to selling draft animals, even when times were good. "This is a cash business," he says. "There's no horse trading in it anymore. You take your yearlings to the sale and bring home cash."

Bill figures it costs about $1,500 to drop a yearling in the sales ring. A $1,500 profit per head on 30 head looks pretty tempting, but the average farmer isn't advised to try it.

"A farmer might make some money on a couple of broodmares," he says, "but he has to be willing to study hard and get a good sound knowledge of bloodlines; he has to keep an eye on the tracks to see what's winning and what kind of breeding may be popular a year or two from now. And most of all, he has to like horses—maybe he has to be kind of horsecrazy. Good horsemen are born, not made. It takes more than the profit motive to make a man a success in this game. You'll find all kinds of people in the business. Some of the men who send their mares to our place are very wealthy. Their mares arrive in the finest vans. Others aren't quite sure where they're going to get the money for the stud fee. But all of them have that passion for a horse."

Son Bill looks on while his father, William Murray, Sr., supervises a shoeing job on their top stud, The Widower.

# There goes the

Today's Chisholm Trail is a narrow roadway of rails, ties and ballast. Every fall, special livestock trains begin to streak along this trail, "hot as a burnt boot," carrying millions of head of cattle in their annual migration from range to feedlot.

In the 36 cars between this Union Pacific Diesel and its caboose are 468 tons of live beef. The herd was assembled from mountain ranches at the rail-

head in Victor, Idaho, and they were travelling 1504 miles to prairie feedlots in Garner, Iowa.

Before the cattle were loaded, the cars had been cleaned and disinfected, per government regulations. They were of the latest design with sides coated in composition paint to keep the warm hides of the cattle from sticking to them in freezing weather. They had been bedded down with fresh,

# Cattle Train

clean straw. From dawn till two in the afternoon it was a battle of cowboys versus cattle—prodding and tail twisting until 1254 steers were loaded.

Since government regulations also require that livestock on a long railroad haul be unloaded at least once every 36 hours for feed, water and rest, their first stop was scheduled for North Platte, Nebraska. To make this 925 miles within the 36-hour limit and still allow for intervening stops for crew changes and routine inspections, the feedlot special put all other trains "in the hole"—on sidings—except the fastest passenger streamliners.

Loaded again after the required 5-hour layover, it sped on through Omaha-Council Bluffs and delivered the cattle to Garner, Iowa, without a single casualty the third day out from Idaho.

Paper work starts at five a.m. for D. Burns, manager of The Pitchfork Ranch.

# Texas Cattle Man

The warm wind that flows over Texas from the southeast is heavy with moisture from the Gulf as it crosses the Sabine River and the coastal plains, the bayous and the tall pine forests. As this humid air is chilled, it drops its rain on the forests and on the rich blacklands where a man and his family are kept humping to farm 15 to 20 acres of cotton. Further to the west and north, more rain falls on land which is less intensely cultivated, where half-section farms rotate meadow and corn and wheat, and where cattle can be pastured one to the acre.

By the time the wind has crossed the Balcones escarpment, the geological fault that divides Texas like a belt from north to south, it has lost most of its moisture; it blows across parched land, stirring the feathery leaves of the mesquite, scouring the earth between the tufts of buffalo grass, tossing up a spray of red dust as it crosses the bleak ranch roads. Even from the realm of the wind, the ranches here seem vast and unfenced—here they trade space for moisture, here it takes 20, 30, and even 60 acres to feed a mother cow and her calf.

The headquarters buildings on one of these West Texas ranches—The Pitchfork spread—are almost lost in the vastness of 165,000 acres. They stand out because of the Chinese elms and the willows on the bank of the dry bed of the Wichita River. The light haze of blowing dust powders the leaves of the trees and sifts against the window of the ranch house, the office, the commissary, the chuck house, and the out-buildings.

Out on the range the ranch manager, D. Burns, sat in his car near a group of holding pens and corrals watching a round-up. He stayed in his car because neither car nor horse will frighten the cattle, but they will turn from a man on foot. The men, horses, and cattle could not be seen, but a cloud of dust rising over the mesquite showed where they were. These mesquite, the bane of the cattle country because they use moisture and rip the hide of men, horses, and cattle, have been sprayed with 2-4-5-T and stand as bare skeletons with only a few of them showing a fern-like regrowth at the base.

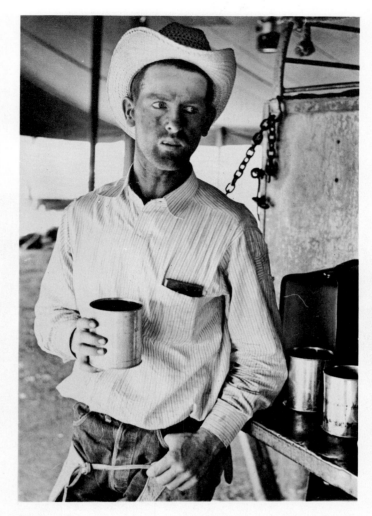

Cattle ranch wagon boss G. L. Procter shows a pale, protected forehead when he tilts his hat. His lips are coffee-washed of dust. Below, in the shade of the chuck wagon, weary cowboys take a noon siesta, sharpen knives or play blackjack.

As the cattle came nearer, Burns could hear the bawling of the cows and the almost sheep-like blat of the calves and then the men's voices, "Haw, there, haw!" "Hi ya ya ya!" and the pop of the reins as they were whipped against chaps. Two horsemen came over the top of the hill and rode down through the trees, followed by the red and white mass of cattle. At a distance the flow of cattle seemed to eddy and ripple as individuals stopped to graze and others pushed around them. Outriders held the bunch together, swinging the loops of their ropes like whips when one tried to stray; three men and a boy brought up the rear—one with a yellow neckerchief pulled up over his nose—weaving back and forth, keeping the cattle moving.

The smell of dust filled the air as the herd of six or seven hundred cattle came nearer. Coy Drennan, the wagon boss in charge of cowboys, brought up the rear. His sunburned, dust-powdered face looked dark as an Indian's between his light straw hat and

his yellow canvas brush jacket. Some cowboys were wearing blue denim jackets; others wore long-sleeved shirts—red and white candy striped, green and white striped, and sun-tans; one had a Second Armored Division patch on the shoulder. All of them wore Levis beneath their dark leather, mesquite-clawed chaps.

The two lead riders reined up beside the gate leading into the holding corral to keep the cattle from spreading while the outriders and the men with Coy Drennan pushed the herd on through. Neither Drennan nor Burns gave an order; the cowboys knew the job and worked as a team as they did it. Inside the corral the cattle ringed the steel tank beside the windmill and drank the alkaline "gyp" water. All of the windmill-pumped water on the Pitchfork ranch is more or less alkaline, or gypy, from the gypsum in the earth, but here it is particularly strong. This is Croton Brakes, so called because a glass of the water will have about the same effect on a man as a dose of Croton oil.

As the cattle were run through a cutting chute where the yearlings were separated from the cows and calves, two large trailer trucks arrived to haul the yearlings off to the railroad to be shipped to the Pitchfork's 32,000-acre Wyoming ranch. This would take some of the burden off the dry Texas range.

When the last of the yearlings were in trucks, D. Burns finished his tallying on a gate slat and wrote the results in a notebook. "I don't remember ever seeing it blow so long from the southeast without rain," he said, wiping dust from his forehead. "It hasn't been this bad since 1934."

"I seen a tarantula this morning, Dee," one of the cowboys said, "and Bill, over there, claims he seen a scorpion yesterday. Those are supposed to be good rain signs, they say."

"Yeah, and I saw a terrapin crossing the road this morning. But they also say that rain signs don't work during a drouth," Burns answered.

Burns and the assistant manager, Jim Humphreys, drove bumpily across the range, passing the cows and calves. Burns said, "Those cows sure look a lot better than the range—better looking than we have any right to expect."

Burns drove some 20 miles to get back to his office. At headquarters, he drove into the yard around which the ranch buildings are grouped. The commissary and chuck house, with its walk-in refrigerator and restaurant-sized range, are on the south side of the yard on the banks of the often dry Wichita River near the site of the original headquarters buildings, which were dug-outs in the bank of the stream. A dairy barn and horse corral form

On some Texas ranches, a helicopter is used to round up strays from the mesquite brush and worry them back to the herd. From his plexiglass bubble, the pilot can spot mavericks which the cowboys miss.

the west side of the rectangle; grain storage buildings, machine shop and windmill repair shop with their forges and power machinery and machinery housing space form the long north side. On the east side is a building which Burns calls "The Monstrosity," a bunk house which looks like an old Bachelor Officer's Quarters. Two pleasant homes for the assistant manager and the machine boss flank the bunk house, and the narrow two-room office with an old locomotive bell in front, from the Fort Worth and Denver railroad, fill in the east side of the ranch yard.

The big ranch home stands back in a clump of Chinese elms near the chuck house. Its screened-in portico has sides made like a very tall fence with screen instead of woven wire fencing attached—this was the best way Burns could describe the structure to the cowboy-partner who made it.

Standing in the high-ceilinged living room with its Catlin prints, sage green chairs and sofas, and cool grey rug, D. Burns looked around at the colonial secretary, the highboy and great fireplace, chuckled and said, "You know, I've ranched in houses where you could see the ground through the floor and the sky through the roof, and I know that all of this isn't *absolutely* necessary to produce beef, but I can't deny that it's pleasant for me and Mrs. Burns." And Burns should know what it takes to grow beef. He has reached that satisfying period in his fifties when a man has the experience of a lifetime to back him up, but is not yet old. Most of

"Git along little dogie, get back to your mammy; there's black buzzards circling and the pasture is dry.
Your gant ribs are showing, your ears are bare leather; git back to your mother or you're bound to die."

Burns' experience has been with cattle; he was raised on a ranch—his father sighted the North star many a time as he rode herd to Abilene and once was on the trail for eight months; his grandfather was one of the cattlemen who sent Jesse Chisholm north with cattle—and he has owned and operated ranches most of his life.

Back in his office, Burns got onto the telephone to make sure that the railroad would have 13 cattle cars spotted on the siding at Narcisco when the yearlings arrived. On the ranch phone—like many of the big ranches, Pitchfork has its own telephone system—he dispatched two men in a pick-up to Pueblo, Colorado, to meet the cattle train and see to it that the animals were rested and fed. Then he put in a call to Wyoming to start Don Webber, his man there, looking for pasture which might be leased for more such shipments.

While Burns was waiting for his call to go through, Tom Thornton, a cowboy in his sixties—Pitchfork has four men over 60 years old who are in the saddle all day—rode up to report a windmill near the Keller-Field camp out of order. Burns promised to have the windmill crew stop by in the afternoon. When Thornton had gone, Burns said, "There's a great cowboy—one of the best. He's been on every big spread in this country—used to be range boss for the Matador's Canadian ranch. When he was young he was as wild as a smokehouse rat, and it takes a pretty good man to keep up with him today."

There were four desks in Burns's office, one of which was loaded down with papers, *The Lubbock Morning Avalanche, The Kansas City Daily Drover's Journal, The Wall Street Journal,* all piled there waiting for a spare moment when he could get at them. His own and Humphrey's desks were covered with ranch papers, invoices, ledger sheets, estimates, registration papers for the purebred herd. The typewriters and adding machine looked strangely out of place with the cowhide-covered chairs and yellow wooden walls covered with an assortment of leather lariats, rifles, Western calendars, aerial pictures of the ranch, and a pair of well-worn chaps. But they are all tools of the practical management that Burns gives this hard-working cattle outfit.

When he had finished his call to Wyoming, D. Burns phoned the Croton camp on the ranch phone. "John, I was over your way this morning. Sorry I missed you; I said, Sorry I missed you," he shouted into the old-fashioned crank phone. "Wish you'd

Texas rancher Joe Bridwell paid $80,000 for a half interest in Larry Domino 107. Bridwell's manager, Bud Thurber, shown here with Larry, says their investment is quickly realized through the multiple breedings with their purebred cow herd, made possible by artificial insemination.

taste of that water in the holding pen tank. I think it may be going a little salt. . . . Hell, you don't have to drink *that* much of it, man, just a little taste. If it's salt, we'll have to run a pipe from the windmill near camp. And the next time the tank is empty, I think we ought to paint it—it's scaley. I'll send over some paint with your supplies. And John, you might pull that water gap out of the upper fence and let the cattle get back on the hill; that lower pasture looks mighty poor; better not overgraze it."

After he had put in another call to Wyoming about a shipping permit and phoned the veterinarian about a health certificate, Burns left his office and got into his car for a drive to the other end of the ranch to check on some plowing and look in on

the purebred camp. He had been up since four-thirty, had worked in the office, and was out on the range by seven. He would drive a couple of hundred miles over rough roads during the day checking the range and the cattle, arranging for land preparation to be ready to plant sorghum in case of rain, talking with his men on work to be done and the progress of the job at hand. He would end the day with another session in the office checking the books, writing letters, keeping up the flow of supplies to the ranch, and arranging cattle sales.

"We put in fairly long hours, all right," Burns said with a grin. "A visitor here at the ranch once told me, 'You can stay all night here quicker than anywhere in the country.' Like any big business, you've got to keep pulling the loose ends together to make it mesh. I tell you, a day in the life of a ranch manager is a nightmare."

The Pitchfork Ranch is one of the oldest in this part of Texas. "We wore out one fifty-year charter here and we're giving our second a good working over," an old-timer on the ranch said. The ranch was put together and the brand established by Powers and Savage about 10 years after the Civil War and was taken over by D. B. Gardner and Eugene F. Williams of St. Louis in 1882.

Pitchfork spraddles over two counties, King and Dickens, at the base of the Panhandle. Its nearest neighbors are other giant ranches. They must be big in this country where in good years one cow must have 20 acres of range. Fifteen miles east is the red stone, castle-like headquarters of the giant 6666. Concerning the name of this spread, Burns said, "There is a legend that Burk Burnett won the ranch at poker with four sixes—I don't know whether there's any truth to the story, but I will say that he was quite capable of it." To the north is Swenson's Tongue River Ranch. And in the rough country, to the west and north of The Pitchfork, is the Scotch-owned Matador Ranch, once second in size only to the million-acre King Ranch. The Matador is now being broken up and sold—Pitchfork acquired some 43,000 acres of rough land from this source.

From the beginning, water was the live-or-die element of the ranch. Like most of the ranches in this part of the country, they depended on wells. Today, Pitchfork has over 100 windmill-pumped wells which are drilled to a depth of from 75 to 500 feet. Fur-

ther east, the ranchers depend more heavily on catching surface water in earthen tanks—huge farm ponds built along any water course by pushing up a horseshoe-shaped dam to form the three sides of the pond.

Like most of the big ranches, Pitchfork operates with a series of camps spotted strategically over the spread. Each camp has a pleasant, modern ranch home where the camp operator and his family live comfortably. The camps are located so that one man can cover a part of the ranch, riding his section of the 300 miles of fences with a pocketful of staples and a hammer, checking the windmills and watering tanks to see that the water is flowing, and chopping holes in the ice in winter, herding the sorry-looking dogies back to the mother cows to get them adopted, occasionally roping a calf to doctor it for screw worms.

Whatever one man can do, the camp operators do themselves; when they need help they call on Burns and he sends out the windmill crew; or the machinist, or, if it is cattle that must be worked, the chuck wagon and cowboys. When new fence is to be built, he sends out a band of Navaho Indians, who arrive like gypsies to make their camp and build the straightest, strongest fence in Texas.

Working the cattle is an all-year job, except perhaps during the hottest part of the summer when they try to let them rest. In the spring, Chalmer Reid, the lanky, placid cook, drives his chuck wagon with its 'possum belly underneath loaded with rattling pans and supplies out across the ranch for the round-up, followed by his helper, Slug Mayo, the

Old Zack Reed drives the hoodlum wagon of bedrolls and branding irons. The hoodlum collects firewood for the cook and for the branding fires; helps spread the big canvas fly over the chuck wagon. His cry "Hot Iron" means the first branding irons are ready.

A welcome breeze fans the hot, dry faces of these cowhands heading for the chuck wagon.

hoodlum. He drives the hoodlum wagon filled with bed rolls and the branding irons. The hoodlum collects firewood for the cook and for the branding fires, helps Reid spread a big canvas fly over the chuck wagon and starts heating branding irons ready for the first "Hot Iron!"

As the smell of burning hair and hide drift back to the chuck wagon, the cook gets out his precious keg of bubbling sourdough and a sack of flour, begins heating a dutch oven, and curses loud and long at the dust which sifts under the lid of a pan of pork and beans. "I aim to feed them a sort of balanced ration," Reid said, "sourdough, beef, beans, fruit and coffee. A man gets all the iron and yeast he can use out of sourdough bread."

For weeks the cowboys comb the pastures rounding up the calves. When they are roped and thrown they brand them, dehorn and castrate the bull calves, inoculate them with a combination shot for blackleg and malignant edema, and slice off the tip of their left ear to show that the other jobs have been done. The ends of the bull's bags are kept in one pile and the ear tips in another; at the end of the day they subtract the bag ends from the ear tips and get their tally of heifers and steers. Later in the year, they go over the pastures again to catch long-eared calves that have been missed.

As soon as the round-up is over, the yearlings are cut out of the herd and shipped to Wyoming to fatten on grass. Around the first week in April, the

Hereford bulls are put in with the commercial cows. The heifers are held back until they are 18 months old to give them a chance to get better growth. In the fall, the calves are weaned—cut out from the cow herd and trucked to winter wheat pastures— and the cow herd is culled. During the whole year the cattle are moved from pasture to pasture as one piece after another is played out and needs a rest.

In the winter, the bulls and purebred cows, the weaned calves, replacement heifers, and cows with unweaned calves are fed pelleted cottonseed cake and sorghum fodder; the rest of the herd roughs it through on range and winter wheat pasture.

Some of the camps on the ranch specialize in a particular branch of work. Veto Austin and his boy run the purebred herd out on the north side of the ranch where hackberry trees compete with the mesquite. Here, the ranch raises all of its replacement bulls and occasionally has a few good bulls for sale. On the rolling, terraced lands near the center of the ranch, Bill Myres, with 4 to 10 men to help him, cultivates the 4,000 acres of cropland and keeps some 25 or 30 brood sows. "No mistake about it," Myres said, "the farmland, like everything else around here, is run for the cattle. We plant oats and hegari and pick them up with a binder for hay for winter feed. And we rotate these crops with wheat. In the fall and spring the wheat fields are pastured up to around March 25 and then we take them off and make a cash crop of wheat. But if it's a poor feed year, like this last one, the cattle will feed right on through and eat every blade of wheat that grows." The pigs are traded to the packing plant for bacon, ham and pork for the commissary.

Bill Myres' duties do not include seeding the range. The only effort that is made to grow more little bluestem, wild rye, gramma, or, most important of all, mesquite grass, is to rotate the herds so that each pasture gets a rest and a chance to make recovery growth. "What we *try* for," Burns said ruefully, looking at the dry range, "is to have a reserve of grass. I know of some of the boys who are trying to reseed the range with red panicgrass and crested wheatgrass. The best management I know is rest and rain."

As he left the shade of the headquarters building, Burns summed up this way: "We like it here, but it's a hard-luck outfit—not an oil well on the place."

In a dusty holding pen, the Pitchfork cowboys cut out the yearlings for shipment to Wyoming so that the dry Texas range will have fewer mouths to feed.

# Forest Pool

A RING of spongy muskeg hemmed the pool, muskeg cut deep with game trails radiating from the water like the spokes of a wheel. Back of the muskeg was a rim of pointed spruce and beyond that a great wall of towering pines. The pool was the shining hub of the wheel, its black surface reflecting the protecting timber. The air was heavy with the redolence of sphagnum and resin. No sound but those of the wilderness had ever penetrated there. At the close of its long primeval period, the pool lay perfect and untouched.

A hundred years ago a white trapper from the settlements to the south followed one of the game trails that led to the pool. Trees were felled and he built a rough log shelter on the rise close to the edge of the muskeg, but even that did not change the quiet that always reigned there. The nasal twang of the nuthatches still came from the pines, chickadees sang, and red squirrels leaped through the sunlit tops high above.

In the pines were marten, and in the swale not far away, beaver and otter. For many winters the trapper took his toll, and then the moose and caribou that used to come to the pool drifted to the north. The trap lines grew longer and longer, and one winter the trapper did not return. The cabin fell into decay, chinking dropped from between the logs, and at last the roof fell in. Pine needles and moss covered it, and after a time it became a mound of duff beneath the trees. Once more the moose and caribou came down the trails and the marten were back in the timber. The forest pool lay as before, smooth and dark in the shadows.

Then, one fall, timber-cruisers discovered the pool and the great stand of pines around it. They repaired the old cabin, rechinked the logs, replaced the roof. For months they worked, blazing long straight lines through the surrounding forest, laying out roadways and trails, cruising the timber. In the spring, when the campaign of destruction was complete, they left the pool and followed the trapper's trail toward the south.

It was September when the logging crews moved in with men and horses, mountains of equipment and supplies. They tethered their teams in the big timber around the pool. For days the woods resounded to the crash of falling trees, the shouts of men at work. Never for a moment were the axes silent or the crosscut saws. Log buildings rose where the trees had been, and for the first time the forest pool knew the glare of sunlight. Until the snow came, moose and caribou returned to their old watering-place and the hunters who supplied the long tables with food shot what they needed without stirring far from camp.

For two winters the loggers stayed, and then they moved on to new stands of timber in the north. For many years the pool lay stripped and ugly, and around it the slashings were barren of life. Only the rabbits remained and the coyotes that preyed upon them. At first the pool had as much water as before, but when the little streams and spring trickles disappeared, it began to shrink and the once-spongy muskeg around it became brittle and dry.

After a summer's drought came a violent storm. Lightning flashed and thunder rolled over the denuded hills. After the storm had passed, a tall dead snag crackled and blazed. When it crashed into a tangle of brush and tinder-dry pine tops, the slash exploded, and for weeks the entire countryside lay under a pall of smoke.

Mosses and lichens disappeared, and then came fireweed, jack pine, aspen, and birch. The water shrank still more in the old pool. Cattails and sphagnum encroached upon its edge from the surrounding muskeg and soon covered most of the open water. What little remained was green with algae scum.

Long after the fire a settler drove his team over one of the old logging roads to the site of the big logging camp at the pool. In the wagon were an axe, a saw, a breaking-plow, and supplies. At the swamp hole he watered his horses and stood there remembering the pines as they looked when he had come in with the crew. One small building had escaped the fire. He moved into it and set to work clearing himself a farm. Day and night he labored, pulling stumps and burning the great piles of roots and brush and windfalls left from the logging and the fire. Gradually a small field was broken to the plow.

As time went on, the little field grew larger and larger, but always in its center was the unsightly swamp hole, which defied all attempts at drainage —an ugly scar in his open clearing, a jungle of blackened and twisted roots interlaced with briars and alder. Because the pool bred mosquitoes, he built a new cabin on a hillside at the far edge of the field.

One day while he was working there, one of the horses wandered back to the swamp hole to crop the sedge, which was greener there than anywhere else. The animal went too close to the edge of the water,

broke through the layer of muskeg which had almost overgrown it, became hopelessly mired, sank deeper and deeper into the muck. When the settler came, the horse was dead.

That day he built a rail fence around the pool and rode the other horse to town for a box of dynamite. He knew what he must do: blast the layer of hardpan that lay beneath so the water could drain away.

In the fall when the swamp hole was dry, he dug down through the black peat, tamped in a charge of explosive, and lit the fuse. With a roar the blast went off and the swamp hole seemed to lift; roots and earth and stones mushroomed high into the air to fall again into the hole from which they had come. After that it was quiet and the air was acrid with the smell of burnt powder. The settler picked up a caribou horn that was golden-brown and in places blackened with age, and nailed it above the door of his cabin across the clearing.

The following spring the shining blade of the breaking-plow cut into the bottom of the little marsh, tearing through what was left of the ancient rim of sphagnum and the game trails that could still be dimly seen, trails that had been followed since the retreat of the glaciers to the north. Now for the first time furrows ran straight across the field. That summer the clearing was planted to corn, and when the crop was grown, it was hard to tell where the forest pool had been except that the stalks were taller and greener.

One night when the moon was full the settler walked out to the center of his field and stood there listening to the rustling of his corn. Now the whole field belonged to him and there was no longer the smell of the swamp, no longer anything to remind him of the cold wilderness. It was even hard to remember how it had looked when the logging crews moved in. That had been a different world. Now the air was rich with the scent of sweet clover and ripening corn. From the hillside beyond shone the lights of home, and he heard the soft tinkle of a cowbell in the pasture back of the barn.

But as he stood there a great horned owl hooted back in the woods, and for a moment the ancient scene returned. Again the pool was there with its rim of pointed spruce and the tall pines. There was a hint of sphagnum and resin in the night air and the pool was silvered under the moon. Then just as swiftly the vision was gone. The corn rustled softly and the tinkling bell in the pasture was very clear.

# View from a window

When city parents are wondering if their budgets will stand the strain of sending their sons and daughters to camp, country kids walk out the back door into a world of sunshine, cool pools, grassy hillsides and an association with the facts of life and death in the most natural setting in the world.

A boy learns to do a man's work and knows the satisfaction of a job well done. And if he gets interested in raising calves or pigs or poultry, there's less trouble keeping him out of juke joints.

Today's farm girl, when she graduates from high school, goes to college just like her city sisters. "You can't tell the farm girls from the city girls, by their dress or by talking to them," sums up a Midwestern Dean of Admissions, "But oh, that difference. The farm girl can cook, and milk a cow, and make her own clothes and drive a tractor too."

How to make home-made bread

A FRIEND stopped by the other day just as we were taking a batch of bread from the oven. When he saw those chestnut-brown loaves and smelled the rich nutlike aroma, he smiled as though he had seen an old friend. "That looks just like the bread my Aunt Vinnie used to make," he said.

"Aunt Vinnie lived down the valley from us when I was just a teen-age boy," he went on. "She baked bread every day in the last of the Dutch ovens I ever saw in action. It was a brick affair out under a shed. She would build a big fire in it, getting the brick hot. Then the fire and ashes were all raked out, the place filled with the loaves of bread, and the door tightly closed. As an oven that fireless cooker did a job that has never been matched.

"The tough-crusted, pully-mixed bread she baked was tops in eating for me. When, eventually, I would leave she always cut a crescent-shaped piece from the side of a new loaf, pasted the holes full of fresh-churned butter, overlaid that with blackberry jelly, then sent me on my way toward home. The road to Paradise could be no sweeter than that path through the pasture was then!"

Like Aunt Vinnie, we bake our own bread at home almost every day because we discovered long ago that store bread bears little resemblance to the substantial, satisfying, aromatic home-baked loaf. Besides smelling wonderfully good, home-made, whole-grain bread is unsurpassed for nutrients.

Who bakes the bread these days? They say it's a man's job, gentlemen, for almost all professional bakers are men. But in our house, most often I start a batch, work it into a dough ready for cutting, and my wife takes it from there.

I'll emphasize in the beginning that temperature is important in baking and it's worthwhile to use a thermometer consistently. Aim for a dough temperature of 80 degrees. To get this just right, the temperature of the water, the flour and the room should all be considered.

But come along on a typical baking day. We usually knock out 24 loaves at a time, but our formula can be broken down to meet your own requirements. Here's how we make it:

I draw one pint of water at 90 degrees because the room is about 70 degrees. Then I crumble one-half pound of moist yeast in and pour in one cup of honey, stirring until the yeast is dissolved and starting to grow rapidly. You can actually see it grow. This mixture goes into the mixing bowl together with 5¼ quarts more of water at 90 degrees. I stir it about a minute or two and then add a half cup of salt.

Then comes the flour—100 per cent whole-wheat as it comes from the mill. No white flour or anything else is needed, just the straight stuff. Since this batch is 24 loaves, I add 24 scoops of flour, each weighing ¾ pound. With water absorption this makes 24 loaves at 1¼ pounds each.

The dough is kneaded for about eight minutes or until the gluten is well-developed and the dough is firm and resilient. We used to do these big batches by hand. Believe me, it's a real workout with about 30 pounds of dough to flip around. Then we got our Hobart electric dough mixer. You can also get old-fashioned bucket-type dough mixers if you like. Phil Wells, in Haddon Heights, New Jersey, makes them and sells them as well as steel-burr flour mills.

After mixing, the dough is allowed to raise in the mixing bowl until the volume is double. This should take place in a spot where the temperature is even all around, or you'll be cursed with uneven fermen-

# spread with fresh country butter
# what tastes better?

tation—the top of the loaf will collapse, or there will be a cavern under the crust.

After it's raised, the dough is dumped out on a floured table and rolled out long so it may be cut into 1¼-pound chunks and shaped into loaves. Weigh the chunks on the kitchen scales if possible. You'd be surprised how important it is. Too much dough and it rolls over the sides of the pan. Too little and it looks like half a loaf.

We like to work with a small pan—3¾" x 7½" x-2¼" deep—sometimes called a loaf-cake pan. If you make a lot of bread, though, it's wise to get strapped pans, that is, six or more pans fastened together with metal strips and spaced so that heat is evenly distributed. Grease the pans to prevent the bread sticking, then fill about three-quarters full with dough. Grease the tops of each loaf or sprinkle with water to prevent too hard a crust from forming, then cover with a cloth to prevent drying out while rising. Raise about an hour in a warm room, around 90°, where the heat is evenly distributed.

Then into the oven with it!

### Oven Lore

Here's a tip a baker gave us recently about the use of our ovens. Directions for baking call for a 350-degree oven. All right, you put in 30 pounds of dough at 80 degrees and what happens? You reduce the temperature of the oven so much that, even though you followed directions, the bread is not properly baked. So this baker told us to start the oven at 400 degrees, put in the loaves and keep the oven at 400 degrees for 10 minutes to compensate for the cold dough. Then reduce the temperature to 350 degrees and continue baking for 35 minutes more. With fewer loaves the compensation is less, of course. And remember, if you're tempted to open the oven to peek at the loaves, you drop the temperature about 100 degrees each time you do it.

When the bread is done, it shrinks away from the sides of the pan and sounds hollow when tapped with the finger. As soon as the loaves come out of the oven, we immediately dump them out of the pans on their tops to reduce the excess moisture. In about 15 minutes we turn them right side up on a perforated rack. The extra screens for our seed cleaner make fine racks. Regular bread racks are available, of course, from bakery supply houses and larger hardware stores.

Variations on this basic loaf are as many as kinds of flour available. The principal thing to remember in working with other flours is that they do not have as much gluten as wheat and, therefore, make a denser bread. On this account we like to make half-and-half loaves, or two-thirds whole-wheat flour and one-third rye, or barley, or corn, or rice flour. One variety we like very much is a Colonial loaf—one-third whole-wheat, one-third whole-rye, and one-third whole-corn flour. We often add raisins to our whole-wheat bread, plus a sprinkling of cinnamon on top, for additional variety.

When making rye-and-wheat bread we throw in caraway seeds and replace the honey in the recipe with unsulphured molasses. That bread, spread with home-made butter and topped with a slab of imported Holland Edam or Swiss cheese, will stand by you while you build a dike or climb a mountain. This bread is called "maslin" in Europe and is not to be confused with pumpernickle, which is darkened with caramel.

A 100 per cent whole-rye bread can be like a brick, just as heavy and hard, unless you know the art of making a "Sauer," which is a complicated method better left to experts. The rye bread of commerce is not rye bread at all, but 90 per cent white wheat flour and 10 per cent white rye flour with the germ and bran removed. It is called "rye" solely out of courtesy and by government consent.

---

## 5 easy steps to homemade bread

1. For a basic white loaf, add 1 package yeast to 1 cup warm water. Dissolve. Mix and add 1 cup scalded milk, 2½ teaspoons salt, three tablespoons sugar, 6 tablespoons shortening.

2. Add 3 cups sifted flour, beat until smooth. Stir in another 3 cups flour. When the dough forms a ball and comes away from the sides of the bowl, turn out on a floured board and knead.

# Old-Fashioned Sponge Bread

Another basic way for making bread is by the old-fashioned sponge, or starter, method in which you save back a portion of each batch of bread to start the next. Mrs. J. C. Turner, who lives on a 600-acre farm near Rising Sun, Indiana, has always made bread this way.

"I used to watch Mother make bread when I was a girl on the home farm," says Mrs. Turner. "For her bread Mother used a sponge, or starter, instead of yeast. She called it an 'Oklahoma starter,' which is different from a regular potato sponge and is made as a part of the bread itself, not separately.

"When I married she gave me two cups of her sponge to start my own bread making. In 33 years of baking, I've lost this starter only once. That was about three or four years after I was married. Luckily, a neighbor had some just like that I'd been using and she loaned me a cup of hers to start again. For 29 years now, I've kept going on my own.

"I sometimes stop to wonder what in the world I would do if I lost my sponge again. I don't know where I could get the loan of another one since so few women bake their bread at home now, and I have never made one from scratch. Though I've never tried it, perhaps one could be made with yeast, just like the potato sponge is made when there is none left over."

Her sponge method takes longer than yeast bread or potato sponge bread because there is an extra raising in the process, Mrs. Turner says, but otherwise the procedure is about the same as that for making all raised breads. This is her recipe for 5 loaves:

If no starter is available, it may be made with yeast in this way: Mix ¾ pound of flour with 1¼ cups boiling water. Add 3¾ tablespoons sugar and 1½ tablespoons salt and enough cold water to make 3¼ cups liquid. Let the mixture become lukewarm, then add 1 cake of compressed yeast which has been dissolved in 1⅛ cups lukewarm water.

Allow this mixture to stand overnight. In the morning it should be light and frothy. Stir it well and remove 2 cups to save and be used as the starter. The remainder is ready for use.

Put 2 cups of sponge in a gallon-size crock, or mixing bowl.

Add: 5 tablespoons sugar, 1 quart *lukewarm* water, 6½ cups sifted flour, mix thoroughly, then set in a warm place to raise to the top of the crock.

Add: 4 tablespoons salt, 1 pint lukewarm water, 9-10 cups sifted flour (save a little of this to use on the board when kneading).

Mix these ingredients by hand, then turn out on a floured board and knead until the dough is smooth and elastic.

Put back in the crock and let raise in a warm place until about double in bulk.

Take out and knead slightly.

Measure into 5 equal portions, shape into loaves and place in greased 4"x8" pans.

Let raise in a warm place until double in bulk and until finger dents remain. The dough will seem much lighter when "hefted" than before it was set to rise.

Bake in a 350-degree oven for 1 hour.

"While the bread is rising the last time," Mrs. Turner says, "I take care of the starter I set aside for my next baking. I sprinkle a little sugar over the top of it to help it ferment and let it rise to the top of the crock. Then I stir it down, put a plate over the top and store it on the bottom shelf of the refrigerator. It keeps cool enough there not to sour—which

3. Place kneaded dough in a greased bowl, cover and let rise in a warm place until double in bulk. Punch down, pull the sides into the center and turn out on a lightly-floured board.

4. To knead dough, flatten it slightly. Fold it over itself toward you, then push away with the heels of the hands. Keep turning the dough and repeating this action until it is smooth.

5. To shape the dough into two loaves, cut in half and press each piece into an oblong 9x8x1. Using both hands, fold each end of the oblong to the center, pressing down firmly.

it might do if left out in the hot summer—but doesn't freeze. Trying to store her sponge in the wintertime so it wouldn't freeze overnight used to be one of my Mother's biggest worries. Freezing ruins the fermentation process and the bread won't rise then.

"The starter will keep for about a week as I store it. If for any reason I don't bake twice a week, as I usually do, though, I mix a tablespoon of sugar and about the same amount of flour into the starter. That freshens it and makes it just like new so that it will keep until I do bake again."

### Potato Sponge Bread

"A lot of our friends made their bread with a potato sponge when I was a girl," Mrs. Turner adds. "Occasionally, Mother would use this recipe:

Boil 3 potatoes, mash or beat soft in the water:
Add:
3 tablespoons honey
1 tablespoon salt
1 cup starter left from previous baking
Enough warm water to make 3½ cups mixture
If no starter is available, dissolve 1 yeast cake in a cup of tepid water, add the potato-honey-salt-water mixture and allow to stand overnight.

Next day take out 1 cup to use next baking, then mix the remainder thoroughly with

      3 tablespoons fat
      10 cups sifted flour
      3 tablespoons honey

Let the dough raise for 2 hours.
Turn out on a board and knead a few minutes until dough is smooth and resilient.
Let dough stand 10 minutes to recover.
Shape into 3 loaves, place in oiled pans.
Raise in warm place until finger dents remain.
Bake 60-70 minutes at 350 degrees.

"When the bread has finished baking," Mrs. Turner says, "I grease the top, then turn it out top down on a cloth or rack and let it cool before storing. I keep my loaves covered with a cloth in a special ventilated drawer in my cabinet. But with a family that likes home-made bread as much as mine does, it doesn't stay there long. I guess that's one reason I still make bread at home.

"Another reason is—if I count my work as free of charge—baking bread at home is much cheaper than buying it ready-made. Bread costs about 20 cents a loaf these days. I get a 25-pound sack of Robin Hood flour for about $2.00. This will make 25 loaves of bread which, if bought, would cost about $5.00. So I figure that I get my bread for half price. This means a lot when six people with healthy appetites sit down to the dinner and supper tables each day."

### To Tell of Taste

Now for the hardest part—to describe the flavors inherent in whole-grain, home-made bread.

The French and Italians, knowing of these things better than we, have just the right expressions. "Bonne mouche" (good mouth) is the sensation you experience when eating it, and the purpose is surely "per amusare la bocca"—to amuse the mouth.

# The Eye of the Farmer

IT WAS early afternoon of one of those hot, humid days of mid-August. As Bob Hiatt and the commissionman walked through the feedlot, the steers roused from their nap and retired to a neutral corner to gaze at the intruders. The commissionman turned to Hiatt. "These bullocks are ready to go, Bob. They're just the kind of cattle that are selling now, Choice grade and right weight; ought to bring a good twenty-four cents."

But 24 cents didn't look tempting to Hiatt right then. He felt the market wasn't right. Most of his fellow feeders were feeling the same way and they decided they would do better if they held a little longer. So they held; and the holding developed into an endurance contest; and finally by the middle of November they found themselves selling heavy, over-fed cattle at prices 25 per cent lower than they were bid months earlier. All of which only goes to prove the wisdom of the old cattleman's axiom, "The first thing a feeder needs to learn is when to give his cattle a good selling." The question is: When should he?

Personal contact with the feeder's closest market is his best crutch. There is the case of the Nebraska feeder who generally sells his Prime cattle at Chicago. He never hesitates to run up a $10 phone bill to call his commissionman for a detailed rundown on current prices and market conditions when he

The early-morning tour of the yards by hard-eyed buyers is an experience for farmers who have fed and babied their cattle along for months.

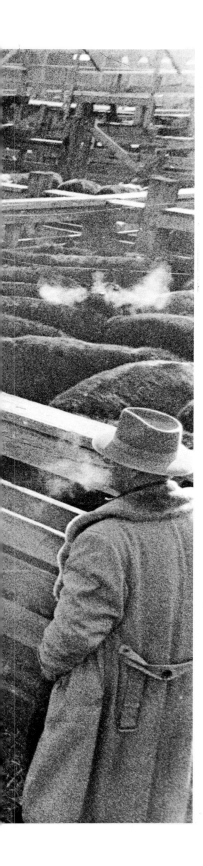

has a load about ready to ship. He will not only get the last word on prices, but advice on exactly what the packers happen to be looking for, the market man's estimate of the immediate market supply, an estimate developed through his personal contacts, those near at hand as well as those reached by long-distance phone, possibly a warning about an up-coming holiday that may have its effect on buyers' intentions.

When prices slip, many farmers are forced to adopt the attitude of Ralph Boals. Boals annually puts 3000 to 4000 head of cattle through his lots in northeast Nebraska, selling them at a Choice grade. When the squeeze is on, his advice is, "Sell whenever you have a profit margin. Don't wait till they're finished.

"I usually lay in cattle to full feed from a hundred and twenty to a hundred and eighty days," he says, "but when prices are down I start topping them out in about ninety days regardless of finish and I try to buy replacements at a lower price to even up."

Capitalizing on margin requires that a feeder be able to make a reliable estimate of the amount of gain necessary to develop a bunch of feeder cattle into acceptable market animals. This means he must not only be able to estimate the amount of feed needed, but must add to this an allowance for risk, interest, overhead and marketing costs. Fifteen per cent of feed costs used to be the accepted rule of thumb to cover the latter items. Today, 20 per cent seems a more realistic figure.

Choice is now the most popular grade in most parts of the country. It is the almost unanimous preference of the chain store trade; the housewife finds it just as tender and less wasteful than the Prime grade. In weight, the 500 to 700 pound dressed steer carcass and the 500 to 600 pound heifer carcass are always in demand. Translated into beef on the hoof, this means that the good yielding animal of 800 to 1000 pounds is always marketable.

Definite variations on this pattern occur throughout the country, though. A man most sensitive to them is the manager of the beef carcass sales division at Armour and Company's general offices in Chicago. According to this expert, anyone intending to feed for markets in the upper New England States would do well to forget the medium-weight cattle just mentioned. "They want big, weighty cattle down east," he says, "carcasses that weigh six hundred pounds and up dressed. They like steers with a thin bark of fat."

"In metropolitan New York, with its tremendous population, there is a market for almost any kind of beef, but six hundred to seven hundred pound steer carcasses are the most popular and there is a ready outlet for Prime beef, too. The Prime moves to the hotels and better restaurants and night spots, to the luxury liners and the dining cars.

"Consumers in Virginia, Tennessee and Kentucky like lightweight steers. We ship them four hundred to five hundred pound carcasses for distributive outlets, five hundred pound Choice carcasses for chains.

"The Ohio market is outstanding in its preference for light heifers. Heifers that will finish nicely at seven hundred and fifty pounds and less have a good demand in the independent stores. The chains like middleweight Choice steer carcasses."

And so it goes the country over. The farmer who finishes his cattle to the preference of his market is always in a much better position than the man who comes in with a bunch fed to his personal taste.

REAPERS AT WORK.

# Now in autumn...

September is a strange and restless month, an in-between month. The cycle of Spring's small grains is complete. Planting, cultivating, harvesting and drying are over. There is a lull and only time can tell whether the equinox will bring drenching downpours to make the fields impassable. The corn is ripening and racing against the time of the first killing frost. Yet there is a strange restlessness, too, for there is fear, rooted deep in the past when man and animal feared hunger and cold and the uncertainties that winter brought.

School opens late in the month and the kids grumble as the time for the school bus draws near. But mothers welcome their absence after a summer of having them underfoot all day. A new schedule of after-school chores gets off to a bad start and it will take a deal of training before the chickens are fed and watered on time.

Then comes October, the brightest and the sad-dest month of the year. There is a clear cold night and a sharp frost and the next day the trees along the creek in the valley sketch a line of color across the countryside. Mist appears over the far hills. The sere and yellow leaf scurries along in front of the cold winds and a family of mice moves into the attic. The shellbark hickory nuts are falling out of their shells and there's a quart or more every morning for the picking.

October slides into November. And now the trees are almost bare and the leaves are ankle deep in the woodlot. A haze falls over the sun and the hills are hidden in a smoky mist. Wild geese point their V's southward, high in the heavens, and the smoke rises straight from the chimneys in the frosty mornings.

Poets call the autumn the melancholy season, but to the farmer it is a fulfillment of the promise of the year, a reward for labor done.

Some people said his extrasensory perception was more than human.

# JIM
## *the wonder dog*

IT WAS a hot autumn day in the Missouri quail country and Sam Van Arsdale headed for a patch of woods along a slope at the far edge of the field. He caught up with his dog, Jim, who was working toward the woods, and called the dog to him. "Let's find us a hickory tree and rest awhile. Do you think you could find us a hickory tree, Jim?"

Sam Van Arsdale, as most hunters do, often carried on a conversation with the dogs he hunted, expecting no response, except perhaps a wag of the tail. This time Van Arsdale got an unexpected and even startling response from Jim. The dog raised his ears, looked at his master, and trotted ahead to a hickory tree. He placed his paw on the tree and looked at his master again.

Somewhat amazed, but not fully realizing what Jim had done, Van Arsdale half seriously said, "Well Jim, if you know so much about trees, show me a pin oak." Jim studied the trees for a moment, then trotted a short distance away and placed his paw on a pin oak, distinguishing it from the other varieties of oak in the woods.

The widow of Sam Van Arsdale, a frail old lady of 87 now living in Clayton, Missouri, told of this incident in an interview.

"Mr. Van Arsdale, very excited and puzzled, drove quickly home to tell me. 'Jim did something this afternoon that has me guessing. He knows every tree in the woods and can find them for me,' he said.

"'Sam,' I said, 'you are pulling my leg.'

"He was annoyed that I doubted him.

"'You get in the car and I'll show you.'

"We went out to the strip of woods where Mr. Van Arsdale had been hunting and I never was so surprised in my life. Jim identified seven trees, one after the other. I didn't see any cedars in the woods and asked Mr. Van Arsdale to have Jim find one. He did that too; ran straight to one about two-hunded yards away, a little old thing we couldn't see."

During the years that followed, Jim's superhuman powers were revealed in countless well-authenticated cases. Each day, it seemed, some new and mystifying trait was discovered by his master. He became known throughout the country and became the subject of newspaper and magazine articles. He identified objects and persons; he understood concepts as well as words; he foretold the sex of babies and kittens; and he predicted the results of baseball games, horse races, and elections.

One of the highlights of his career was his appearance before the Missouri Legislature. One day in 1933 the Missouri Legislature recessed for a very special and unusual occasion. Senators and representatives gathered in the chambers to pay tribute to Jim, The Wonder Dog of Sedalia. Jim sat calmly beside his master as the lawmakers and a gallery of several hundred took their seats. With the exception of a few who had previously seen the dog perform, the spectators were frankly skeptical about the amazing feats attributed to him.

There is some trick in this, they said; no dog could do what this dog is reported to have done.

For an hour and a half Jim was put through his paces. Questions and requests were given to his master who passed them orally to Jim. "Find the man who is known as the Beau Brummel of the legislature." Jim left the platform, passed down the aisle and placed his paw on the man. "Jim, there's a man with a moustache in the fourth row of seats. Find him for me." Jim made no mistakes; unerringly he carried out the requests of his master. In a final attempt to trip him up, one of the senators suggested that the state telegrapher be brought in and a message be given to Jim in Morse code. The senator whispered a message to the operator. "Jim," said Van Arsdale, "listen carefully now and do what it says." Jim watched the instrument intently while the message was being tapped out. When it was finished he walked down the center aisle of the room to the rear, edged down a row of seats, and placed his paw on the knee of a man.

Mrs. Van Arsdale remembers well the drama of the incident. "There were only two men who knew the question," she says, "the senator who whispered it to the operator and the operator himself. Mr. Van Arsdale did not know the Morse code, so he could not have given Jim any sort of a sign, as many people thought he did in similar cases. When Jim identified the right man there was a deep silence in the room. Then the telegraph operator sprang from his chair and shouted, 'My God, he has done it!' The message was, 'Point out the senator who sponsored the race horse law in the legislature.'"

Jim was a pure bred animal, a black and white Llewellin Setter. He was related to one of the great dogs of dogdom, Candy Kid, famed wherever setters are known. He was born on a Louisiana farm in 1925, and when he was just a few weeks old was given to Van Arsdale. While his brothers and sisters were valued at $25.00, a good price for a dog in those days, Jim was offered for $5.00 because, as his new master said, he was an ungodly looking dog.

Van Arsdale kept a large string of setters for hunting quail. The keeper of the kennels was Ira Irvine, who trained the dogs, and turned them over to Van Arsdale when ready for field work.

Jim was either too lazy or too smart to go to school. While Ira was working the other pups in the field, Jim sought the shade, and watched the proceedings. Van Arsdale became discouraged with the dog and offered to give him away. "I wouldn't do that, Mr. Sam," said Ira. "He's the smartest dog I ever saw. Take him out alone and see what he will do."

Van Arsdale did take him out alone, and on his first hunt Jim pointed a covey of quail perfectly and followed through to point the singles after the covey was scattered. He brought the dead birds to his master without mutilating them.

Until the incident of the trees, Jim had been used solely as a hunting dog and lived in the kennels with Van Arsdale's hunters. Now he was taken into the Van Arsdale home, and until the dog's death at 12 years, he and his master were rarely separated.

A favorite stunt was to identify cars which Jim did both by make and license number. Jim's talents seemed to have no limit. A hotel guest, J. Wilbur Cook, of the F. A. Owen Publishing Company, found a kitten in the street, and brought it to the hotel where it was given a home. On his following visit he was informed that the kitten, now grown, was expecting. "I wonder if Jim can tell us how many kittens there will be?" he asked Van Arsdale. Jim was called, and as always he sat down on the left of his master and looked up at him. "Jim, here are some pieces of paper on the floor. Show us how

(Text continued on page 142)

# Jim answered questions like these:

## in English

Who is Mayor of Steamboat Springs?

## Spanish

Donde esta la niña pequeñita?

## Shorthand

## Morse Code

Dr. A. J. Durant, Dean Emeritus of the School of Veterinary Medicine at the University of Missouri, with his own Pinbone hound and wildcat trophy.

# He's a rare dog

Learned men, doctors and scientists, were curious about Jim and many attempts were made to fathom his mysterious powers. On the invitation of a group of the faculty of the University of Missouri, Jim was taken to Columbia for an examination and demonstration. A Paramount News crew was on the scene to record the tests, which were made in the open air on a tennis court. Hundreds of students and faculty saw Jim follow every request made. Dr. A. J. Durant, Dean Emeritus of the School of Veterinary Medicine at the University, recently described this demonstration.

"I had never seen the dog nor did I know Mr. Van Arsdale, but I had heard a great deal. I was skeptical and I watched very carefully for some cue or sign Mr. Van Arsdale might give the dog. My doubts on that score were soon dispelled. Questions were asked the dog whose answers Mr. Van Arsdale did not know. For example, there was a professor in the audience who was known as 'Piggy' to his students. Mr. Van Arsdale certainly did not know this, yet Jim searched him out in the crowd. To the question, 'Can Jim read?' Mr. Van Arsdale's answer was that Jim had read messages and could identify every letter of the alphabet. On request, Jim pointed out the letter 'O' in the word Paramount on the sound truck. A professor wrote a message in the Greek alphabet. 'Read this Jim', said Van Arsdale, 'and do what it says.' Everybody thought that at last Jim was stumped, for he made no movement from his master's side. However, the professor at once confessed that he had merely written out a portion of the Greek alphabet. Later Jim read messages in French, German, Spanish, and shorthand.

"Jim was asked to point out a man wearing a blue shirt and a red tie. 'Now they've caught him', I thought. Knowing a dog is color blind, I was sure that Jim could not identify the man. However, he had no trouble at all. Apparently it was not necessary for him to distinguish a color. All he needed to know was the man—and he knew, how I don't know.

"We were baffled and it just didn't occur to us to go further than we did at the time. Later I attempted to get a group from the psychology department to go to Sedalia and test Jim, but they were not interested; probably the delicate question of who was smarter was in their minds."

Will Judy, editor of *The Dog World,* never saw Jim perform but is skeptical of claims made for him.

# I can't accept the story of Jim

There were few doubters among those who saw Jim perform. However, there were skeptics, those who refused to believe the unbelievable. Among the most prominent of these is Will Judy, editor of *The Dog World,* and an international authority on dogs. Mr. Judy, who never saw Jim, steadfastly refuses to believe that his gifts were anything more than a trained high intelligence, plus good guesses and coincidences. He says of *Jim the Wonder Dog,* a biography of Jim written by Clarence Dewey Mitchell, of Columbia, Missouri, "Frankly, I do not believe that the book is telling the truth. If I am to believe a great part of what is in this book I must revise entirely my whole basis of information and opinion on animal psychology.

"Jim deserves remembrance, but his accomplishments were so great and so varied that I have difficulty in accepting them. If only a very small percentage of Jim's accomplishments were actual and probable, he deserves a high niche in canine history."

(Continued from page 139)

many kittens our cat will have." Jim pulled out five pieces of paper. "Now tell us what sex they will be." Ten pieces of paper, five with the word female and five with male written on them, were put down. Jim pulled out three female and two male. A few weeks later the cat gave birth to three females and two males.

Having established a reputation, Jim was greatly in demand to predict the sex of babies. One visitor to the Van Arsdale home, Judge J. V. Kesterson, was about to become a grandfather. Jim repeatedly predicted it was to be a boy, and a boy it was.

During the following months Jim correctly predicted the sex of five babies. At this point Mr. Van Arsdale threw in the sponge. "Jim and I have more to do than predict sex," he said, and went hunting.

One of the most controversial aspects of Jim the Wonder Dog was his reputed ability to predict the future. Jim's prognostications were the least documented of his feats, but we must take the word of many intelligent and responsible people that he did make infallible predictions.

It was the custom of Mr. Van Arsdale and a group of his cronies to gather each evening in the lobby of the Sedalia Hotel for small talk and cigars. In one of the sessions the coming Kentucky Derby was discussed. One of the party asked, "Do you suppose Jim could tell us the winner?" Mrs. Van Arsdale tells the story: "Mr. Van Arsdale wrote the names of the entries on separate pieces of paper and gave one to each man. They were folded and no one knew what was on his slip. Then he said to Jim, 'Jim, I want you to pick out the man who holds the winner of the Derby.' Jim placed his paw on the knee of one of the men. Mr. Van Arsdale put the slip in an envelope and gave it to a banker friend in the group who locked it in the bank safe. When the Derby was run the envelope was brought out.

"For seven straight years Jim picked the winner. But Mr. Van Arsdale never allowed anybody to see the sealed selection until after the radio announced the results. He was very much afraid that something evil might happen—that it would be dangerous to have bad men know that Jim could do this."

Jim correctly predicted that Roosevelt would win over Landon, and someone remarked in a newspaper editorial that the *Literary Digest* would do well to hire Jim. Picking the World Series winner was a routine job for Jim.

Van Arsdale received a number of offers from sportsmen who saw in the dog a much more reliable tipster than any tout. Opportunities to capitalize on Jim's talents came from many sources. An offer in six figures to sign a Hollywood contract, and an engagement at the Century of Progress Fair in Chicago, were turned down by Van Arsdale. Dr. Durant said of him, "He never made a cent off Jim. He resolutely refused to commercialize him."

While Jim was an obedient and well-mannered dog; with one exception he was not responsive to any person other than his master. The exception was Dr. J. C. Flynn of Kansas City, Missouri. Dr. Flynn was president of the National Veterinary Association, a distinguished veterinary surgeon. Jim was sent to Dr. Flynn's hospital in Kansas City for treatment during an attack of rheumatism when he was eight years old.

Jim spent the first few days of his illness at the hospital, but was then taken to Dr. Flynn's home. It was during this time that the veterinarian discovered, quite by accident, that Jim would "perform" for him as he did for his master.

"Jim seemed to be unhappy at the hospital," Dr Flynn reported later, "and one evening I took him home. When he got out of the car at my home I said to him, 'My little niece is in the northwest room. Go on up and see how she is while I put the car away.' This request was entirely unconscious and I had no intention of testing Jim. I always talk to animals and when I opened the door for Jim I said it more to assure him. When I put the car away and went into the house I found Jim sitting by my niece's crib with his paw on the pillow. To find the room he had to go up a flight of stairs, down a long hall, and make a choice of several rooms."

Thereafter, Dr. Flynn gave him every test he could think of in an effort to discover the secret of his power. "The most amazing thing about Jim was that he never failed," Dr. Flynn continued. "He was, like nature, infallible. I took him to a large party one evening. One of the guests was a stenographer. She wrote a number of requests in shorthand and Jim followed them perfectly."

Van Arsdale did not believe telepathy could explain Jim's powers—too often he did not know the answer himself. For example, he stopped at a filling station one afternoon and the attendant, recognizing Jim, asked to have him "do a stunt." Van Arsdale was inside the station office at the time, paying for his gas. "Jim," he said, "show us where the man keeps his money when he goes home at night." He had seen a small safe in the office and fully expected Jim to walk over and place his paw on it. Instead, Jim went to a corner where there was a pile of old tires and placed his paw on the bottom one. The attendant was amazed. "I guess I'll have to find a new hiding place. That's where I hide the cash box. The safe's been robbed twice."

Among the most competent men to comment on the story of Jim the Wonder Dog is Dr. J. B. Rhine, Director of the Parapsychology Department of Duke University. One of the world's foremost authorities on the extrasensory phenomenon, Dr. Rhine says of the story of Jim, "Perhaps the best service this story renders is to remind us how little we really know. There are many more mysteries in the behavior of dogs than anyone would believe who did not start putting them down, adding them up, and keeping at it for years. In the story of Jim there is perhaps more of a concentration of these mysteries than in any other dog on record. But I think we will have to assume, as we do in all the sciences, that in due time by proper study we shall find out how dogs like Jim do what they do.

"I can go only part way with Mr. Judy's opinion. I agree that we must be very cautious about accepting free accounts of an animal's doings, because animal lovers like to be generous and storytellers like to be interesting; but being careful is not the same as closing one's mind. Jim lived in a sort of goldfish bowl and there were plenty of people doubtless eager to 'explain the trick.' If pure fabrication were involved it would not have got by very long. I do not find it difficult, even for introductory scientific purposes, to accept these claims of the striking things Jim was able to do. But what they do to me is start me looking for more cases like Jim's to strengthen the case, if there is one, and to allow the study necessary to explain the doings if they occurred as reported. Such a study could be a very important one if it led to the discovery of powers of such revolutionary character and such great potential value.

"And there is one more difference I would stress, and this is with Mr. Van Arsdale himself; it is reported that he was frightened by Jim's performance or, rather, by the implications of it. But this could only have come from reading into it some theory that was not necessary. Accepting the facts is one thing, but forcing an interpretation is a very different matter.

"Many thoughtful people who know about Jim seem to be hesitant to say telepathy and other capacities for extrasensory perception could account for Jim's remarkable behavior. I have been investigating these capacities for many years and have even worked with dogs in the line of investigation. There is some fairly good experimental evidence of telepathy between man and dog, and allowing that Jim was an exceptional case, as he was, whatever the ability concerned may be, I find that telepathy is a pretty useful type of explanation of the results. Van Arsdale thought he had ruled out telepathy when he himself did not know the answer. But telepathy is not a one-party line; even in experimental demonstrations two people have acted together as senders for a single receiver. The man who knew where the money was hidden was right there in the room with Van Arsdale, and if minds start getting together, what is to keep three from working together as well as two?

"But all of this leaves me far from the conclusion that telepathy was actually in operation in Jim's performance. A sensitive hunting dog, used to working with his master and bending his whole body in the direction of his master's interest, might easily develop a great capacity for catching the most subtle cue of eye or posture. It could thus, like Jim, be guided to a tree in a woods, a person in the crowd, an automobile on the car lot.

"It is true that as the stories are told this would seem to have been very nearly impossible in some cases of Jim's feats, but we must remember that these are accounts by witnesses who were not trained to look for subtle signs of the type I am referring to. So I say it is better not to try to say that telepathy *did* operate in Jim's performances but, rather, that it may very well have done so and if it did, this ability, along with the dog's intelligence and his very great responsiveness to his master might explain most things reported."

Jim did not seem to think of himself as a dog. It was with difficulty that he was induced to sire a litter of pups. These pups, of which much was expected, turned out to be just plain dogs.

Jim passed away, the victim of the infirmities of old age, on March 18, 1937, age 12 years and 8 days. His body was embalmed and buried outside the gates of the Marshall, Missouri, cemetery, the secret of his remarkable powers buried with him.

# The dilemma of the Grain Farmer

CAN a wheat farmer be too big for the soil bank, acreage quotas, price supports? Are these government restrictions and regulations valid for the big fellow as well as for the little operator? Some big wheat growers of Montana have found that planting it all, ignoring the restrictions, paying the penalty, brings them more profits. Henry Kolstad is one who plants it all and comes out ahead.

Liberty County, Montana, is long, narrow, dry and treeless. For the most part, it is a flat piece of real estate, extending from the Canadian line for about 60 miles into the sovereign territory of the United States. The main line of the Great Northern Railway cuts the county about in half, the part north of the tracks being spring wheat county, that south of the right of way growing winter wheat. In the lower part of the county the traveler comes upon a completely unexpected scenic attraction, the Tiber Reservoir, a huge, blue lake produced by impounding the upper reaches of the Marias River behind a dam which the local residents modestly refer to as "the world's largest earth fill." This is only one of the superlatives in the county.

Close by this lake lies the 22,000-acre Kolstad Farm, a place of no unusual proportions in this land of semi-arid vastness where the average farm is close to 3,000 acres and government experts estimate that it takes a minimum of 1,200 to 1,400 acres of crop land to make an economic unit. But this "south" place is only one segment of the domain of that operator extraordinary, Hank Kolstad, who also has a 5,500-acre place on the north side of the river, 1,480 acres in neighboring Choteau County, and 80,000 acres of range and crop land, including 3,500 acres of irrigated meadow, in Valley County, almost 200 miles to the east. He runs a tractor and implement agency in Chester, the county seat, and

has a big grain elevator at Lothair, a few miles to the west along the Great Northern tracks.

Kolstad doesn't mind characterizing himself as "the meanest SOB this side of the Rocky Mountains" when he's in a corner. But when the chips are down, he gets his biggest thrill playing Santa Claus for the kids of Chester every Christmas, a role for which he has a natural build. He is a tough, hard-driving survivor of the homesteading days of the second decade of this century. Those were the days when railroader Jim Hill's dreams of empire combined with the government's ill-conceived land policies to lure thousands of emigrants to this section of "The Great American Desert" to settle on undersized and uneconomic farming units. The government, it was said, was willing to bet title to 320 acres against the homesteader's filing fee that he would starve to death before proving up, and the government usually won. But not against Kolstad.

Hank's father, a North Dakota farmer of Norwegian descent, came to Liberty County in 1910 and filed claim on a quarter section for himself with another quarter in his wife's name. Hank stayed with his grandparents back in Dakota for two years, then joined the family in the 12x18 homesteader's shack when he was 10.

It took three years to prove a claim. Most of the homesteaders came about 1912. After they proved their claim they could mortgage it. Most of those who lasted that long did, and moved out. The Kolstads stayed and started adding land to their holdings. The 5,500-acre piece on the north of the river, now farmed by Hank's son-in-law, Bill Fraser, is built around the nucleus of the original Kolstad half section. The other pieces Hank picked up as opportunity presented itself. Opportunity generally meant drouth, grasshoppers, depression and other

circumstances usually labeled calamity. As Kolstad says, "There have been times when you could buy land out here for 50 cents an acre—if you could scrape together the 50 cents."

Topography and climate combine in this country to make it a land that cries for large-scale farming. It is also a region where the scale of operations and the hazards involved in raising a crop often make a mockery of restrictive governmental programs. Hank Kolstad is one of the biggest of the big and the story of his operations is a dramatic picture of modern large-scale agriculture.

The Kolstads have a son, Allen, and four daughters. Two of the daughters are married and sons-in-law Bill Fraser and Cliff Lingen each are in charge of one of the farms. Fraser is on the 5,500-acre home place from whence he can take off in his Cessna to rush a part for a broken-down combine down to Lingen's place in Choteau County, help spot strays during the roundup on the big "south" place presided over by young Allen Kolstad, or fly in help to lend a hand at hay time on the Valley County ranch.

Hank, himself, dashes from place to place in his big, two-way radio-equipped Oldsmobile. Dodging chuck holes as he approaches Tiber dam at a 75-mile-an-hour clip he suddenly reaches over to the

Montana wheat farmer Hank Kolstad has four farms with 20,000 acres in cultivatable land. His parade-formation of machinery on just one farm, below, is a $150,000 investment.

dashboard and grabs the microphone. "Car one calling 207 . . . 207 . . . come in 207."

"This is 207."

"There's a flatbed leaving down at Allen's going over to Valley. Anything you want to send along from the store?"

"Don't think so, but I'll check and see. Vern says to remind you about that meeting at the bank at two."

"I'll be there. Roger and out."

A few minutes later the speaker begins to squawk: "Car four calling car one . . . car four calling car one."

"This is car one, come in."

"We're down here along the breaks and we're about out of gas. Have somebody bring some gas down from Allen's for us."

"OK, I'll bring it myself. I was coming down to see how you boys were getting along with that fence, but I was going to stop by to give the kids their 'prize' first."

The Kolstad grandchildren always get a treat whenever grandpa Hank drops by.

Wheat is the big wheel of the Kolstad fortune. The elevator and the implement store are mere sidelines, though intimately related to the wheat operation and almost demanded by its size. The elevator, naturally, grew out of the need to acquire more control over the disposal of the harvested crop. The implement business, according to Hank, also filled the need for something to do during the slack season. "We moved into town in 1942," he says, "so the children could go to high school. I had to have something to do during the winter, so I bought the John Deere dealership." A dealership is a mighty good way to whip the farmer's old problem of buying at retail, too.

It is easy to see how a man who farms on this scale not only finds little need for government assistance, but is inclined to shout like the rookie retreating from Bull Run, "Get out of the way for a man who can run!"

His total cultivatable land adds up as follows:

Kolstad Farm (Allen's place).......12,000 acres
Bill Fraser Farm................... 5,000 ”
Lingen Farm..................... 1,480 ”
Valley County Ranch............. 2,000 ”

     Total........................20,480 ”

This being dry farming country where half the crop land is left in summer fallow every year to conserve moisture for the next crop, roughly 10,000 acres of wheat or barley are the normal Kolstad production.

The cropland on the Valley County place was sown to Durum wheat and flax last year. The 1957 wheat allotments for the other three places were:

Kolstad Farm....................... 3,076 acres
Fraser Farm....................... 2,298 ”
Lingen Farm..................... 400 ”
_____
Total....................... 5,774 ”

This was just too restrictive for a man of Hank Kolstad's proportions. Take the south place, alone. Allen has over $150,000 tied up in equipment there and storage space for 160,000 bushels of wheat. According to the county Agricultural Stabilization and Conservation committee the normal yield on this place is 13 bushels to the acre. In a good year it can easily double that yield and even 30 bushels is not uncommon. Kolstad had the choice of staying within the allotment and either letting his excess acres remain in fallow or sowing them to barley, a crop he holds in low esteem, not only because of its unattractive price but because it is hard to combine; or he could shoot the works and overseed.

If he stayed within the allotment he could sell his grain and get the full government support price, around $2.05. If he overseeded he would lose the support of the entire crop. He could sell on the open market, but that part of his crop equal to his normal yield times his overseeded acres would be classified as "hot" wheat and subject to a penalty of $1.12 per bushel. (In some cases the entire yield from the overseeded acres is considered "hot" wheat.) He could sell this "hot" wheat at harvest and pay the penalty, or he could store it, post a bond for the amount of the penalty and if his crop this coming year should fall below his quota (normal yield times allotment), a distinct possibility in that dry country, he could sell this "hot" wheat without penalty as part of his new quota. There was another possibility, too. If he seeded the works and his actual yield was less than his quota (39,998 bushels on Allen's place) he could dispose of it all without penalty. This last is what the growers refer to as the "Christmas" amendment designed to bail them out in case of crop failure.

Having plenty of storage space, Kolstad, like most other big growers in a similar position, looks upon "hot" wheat as insurance. "A man would be a fool if he didn't overseed," is his attitude. So he put the works in wheat—9,100 acres on three farms.

Here's the way it balances out in some pretty simple arithmetic. Since the normal yields vary from farm to farm it will be best to use just one of the farms, Allen's, as an example.

Wheat out in that Montana country brings a premium for protein content. This may run anywhere from 12 to 18 per cent and bring a premium of from 6 to 34 cents per bushel. However, protein content usually runs in inverse ratio to weight so the higher yielding wheat (weight-wise) is usually of lower protein content and vice versa, and whatever premium the lighter weight wheat might command for protein may be counterbalanced to a considerable extent by the discounts for weight. So, for the sake of example, it is safe to use a figure of $2.05 per bushel for the crop. A crop of 76,900 bushels (3,076 acres times the actual yield of 25 bus.) at this price would bring $157,645. That would be the maximum Kolstad and his son Allen could get if they stayed within the allotment on the south place.

Unsupported wheat in northern Montana this past winter was bringing around $1.80—a price admittedly higher than would have been the case without the protection afforded the supported part of the crop. After sowing a total of 6,000 acres (of which 2,924 acres were overseeded) Kolstad got a yield of 25 bushels per acre for a total of 150,000 bushels on Allen's place. Of this 38,012 bushels (2,924 acres times the normal yield of 13 bushels) were "hot" wheat which could net only the difference between the market price ($1.80) and the penalty ($1.12) or approximately 68 cents per bushel for a total of $25,848. The remaining 111,988 bushels he could sell at the market price, realizing $201,578. Total receipts $227,426. Obviously, this was a better deal than staying within the allotment, particularly when his costs ran about $20 per acre and because of his large fixed investment would have been higher with reduced acreage.

Using this cost figure he ran up a total bill of some $120,000 on 6,000 acres, leaving a net of $107,426. Even if he could have held his costs to $20 an acre on the 3,076 acres of allotment his expenses would have been $61,520 and his net only $96,125.

Actually, he did not dump the "hot" wheat on the market. He held it on the farm, posting a bond in the amount of the penalty. If dry weather, hail, grasshoppers or any of the other hazards to which wheat is heir take their toll of this year's crop he can pay out the "hot" wheat against it. There is a certain amount of risk involved, of course, in holding the grain and added expense in the way of depreciation on granaries, insurance premium, premium on the bond on the "hot" wheat, possible outlays for moving or treating the grain, and the county tax based upon a valuation of 70 cents per bushel. Yet the grain in the bin is good property and its value will far exceed these expenses.

Each of the Kolstad farms is a completely independent unit with its own line of equipment. Allen's place is, again, a good example of the setup. Here there are 10 tractors, 2 big International crawlers and 8 John Deere R's, 8 14-foot self-propelled combines, 6 20-foot pull-type combines, a 60-foot hitch of Noble blades (those big 6-foot blades pulled 4 to 6 inches below the surface for the first cultivation), a 60-foot hitch of duckfoot plows (known more commonly in some parts as the Graham-Hoeme) behind which are pulled a hitch of rod weeders, and 3 hitches of shovel drills—one an 84-foot hitch of 7 12-foot drills, one of 4 12-foot drills, and 2 of 2 14-foot drills.

Besides this the farm keeps 6 or 8 pick-up trucks busy and has 3 big tractor and semi-trailer outfits. There are 3 or 4 long grain augers to fill the four big granaries with their 160,000-bushel capacity. And to keep everything in perfect working order there is a completely equipped workshop with a full-time mechanic in charge.

The manpower requirements vary greatly, of course, on an operation like this. Cliff Lingen locks his place up and goes to town to teach school after the wheat is seeded in the fall. Even on Allen's place, where there is a 600-cow herd of whitefaces, three or four men are all that are needed during the winter. At seed time and harvest the labor demands double or even triple.

Being winter wheat, the crop is sown in September on ground which has been fallowed all summer. The big 84-foot hitch of drills can cover close to 450 acres in a day, rolling along behind one of the crawler tractors. No fertilizer is used. The seed is sown at the rate of about 30 pounds (½ bushel) to the acre. Placement is made about 1 inch deep though there are times when the seed is put down deeper to insure contact with moisture.

According to Kolstad, it was the introduction of the shovel drill, a drill equipped with a small duckfoot-type shovel to open up a furrow for the seed, which assured the success of winter wheat in that part of Montana.

Blowing is one of the great hazards in that country so the seed bed is left in a comparatively rough or trashy condition. "We used to use the disk," Kolstad says, "but it worked the soil up too fine, so we have discontinued it." Seed bed preparation actually starts in the spring with the fallow treatments. This is when the big Noble blades are pulled along 5 or 6 inches below the surface to break up the hardpan and cut weed roots. The surface is relatively undisturbed. After this, every time there is a bit of rain the tractors hit the fallow land with duckfoot hitches and rod weeders, killing weeds and volunteer wheat and conserving every possible drop of moisture.

With the 60-foot hitches a piece of equipment traveling 4 miles per hour can cover about 320 acres in a 10-hour day.

During the growing season the wheat is sprayed, either by plane or by surface equipment, for weeds and, if need be, for insect pests. No spraying for weed control is attempted on the fallow ground. One of the biggest problems is volunteer wheat, against which the ordinary weed sprays are ineffective.

While there is one huge field on Allen's place a

Country elevators receive all night long in the harvest season.

Western wheat farmers like Kolstad need huge storage terminals for their 100,000-bushel production.

half mile wide by three miles long, most of the wheat land is a pattern of alternate strips of growing wheat and fallow to control blowing. Since the prevailing winds are from the west and southwest, the strips run north and south.

Kolstad estimates that it costs around $7.50 per acre to maintain summer fallow up to seeding. To seed the crop, spray, combine, store and carry the wheat up to marketing costs another $12.50 per acre, making the total $20 per acre. That, however, is when he is sowing his full acreage. With his tremendously heavy fixed investment in equipment his per acre costs would advance rapidly on a reduced acreage. Basically, this is the compelling motive behind these large-scale operations. Liberty County boasts that it has the highest percentage of big farmers of any county in the state and Montana is a state with a lot of big farmers. Just about half of Liberty County's wheat growers ignore their allotments and seed the works. With their huge investments in equipment and plenty of storage space for the crop they can't afford to seed less. They are geared for a big job. Reduced acreage increases their cost per acre and robs them of a reserve against the ever-present possibility of next year's failure.

### Who Makes The Surpluses?

A farmer from the Midwest recently made a remark to Hank Kolstad about fellows like him being the cause of the surpluses which are agriculture's millstones. The Montana grower had an answer for that one. "We don't cause the surplus. Wheat is the one crop we are really able to produce efficiently. If we have a bad year and our production falls off, the whole country feels it and the price goes up. It's those farmers back in your part of the country who make the surplus. They can grow corn, or soybeans, sorghum, a variety of small grains; but each of them is allowed to grow 14 acres of wheat—any kind of wheat, soft, low-protein, low-quality stuff. And they grow it, too. That's what makes the surplus."

The contenders will now retire to their corners and come out fighting when the bell rings.

149

# The Blind Farmer

"THE EYE of the farmer fatteneth the ox" says an old English proverb. There is a world of truth in this saying, for much of the farmer's success depends on the careful observation of his livestock and crops. He must cull his flock and look over his herd to see that his animals are healthy and producing; he must check his fields to see that the crops are harvested at the right time; and he must watch the growing crops for signs that show lack of proper fertility. He must look over his land to see that erosion is not gnawing away the slopes and he must look at the sky to make his best guess about the weather. In the evening he must read to keep up with this changing world of agriculture, and strain his eyes with the drudgery of bookkeeping if his records are to be kept in order.

But there are farmers, and good ones, who have been blind from birth, or have lost their sight for so long they but dimly remember the world of light and color and form. These men can do their own milking; are good enough judges of cattle to enter judging contests at the county fair and come

off with honors; and cull their own poultry. They are accomplished in the small crafts of farming such as carpentry, electric wiring and repair, plumbing and metal work; are competent farm managers with all the record-keeping that management involves; and can even plow a straight furrow when necessary.

One of these sightless farmers is Jack Caldwell, who runs a 115-acre dairy farm near Burlington, Kentucky. Caldwell lost his sight over twenty years ago when he was a boy. He and another 13-year-old had poured a half pound of black powder into a toy cannon and failed to provide a long enough powder train. The resulting blast left him permanently blind. After high school and college he and his sister saved their money and, with their father, bought the farm Jack now operates.

Standing on the porch of the house, watching Caldwell and his hired man work in the barnyard, it is impossible to tell which is the blind farmer and which the seeing helper. The tall, slim Caldwell works around his farm with complete assur-

Feeding his herd of 13 Brown Swiss is one of Caldwell's daily chores on the farm. His hired man, Arthur, does the milking and Caldwell cleans the machine.

ance. There is little or no fumbling, and he scorns a cane or a dog helper. When he walks to the house he follows a definite path, where his feet know and recognize all of the guiding contours. At the end of the path he turns down the edge of the hard road, and when he comes to the lane that leads to the house he turns into it without hesitation.

Like most farmers who love their farms and are proud of them, Caldwell enjoys showing visitors around the place. He likes to take them up the road and into the field that he is converting from crop land into hay production. With no other guide than the feel of the road under his feet he turns and walks into the field.

"During four of the five years I've had this farm this land has been used for row crops, as it was for a long time before," he said. "The first hired man I had was an excellent worker and very conscientious, but he refused to contour farm—felt there was something wicked about plowing a crooked furrow. When I began finding small gullies between the rows of corn and deltas of top soil at the end of each furrow, we came to the parting of the ways. Arthur, the man that helps me now, used to be with the Soil Conservation Service and he and I see eye to eye on conservation. One of the first things we did was to lay out the contour lines —he used the transit and I held the pole and

# Jack Caldwell sees

drove stakes—and later we put the field into alfalfa. Down the slope here you can see how we are healing the gullies that were starting. You see that bare line running across the field," Caldwell said, pointing directly to the thin patch and following it across the field with his finger, "that is the old fence row. We took out the fence when we converted all of this land to forage crops, but we haven't got the alfalfa to grow so well there.

"Our land on this side of the road goes clear up beyond the stream to the sassafras trees," he continued. "At one time I intended to cut out the trees, but they are so beautiful, especially in the fall, that I decided to leave them there. That is one of the things I remember from the old days, driving along and seeing the sassafras trees in the fall."

Asked about his ability to get around the farm, he said, "The best way I can put it is this: It's as though a seeing person were walking around the farm with his eyes fixed on a map. He would always know where he was without looking off the map for a moment. Of course, I do get lost sometimes, and then I just wander around until I find something familiar and then I'm not lost. It's nothing to get excited about. Maybe the church bell rings or the noon whistle blows, or maybe Arthur starts the tractor. You know where the town is and where the tractor is so you know

where you are in relation to them. One day, soon after we moved here, I was out in the field and got completely lost. I walked around until I was tired and finally ended up on a little island in the middle of the creek. It was nice and grassy and the sun was shining on it so I just lay down and went to sleep. When I woke up all the cows were standing around sniffing at me."

The division of the work between Caldwell and his man Arthur, is on the basis of who can do the job most efficiently. "I am sure that, with help, I could do field work" Caldwell explains, "but I wouldn't do it as well or as quickly as a seeing person, so I let Arthur do it." Caldwell keeps all of the records, either typing them or punching them out in braille, and takes care of the other management duties. Both of them do necessary repair work around the place, though they rarely work together on repair jobs. "I have my own way of doing things," Caldwell says, "and it is usually more efficient to work alone. I have taken our combine apart and put it together again and feel that I can make any necessary repairs on it, but when Arthur works on it I don't try to help him."

Caldwell built the bull pen and dug the trench and laid a third of a mile of pipe to bring water from the pond to the horse barn. "I hired a young boy to help me line up the pipe. I could have done it alone, but you have to lift each section in the

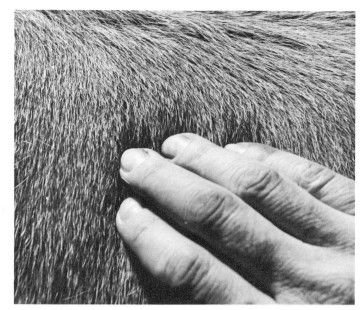

# with his hands

middle and since they are 24 feet long, I'm just not long enough to reach back and feel if I have it lined up with the last section."

When haying time comes, Caldwell has his hay put up by a custom baler. He works in the field with the men loading the hay, and later unloads the wagon himself at the barn.

Arthur drives the tractor and spreads the manure, but when the spreader is empty he leaves it parked near the loafing shed where Caldwell fills it. Arthur milks the herd of 13 Brown Swiss and Caldwell feeds and cleans up the milking machine. On Arthur's day off Caldwell does all of the milking and cleaning.

"Of course, you always have something coming up that changes the schedule," Caldwell says, "like the time one of our best cows had a bad udder condition. We decided to milk her four times a day to keep her from having too much weight in her udder. Arthur milked her morning and evening and I milked her at noon and midnight. And then there was the time that we had one of them with a bad case of foot rot and I had to go out into the field and feed and milk her there."

Walking through the loafing shed one of the cows brushed past him. "That was Queen, I think. I didn't get a good look at her." He ran his hand along the backs of the cows as he passed, "This is Bess and this is Silver, one of our best animals."

Asked how he knew them so easily he said, "They all feel different. Take Silver here, there isn't a silkier coat on any cow in the country, just feel it. You get so that the shape and texture of things is very revealing. I can tell any of the feeds we use by their feel and I can tell the difference between hay and straw or between kinds of hay either by feel or smell. When I'm walking, the slope and the texture of the ground under me is a guide that I don't miss even with overshoes on."

A friend who visited Caldwell one winter evening when he was finishing his chores says, "It was quite dark when we left the dairy barn and walked up to the other barn where he keeps his calves. Jack walked along easily and confidently while I stumbled along behind. When we got inside the barn it was pitch dark and I found that I was the blind one. I heard him set out the feed boxes and pour oats into a bucket. I knew that he must be measuring the amount, as I had seen him do, by holding the fingers of one hand at the point he wanted to fill to and pouring with the other hand. It was so dark in there that I couldn't see him as he brushed past me to put the feed boxes into the horse stalls. A moment later I heard him climbing the ladder to the loft and then the swishing sound as he dragged a bale of hay toward the opening. Suddenly I felt lost and rather afraid. When he came down, I told Jack that for the first

Walking the edge of a 12-foot loft does not bother Caldwell. The locust pole is a guide and he feels for the edge with his toe.

time I knew how it felt to be blind. 'That's how you feel after a five-minute taste of blindness,' he told me, 'but the feeling of being utterly lost in a dark world wears off. After a period of years you forget about it so completely that it's a surprise to be reminded that you can't see'."

At night, when seeing people are handicapped, he likes to go down to the barn and check over the cows. "I usually come down late and look them over. If any are in heat we like to pen them off quickly so that they won't do any damage. Even if I know they are all right, I like to go down and stand there and just listen to them breathing and

groaning in their sleep and smell their good smell."

One of the visitors who stopped by Caldwell's farm to look over his herd was Steve Elsaesser, who has been totally blind since infancy. "My nephew asked me to go with him to look at a calf that Caldwell had for sale," Elsaesser recalls, "but we hadn't heard that he was blind. You could have knocked me over with a pin when I got out of the car to look at the calves and the man who was to show them to me told me that he was blind."

Elsaesser operates a 260-acre farm in Ohio, where he milks 38 holsteins and raises chickens, turkeys and ducks on the side. All this he does with the help of a man in his late sixties and a boy of 18. Not content with merely farming, Elsaesser has a growing retail business in milk, butter, eggs, and dressed poultry. "I am confident that I could make a living on turkeys alone if I wanted to specialize in them," Elsaesser says. "They are a good project for a blind man when you raise them on wire the way I do. These Muscovy ducks are not so easy to raise, but I like to keep them to clean up under the turkey pens where grain and mash is spilled. I raised 400 turkeys last year and sold them at slightly below butcher-shop prices right here on the place.

"Chickens are another good project for the blind, either broilers or layers. A fellow should be able to do all the work without outside help. I know I do. Once I hired some fellows to help me with the culling. I generally do my own culling, but I was pretty busy at the time and thought that they could help me out. The first thing I learned, of course, was that they couldn't work like I do. I go in at night and work right down the roost, handling every bird. Why, I can spot a case of roupe as quick as you can tell your nose is running. These fellows needed light and before long all of the chickens were off the roosts and we had a terrible time trying to catch them. I tell you, sometimes people who see are a blamed nuisance," says Elsaesser.

Elsaesser learned farming as most seeing farmers have, by being raised on a farm and doing his part of the day-to-day chores. At the time he attended school there was no course in agriculture available for the blind. Until a few blind farmers proved that it was a practical profession for the sightless, there were no organizations for the blind willing to assume the heavy financial burden of an agricultural school. In 1942, the Barnes Agricultural School for the Blind was started in New Hampshire. It became the first and only agricultural school for the blind in the world. After five years of operation it was closed for lack of financial support. Its director, Fred Ward, was later invited west by the Cincinnati Association for the Blind, however, and a new school has been started in Mason, Ohio. So far as Ward knows, the school at Mason is the only one of its kind in the world, but he is hoping that two of his former students will soon have another agricultural school for the blind started in Greece. Ward would like to see other schools opened because he feels that farming is another way of life in which the blind can

find themselves. He does not, however, feel that farming is the answer to the problems of all of the blind. "The blind, as a group," Ward says, "make up a cross section of the American people. It would be just as silly to say that farming is the answer for the blind as it would be to say it was the answer for every American. For some of us it is an excellent way of life that we can enjoy quite fully in spite of our handicap."

Ward's work for the blind who wish to be farmers is a logical development of his own past. He too is totally blind, having lost his sight when he was a child of four, and he has operated his own farm in New Hampshire for over 20 years. In operating a general farm with dairying and broiler raising as the chief sources of cash income, Ward, like Caldwell, felt that the most economical use of labor was to hire a man to do the field work. This plan worked out very well for him until the war years when he found that he couldn't get extra help.

To meet this crisis, Ward took his oldest boy, Lawrence, who was five years old, out to the fields on his tractor. Ward started the machine, made the gas adjustments, and manipulated the gears while Lawrence sat in his lap and steered. With a little practice they developed into a surefire tractor driving team. "During the time we were driving the tractor every day," Ward says, "together we made as good a field man as you could find in New Hampshire."

When Lawrence graduated to driving the tractor alone, his younger brother, Robert, and sister, Barbara, took their turns as apprentice tractor drivers. With Lawrence able to drive the tractor it wasn't that they were particularly needed for the job, but by this time so much family prestige had become attached to it that it wouldn't have been fair to deny them the chance to serve as their father's eyes.

Around the farmyard Ward needs no help in finding his way about. "I did use a cane around here for a while" he says, "when we had a seeing hired man who couldn't seem to realize that there were blind people around. The day I finally decided to use a cane as long as he was with us, he left two garden tractors on the sidewalk between the house and the shop. They were so low that I didn't notice them and stumbled over one, got up and promptly fell over the other.

"Low obstacles are much harder for a blind person to detect," he said by way of explanation.

"You would never find a blind man walking into a wall or the side of a building; he would sense that they were there and avoid them. There is a difference of opinion as to how we do this; some feel that facial perception is the most important and others, I among them, feel that sounds rebounding from objects is the thing that does it.

"Facial perception," he continued, "is the ability to sense the presence of an object. Mostly, we find, the sensing is done with the nerves of the face and forehead. It is like my knowing that there is a wall next to me right now. I would know it even if I hadn't felt it there with my hand. I agree that there is facial perception too, but I feel that hearing is more important.

"I can fully understand the feelings of dread some people have about blindness," Ward said with a slight shiver, "for I have the same dread of being deaf. As a matter of fact, I was deaf for a little while during a mastoid infection and the world closed in on me. I think it a worse handicap than blindness. With sight you can only see what is directly in front of you, but you can hear sounds from any direction.

"When I was going into town a good deal I always wore leather-heeled shoes so that I could hear the sound bounding off the buildings," he said, continuing his argument. "If a truck rumbled by, however, it was like a seeing person might feel when the light is turned off, for as long as the noise continued you were completely lost. It is low objects, like fire hydrants or garden tractors, that are troublesome. You don't get a good sound rebound and you can't seem to sense them by facial perception, so you wind up stumbling over them.

"In getting to know a place you use all of your senses, of course. And they are so integrated that you rarely are conscious of using one or the other of them. Yes, we do have some landmarks that we remember. I know, for instance, that there is a rough spot on the sidewalk just before you reach the cement steps and I know the inward slope of the road as it turns near the shop and goes down to the barn. We teach the students as many of these landmarks as we can remember when they first come, just to save them time in getting acquainted.

"Our hope in teaching," Ward continued, "is to give the students as much theoretical training and as much practical experience in farming as we can in a one-year course. The main emphasis is on actually doing the various jobs so that when they leave here they will have have enough self confidence to tackle any job that normally comes up on the farm and go on from there."

The school started out several years ago with one student, Edward Konieczski, who came to the school from Michigan where he had had three years of High School Vocational Agriculture. In February the next year their second student was enrolled, James Richard, a veteran from the last war with no previous agricultural experience. Eventually the school hopes to help many blind students find a new life on the farm.

Instruction must be on a personal basis. To introduce a city-bred boy to the intricacies of a dump rake, for instance, Ward must first explain the function of the rake in farming and give a general description of it and of the other equipment that could be used in doing the job of gathering hay. He then takes the students by the hand and goes over each part, feeling the general shape of the machine. He then explains the relationship of the parts and how they function together.

In teaching electricity, plumbing or carpentry the instruction includes the actual use of tools. The project in carpentry, used in teaching Edward Konieczski, was the construction of roosts for the chicken coops. Konieczski helped Ward build one of the structures, a sturdy table with a hinged, wire-covered top, and was then permitted to make one entirely on his own. A seeing poultryman who saw the roosts said, "They're too good. You just don't do such a finished job for chickens." The neat firmness of the joints, the alignment of the boards, the fit of the hinged top to the table, and the finish was as good as that generally found in kitchen furniture.

Whenever possible, regular farm chores are used for instruction. A student learning about cows and milking will take care of some of the cows in the school herd and run the milking machine; classes in poultry raising are conducted while working in the coops. At times a job that has been set aside for instruction work just won't wait. "We were milking the other morning," Konieczski says, "when the milking machine motor slowed down and began to smell. We figured that the trouble was in the switch. Mr. Ward had promised to let me help him install a new switch, but the one that they had sent out was a kind that he had never used before so he was waiting for another to come

before we tackled the job. Well, when the motor started heating up, Mr. Ward turned off the switch, but the motor kept right on running and the burning smell got worse. Later we found that the heat had fused the switch. Mr. Ward jerked the wires out of the switch box, shut off the electricity at the meter, studied the new switch, and in minutes had the new switch in and the machine going.''

The students are taught field work with different crops and different pieces of equipment. "I know that field work is not efficient for the blind," Ward explains, "but they should have it in order to understand the management problems involved. Furthermore, there may come a time, as there did with me, when you either know field work and do it or you fail as a farmer."

Most of the instruction must necessarily come in lecture form since there are a very limited number of agriculture books that have been written in braille. Poultry farming is best covered, with several standard books and bulletins in braille; dairy farming has but six bulletins; hog raising

has one and home gardening a single bulletin. The number of texts indicates the current belief as to the types of farming most suitable for the blind, with poultry and dairy way ahead. Ward feels, however, that for those who want to devote themselves to management there is no branch of farming that is closed to the blind. "It depends on the individual whether or not he should be in farming at all. At the school here we are most concerned with whether the student has the proper aptitudes for a farmer. We take them on probation for two months, during which time we watch them very closely to see if we think they fit into the life."

Those who do love the life of a farmer and are able to adapt themselves to it go on with their studies. The life they have chosen will be difficult, but it will also be rewarding. They at least know that others with the same handicap have made a success of the job and have shown that the eye that fatteneth the ox can be replaced by the touch of hands that can see, and ears that can make visual the sounds that come to them.

# Judd McKnight
## built a sheep kingdom

ON A fall morning in 1901 Judd McKnight stood on a headland above the Pecos River in New Mexico and watched his herd of 1100 mortgaged sheep snake down the dusty trail to the river. Judd was nineteen years old and he had two dollars and some loose change in his pocket.

Judd and his sheep had come a long way—from Eldorado, Oklahoma, across the Texas Panhandle and into southeastern New Mexico, a dry, dusty trek of close to 400 miles, not counting the meanderings of a herd of sheep. His jeans were patched, his boots were run down and his sheep needed salt. Winter was coming on.

If Judd was bad off he didn't know it, for as he stood there above the Pecos a dream took shape —a dream that until now had been only a vague, nameless urge that made him restless, and kept him always on the move.

Now he knew what he wanted—sheep and land, land and sheep—thousands of sheep and thousands of acres of land. He saw the ochre-colored plain dotted with sheep—his own sheep, and his domain stretched away to the purple dome of El Capitan on the far horizon. He wanted to be a big man in this big land. That dream was never to fade, and it carried Judd McKnight over recurring drouth, two depressions, staggering debt and falling markets.

Today, sixty years later, Judd McKnight can stand on that same point and look out over 200,000 acres of good grazing land—the McKnight Sheep Kingdom—with 20,000 sheep grazing in tight-fenced meadows. It wasn't easy. He had no education, no inheritance, no background of family or position. But he did have one thing beyond all else —a bulldog tenacity, a singleness of purpose that shaped every move he made in the next half century. The Mexican sheep hands called him *El Chato,* The Bulldog. And Judd McKnight, at seventy-nine is still The Bulldog, a survivor of an era of the West when the weak perished and the meek inherited nothing.

A good many of Judd's rough-and-ready ways came from his father, Tom. Tom was a wrangler on the old Chisholm Trail when he was fourteen years old. He married and settled in Davilla, Texas, as a storekeeper. Judd was born in 1882. The McKnight family moved to Quanah, Tex., soon after Judd's birth. Then, when Judd was still a youngster, the family decided to move to Eldorado, Oklahoma, about twenty miles north across the Red River. Judd liked the move, but he did have one regret. He was in the throes of a puppy-love affair was a pretty little neighbor girl, Nannie Potts.

Tom McKnight opened a general merchandise store in Eldorado, but that petered out and he homesteaded a sand-blown farm that wasn't much good. Judd grew up there. The country settled and money was tight. The water was bitter, the farms were small, and they never seemed to raise a decent crop. But his father refused to move, perhaps because his wife died there. He remarried an Oklahoma girl.

When Judd was thirteen, he got his first, and last, exposure to book learning. It was brief. A

teacher was induced to come to the community and Judd took his lunch and trudged reluctantly to the one-room school. His seatmate was a six-year-old who already knew the alphabet and could write real well. Judd felt inferior, and that is one feeling he never learned to like. He learned to write "The dog runs" that first day, and concluded that was enough for a sheep man. He never went back.

That evening when he got home he found the four sheep owned by the family had broken out of the pasture. Judd persuaded his father that he could not go back to school until he found them. During the two days it took him to find those sheep the humiliation he had suffered in school kept gnawing on his mind. He explained to his father that what he wanted most in the world was to own a herd of a hundred sheep—and you couldn't own that many sheep sitting in a schoolroom learning the three R's. Finally his father, being what he was, agreed. Judd was to take his lunch and herd the sheep, and manage the business of increasing the herd. Father and son were to be partners. Judd's first step was to get his father's permission to trade a litter of skinny, no-good pigs for sheep.

Taking a pig in a sack, Judd rode to the farm of a neighbor. He found the neighbor washing up for dinner.

"I'm thirsty," Judd said.

"Light and get a drink," the neighbor invited.

Judd was invited for dinner. He put the sack under his chair and was very solicitous of the pig's welfare during the meal. Finally, his host's curiosity got the better of him. "What you got in that sack?" he asked.

"What sack?" Judd asked innocently.

"That sack under your chair."

"It sounds like a pig and that's just what it is."

"What are you going to do with that pig?"

"Trade it for some sheep."

The host rolled a smoke. After a while he said, "I've got a sheep I'd like to trade for a pig." Judd McKnight made his first deal. It was mostly through young Judd's teen-age trading that the McKnights ran up their string to several hundred head. Then they mortgaged them and doubled their count.

As his ability as a trader sharpened, Judd started to fret over his lack of education. He couldn't be out-traded, but he found that he could be out-figured. He began his own schooling. He spelled out words on canned goods. While he was watching the sheep he counted sticks and pebbles, and scratched out problems in the dust with a stick.

Then one day when he was eighteen his father brought home a watermelon. It was wrapped in a Roswell, New Mexico, newspaper and it changed Judd's whole life. As he spelled out the newspaper, a great idea burst upon him. His dream was beginning to sharpen. In Roswell watermelons were a dollar each, and eggs were eight dollars a dozen. In Eldorado watermelons were ten cents each and eggs were eight cents a dozen.

Judd went to his father. "Somebody's got money down there. Maybe we could get some of it if we'd move there."

Tom McKnight shook his head, but Judd didn't forget. He hung on to his dream. A little later he heard that a man by the name of Al Garrett had drilled a well on the Blackwater River thirty-five

miles northwest of Roswell and found water as pure as snow water. Judd thought of the bitter gyp water they drank in Eldorado. The dream of New Mexico taunted him day and night. He could talk of nothing except what fine country it must be, of how rich a young man could get in a country where a watermelon cost a dollar. An old friend, Hubert Blackwell, had gone to Lincoln, New Mexico, and Judd had his stepmother write Blackwell and ask him to send a map telling him how to get there. In the spring of 1901 Judd got Blackwell's map and an encouraging letter. They could range their sheep south into the Big Bend country of Texas, Blackwell said. It was raining there. The tallow weed was lush. They could fatten their sheep and sell them for good money.

Tom McKnight's resistance finally broke. On September 20, 1901, Judd and a friend, George Foster, headed the McKnight sheep toward Paducah, Texas, then to Lubbock, past the Yellow Houses division of the three-million acre XIT Ranch in West Texas. On a rainy day late in October, Judd drove his chuckwagon into New Mexico on a dim wagon road just east of Portales. A few days later he was standing on the banks of the Pecos, with the blue-hazed mountains in the distance and the grasslands rolling into the horizon. "George," he said, "this is the best damn sheep country in the whole world."

During the long, golden days of autumn, Judd and Foster herded the sheep toward the mountains, grazing them on grama and buffalo grass. One day from a rise they saw the sprawling outline of Roswell in the valley. "I'd better go get some grub and clothes," Judd told his friend. "Winter is coming on. I'll have to get credit somewhere." He had only the two dollars and a few loose coins in his pocket, but no doubt about the credit. After all, he had a big herd of sheep. The mortgage on them was less than a dollar a head. Certainly he could get credit.

Soaking wet, Judd would have weighed less than eighty pounds. He was lean and he looked hungry; his clothes were patched and months on the trail hadn't helped their appearance. He looked like a poor risk as he tied his team to the rack in front of Joyce-Pruitt and Company—General Merchandise. Hipshot cow ponies were tied in front of the saloons; cowboys whooped and spurred through town; Mexicans loafed in the shade of cottonwoods. He hadn't seen so many people for a long time. Roswell was a thriving town of 1500 souls in 1901.

Judd walked into the Pruitt store. A solemn man walked up to him.

"I'm looking for the boss," Judd announced.

"I'm Abe Pruitt," the man said gloomily.

"I want some credit," Judd said. "I have some sheep. I'll pay it back when we shear next spring."

Abe Pruitt's back stiffened. "You know it's boys like you that are ruining this country." He swept his hand toward the street. Walking past was a boy about Judd's age. "That boy owes me twenty dollars," Pruit said. "He'll work on some cow outfit until he draws his wages and then he'll pull out without paying me. I'm not going to lose another dime by crediting you boys."

Judd shifted his attack. "But you don't understand. I've got some sheep up north of here. I've got to have salt and flour and stuff." He looked down at his ragged jeans and boots. He started to say he needed some clothes but his pride got the better of him. Pruit said, "I'm sorry."

Judd stared at the floor. He felt numb. He thought of the long trail drive, of bitter water and poor grass and small farms back in Oklahoma. Almost fiercely he turned to Abe Pruitt and said, "I won't take no for an answer. I won't cheat you."

Pruitt said nothing. All day long Judd dogged his footsteps. He did not leave the store. Every time Pruitt looked up he met Judd's determined eyes. Toward evening Pruitt said, "Come and meet my partner, young man." He introduced him to his partner, Joyce, and called to a clerk, "Give this boy all he wants."

Judd wasted no time in piling salt, flour, bacon, beans, dried fruit, socks, and a coat on the counter. Pruitt walked up and said, "That's not enough. Get whatever you want."

Judd doubled the order. The bill totaled $17.60. He put the supplies in the wagon and drove back to camp. When he got there he realized he didn't really know if he had $17.60 worth of supplies or not. He put the items near his campfire and gathered up a bucketful of rocks. Small ones for nickels, bigger ones for dimes, for quarters, half dollars, dollars. One by one he put each item in a line and placed beside it enough stones to represent its cost. When he finished he had counted out $17.60 worth of rocks. Abe Pruitt was honest. He would give his business to Abe.

Spring came; Judd sheared his sheep and paid his debts. He wrote his first letter . . . to his father. Then he wrote to Nannie Potts. He told her of the opportunity in New Mexico, of the grass that grew in the mountains even when the plains twenty or thirty miles away were brown and sear. His letter to his father must have been persuasive, for that summer of 1902 Tom McKnight moved his family to New Mexico. The sheep partnership was resumed, but now Judd was the manager.

The next two years were good ones. Their herd increased; they traded, sold wool and wether lambs, bought more sheep. In the fall of 1903 when Judd was 21, he homesteaded a place about halfway between Roswell and Mesa. He built a one-room shack and his family moved in with him.

Judd reached out, never satisfied. They ran their sheep on free range but they were in debt over their heads. Then an outbreak of scab gave them their first break. Judd was learning that the man who holds on when the pinch comes reaps the harvest of the weak who fall out. A government sheep inspector suggested that Judd build a dipping vat. He could make thousands of dollars, the inspector hinted. Judd followed his advice and he and his father and brother dipped 116,000 sheep at five cents each. Elated, they paid some debts, bought more sheep.

Here Judd decided that he would go alone. His family lacked his vision, and held him back. He sold the homestead to his father and brother, divided up the sheep, and moved out. He dreamed of a mountain ranch where there was always grass and water. Herding two thousand sheep before him, he set out to find his Shangri-La.

It was a two-year search. He ranged his sheep all through the White Mountains and got to know every waterhole and canyon in them. During the long days he had much time to think and plan. He composed a letter to Nannie Potts back in Quanah, Texas, hoping that she would be able to read it. Judd's prose was halting and he couldn't spell, but Nannie got the message. One day Judd left his sheep in charge of a Mexican herder and struck out horseback for Davilla, Texas. When he came back to the mountains in the spring of 1908, he brought Nannie with him.

In the fall of 1908 he and Nannie were herding sheep near the Pajarita Mountain, south of El Capitan, when he met a French sheepherder, Capt. Charles DeBremond. They were sitting around the

# He bought good animals

campfire one night when Judd said, "I've got to find a place, but I don't know where there is water. Where would be a good place to homestead?"

"Do you remember an old pine tree at the head of Mountain Canyon?" DeBremond asked.

Judd nodded.

"You back off from the pine tree on a level spot and drill a well," DeBremond told him. "You'll find water and you'll never go broke."

The well came in at 715 feet. Judd rode into Roswell and signed his homestead papers; the Home Ranch was born. Judd and Nannie picked out a site on the slope above the well and built a dug-out. They covered it with boards and piled dirt on top and lived there three years. But it was uncomfortable and damp and Nannie preferred to stay in the sheep camps with Judd. Finally they built a small house of concrete and abandoned the dug-out. Judd kept reaching out . . . buying land . . . sheep . . . trading. In 1912 he was running 14,000 ewes.

That same year a young Mexican, Antonio Gallegas, went to work for Judd. He became Judd's confidant and first lieutenant. Rather than feed mutton to the thirty men working for him, Judd and Antonio hunted the big mule deer that ranged the mountains and the antelope that foraged on the plains to the east. A haunch of venison was always worth a sack of beans in trade to the Mexicans living along the Hondo River to the north.

Judd became a father in 1912. It was a boy and they named him Joe. When Joe was old enough to go to school Judd and Nannie moved to Roswell and built a two-story house.

Judd hired a bookkeeper, but the five-dollars-a-day wage was big money to Judd, and he fired him and made up a system of his own. It was simple—he set his bills down on one side of the page and his income down on the other. He hired a surveyor for five dollars a day but the surveyor made a mistake in a section line and Judd fired him, too. He bought a transit and learned to do his own surveying. He

## turned them loose on the open range

## and wasn't afraid to take a chance

was good enough that he was often called upon for his expert knowledge of land boundaries in Lincoln County.

Judd's appetite for land knew no restraint. He kept buying, going heavier and heavier in debt. The Home Ranch grew up to 70 sections, but he owed $300,000. One day his banker asked him, "Why don't you stop buying land? You've got enough to make your living. You can always buy more some day when you get money ahead."

Judd shook his head. "They may grow big corn crops in Iowa, big wheat crops in Kansas, and big lamb crops in New Mexico. But there'll never be another of land. Some day land will be hard to buy."

Judd's family kept pace with his land and his sheep. After Joe came Minnie, J. P., Joyce, and Wade. Between Minnie and J. P., they lost six.

Then in 1917 came the great drouth. With fourteen thousand sheep on hand, with grass burned up, with waterholes and rivers dry, Judd didn't

think he could last thirty days. But he wouldn't let go. He ranged his sheep a hundred miles north and south of the Home Ranch, and kept his wary eye on neighbors whose land and sheep were on the line. The bankers urged the ranchers to sell out before they went broke. Judd put up a big front. "My grass is fine," he said. "Got lots of it." The poor forage kept his ewes from breeding that fall and the next spring he didn't raise over a ten per cent lamb crop. However, he kept his breeding herd together and was still in business when the rains came the next year. In 1920 he sold 9,924 head. It was the proudest day of his life when he and Joe and his herders drove them through Roswell to the stockyards on the east side of town. The stockyard pens couldn't hold them all and they had to be grazed out on the East Grand Plains where irrigation from artesian water was just beginning to excite residents of the Pecos Valley.

He seemed to be free and clear at last. But he wasn't. In 1923 drouth visited again. He had lots of sheep, was hiring forty herders. Markets were glutted with sheep. Prices broke. Judd knew he was going to have to change his methods of management if he stayed in business. Too many times drouth had threatened to ruin him. One day a neighboring rancher came by to sing the blues. Judd snorted. The drouth wouldn't last forever. The ranchers who outlasted it would be in a strong position to make money and pay their debts. "Besides," he said, "I've got a plan that will let our sheep make better use of range and water. Best of all it'll cut our herding costs to nothing."

The next day Judd went to see Abe Pruitt. "Abe," he said, "I want you to buy me enough wire to fence my land. I can turn my sheep loose and they'll range into country that has never been grazed."

Pruitt thrust his hands into his pockets and pursed his lips. Finally he said, "It'll never work. Coyotes will eat you up. You will go broke."

Judd said quietly, "I owe over $300,000 right

Workers on the McKnight ranches are mostly Mexicans. They are handy with sheep and Judd gets along well with them. They have reason to call him *El Chato, The Bulldog.*

now. I'm not good for half of it. If that's not being broke, what do you call it? If you back me with that fence wire I can pay out."

Judd got his wire. When he had it loaded on wagons, along with posthole diggers, staples, crowbars, axes, hammers, and wire stretchers, the caravan swung south on Main Street and halted in the busiest section of town. Judd climbed atop a wagon and shouted to the gathering crowd. "There's a dollar a day and all you can eat for every man who wants a job building fence. When the wagon comes to town Saturday nights, you can come with it."

Twenty-one men pushed toward the wagon. Judd said, "Get your bedrolls, boys, and kiss your gals good-bye."

In a few days, 6000 acres of virgin range land went under woven wire fence. The first major change in the history of range sheep business was underway. As each pasture was finished, Judd would lay off the two herders and the cook necessary for handling a band of 2000 sheep, and put the money back in wire.

Judd's troubles, even when the entire ranch was fenced, were not over. He fought coyotes for years. His hunting crews rode hard from dawn till dark with shotguns, strychnine, traps and clubs. With the help of neighbors they so thoroughly cleaned the area of coyotes that they are rare even today.

Though land for himself and his children has been the motivating power of Judd's life, he has used sheep as a medium of exchange to build up his kingdom. The McKnight sheep of today are third and fourth generation Corriedales from Delaine and Rambouillet stock. Last year's wool clip on the ewes averaged 12 pounds and the lambs weaned off at a husky 75 to 80 pounds. Judd has always placed great stress on wool. "The first ewes I had here sheared only five or six pounds," he said. "The hardest job I found here was breeding up ewes to where they'd make a profit."

Besides being the first sheepman in the Southwest to turn his sheep loose in fenced pastures, to fend for themselves much like wild animals, Judd was the first to shear his ewes before they lamb in April. He was warned that many ewes would die from exposure, but only in one instance has this proved true. A bunch of about 150 freshly shorn ewes were penned south of a barn on the Blackwater one March, and a sudden sleet storm roared out of the northwest. The ewes could not be driven into the face of the wind to the protection of the

In the early fall comes the annual roundup, payoff time for the McKnight ranches. The sheep are brought off the ranges, the ewes and lambs sheared, culled and "toothed," and the lambs are sorted for market and breeding.

barn standing two or three hundred yards away, and about 100 died.

The early shearing has been credited with raising the lamb crop percentage of McKnight outfit sheep to about 92 per cent. "Take ewes like ours with three or three and a half inch staple wool," Judd said, "and a lamb has a hard time finding the teat. Get that wool out of the way and he don't have a bit of trouble."

Judd's search for better sheep, especially for rams that would sire the right kind of replacement ewes, has led him all over the United States and Canada. In 1950 he defied the warning of friends that he was wasting money and flew to Australia and bought almost the entire yearling crop from one of the leading breeders there. He is confident the importation increased the wool clip of the sheep by two or three pounds and the weight of lambs by 12 to 14 pounds. Even though the trip cost him $50,000, he feels it was a good investment.

He is not only tough in spirit, but tough in body. He packs a hard-twisted 190 pounds on a five-foot, eight-inch frame. His nose is wide and flat and he has a rock-like jaw. He walks with a belligerent swagger, like a man bent on twisting the tail of the world and carrying it off over his shoulder. He knows the value of looking prosperous—his jeans are creased to a knife-edge, his boots shined to an expensive luster. He spends a lot of money on his hats. A string tie fastened at the throat by a miniature thunderbird, presented to him by an Apache friend, decorates his shirts. He has trouble with his teeth, which he usually carries in his shirt pocket or near him on the seat of his car, ready to pop into his mouth on a moment's notice. His voice is high-pitched, but as direct and positive as desert sunlight.

Judd had a method of getting credit for himself —he often needed credit, for while he was expanding he was never out of debt. He always looked prosperous, and when he faced a banker he was as full of confidence as a pickpocket at a country picnic.

A banker once said to him, "You're hiring too many herders. They cost you lots of money."

Judd said, "I'm out of grass. I've got to have herders to take my sheep up in the mountains where they'd never go by themselves."

The banker reached out and asked for Judd's hat. He turned it over and examined the label. "That hat cost lots of money. How can you afford an expensive hat when you're almost broke?"

Judd looked the man squarely in the eye and said simply, "I want to look better than my men."

He has been known to plan for years just how to buy a piece of land from a stubborn owner and admits he works out many of his deals in bed, when he ought to be sleeping.

When Judd was a young man he once heard a representative of an eastern packing company was coming to Roswell to contact an order buyer. He got an order for 15,000 lambs before any other rancher knew the buyer was in town. The packer agreed to pay market price. Riding horseback, Judd scoured the plains and mountains, buying lambs in bunches of fifty to two thousand, and paying about a third less than market price for them.

First thing when he got back to Roswell, his best friend, Abe Pruitt, buttonholed him on Main Street. "Boy," Pruitt exploded, "I just found out what you're selling those lambs for and I know what you are paying for them. If these ranchers find it out, they'll mob you. They'll never deliver, either."

Judd grinned, "I bought them fair and square. They'll deliver." And they did. Inside of a week Judd loaded 14,000 lambs on the cars at Roswell just 1000 short of the order. He cleared nearly ten dollars each on them.

Judd has the reputation of being an extremist. There is no gray in his life—it's either black or white. He'll take the last penny in a trade and expect the same treatment in return—he expects no more from any man than he's willing to give.

The greatest joy in Judd's life was to see his children grow up with his own fierce love of ranching. He set each of them up on ranches of their

This is the working team which operates the McKnight sheep empire. In the foreground are Judd and Mrs. Knight, "Granny." Behind them: two sons, two daughters and their husbands and wives.

own. In 1950 the McKnight Sheep Company, a five-way partnership, was organized.

And it is the roundup each autumn which is the big event for the McKnight oufit. That's when old ewes are culled and lambs sorted out for sale or for breeders. It is at these roundups, when the boys are together and working the sheep, when the wives gather their broods and prepare a barbecue of mutton at the Home Ranch—where the fall's work traditionally starts—that Judd McKnight is the happiest. From the time the riders head out to round up the thousands of sheep until culling

and loading is done, Judd is where the dust is thickest and action is heaviest.

Last fall Judd rode his dun pony through a mass of sheep in the big corral to watch four of his grandsons as they helped the Mexicans "tooth" the sheep. A visitor asked him. "What's going to happen to this place when you're not around to run it, Judd?"

Judd's mouth lifted at the corners in a quiet smile. The saddle leather creaked as he half turned to watch his grandsons at work. "It looks like the good Lord has taken care of that for me," he said.

# The Farm's Wildlife

THE cock pheasant that fails to flush in front of the farmer's hungry sickle bar presages the fate of most wildlife on American farms. For the way the farmer manages his land will be the deciding factor in keeping pheasants, quail, song birds, and other wild things living and maintaining nature's balance.

If fence rows are mowed up to the wire and fallow fields burned in the spring, the pheasant may have no place to live; if there are occasional rough spots on the farm, the farmer will have game to enjoy during the hunting season and song birds to help him fight insects.

Until a few years ago the sportsmen who invaded the fields and forests each fall took wild game for granted. They took it for granted until their motorized battalions began to outnumber the game. Then they demanded that their state game departments look into the growing scarcity of wildlife and do something about it. In response to this demand, the game departments began to develop a new breed of scientists—wildlife biologists—and the things they found out upset old theories of game restoration and established the farmer as the key man in wildlife management.

The biologists discovered that the things the farmer does with the land have more effect on small-game than anything else except, perhaps, the weather. They became convinced, and so reported, that soil erosion has destroyed more game, by destroying the homes and food of wild things, than all the guns and dogs, and ruined more fishing, by silting the streams and lakes, than all the nets and baited hooks.

As first it looked like a one-way street. Wild game, in numbers to provide good sport for all Americans who wanted to go hunting, seemed doomed. The thing that made it look dark was the fact that the "better" farmers of the day had the least game on their land.

If one wanted to go hunting, he visited the land of a "careless" farmer with its untended fence rows,

# A bird in the bush......

The soil in this field has gone down the river and each spring the gullies will lengthen.

Planted in locust trees and grass mixtures, erosion is stopped and wildlife gets more living space, to keep up the battle against insects.

its uncut briar patches and ungrazed woodlots.

Unable to influence the trend of agriculture, state game departments tried to cover their pessimism with popular panaceas, most spectacular of which was artificial propagation and restocking. The theory was that to restore good hunting all one had to do was raise the game in batteries and pens and release it to the wild. The theory had four big holes in it. In the first place, no state game department ever had enough money to replace by incubator methods a significant fraction of the game taken by hunters. Further, certain wild species, among them prairie chickens and squirrels, couldn't be raised in captivity. Others which took to pen-rearing, like quail and wild turkeys, developed domestic tendencies which left them largely unfitted to shift for themselves in the wild. The fourth fallacy was that the products of the game farm had little chance, anyway, to survive in a habitat where truly wild birds could not live and reproduce in numbers. As one game expert described it, restocking was like pouring water into a leaky bucket. Survival of from 3 to 5 per cent, as indicated by return of bands placed on the legs of released birds, was a good record. The Indiana Department of Conservation figured that every pen-reared quail or pheasant bagged by Hoosier hunters cost $50.

## Soil-Saving Helps

Meantime, however, something happened to change the mood of wildlife men from defeatism to smiling optimism. It was a by-product of the soil-saving programs that started during the drought-ridden 1930's. Soil conservation, it was observed, also helped wildlife.

Technicians recorded a 32% increase in quail coveys in a single year on a demonstration area near Fulton, Missouri. Similar results were obtained in other states. At first glance the reasons seemed obvious. In order to check soil erosion, new cover was put on the land. Gullied hillsides were planted with trees; waterways were kept in deep sod. Lime and fertilizers were used in unprecedented quantities, and rotations were changed so cover crops followed row crops. Thus, given new places to live, wild game responded with a sudden increase, but the effects, it was later to be discovered, went deeper than the cover on the land. The wild animals, like farm livestock, found more nutritious food when soil fertility went up.

Research into the effects of soil fertility and land-use on wildlife probably has been carried farther in Missouri than any other state. Following an idea of Dr. William A. Albrecht, of the University of Missouri, who has studied the benefits of feeding livestock by feeding the soil, the game technicians began to study wildlife distribution on the basis of soil types.

Lying mostly south of the 40th Meridian, which seems to mark roughly the boundary between quail country and pheasant country, Missouri runs to bobwhites rather than ringnecks. The former Fish and Game Department spent twenty-five years trying to get pheasants started. The only places the birds survived in shootable numbers were small regions in Missouri and Mississippi river bottoms and on the black prairie land of northwestern counties—the richest soil in the state. This curious fact led to the suggestion that South Dakota's predominance in pheasants may be due in part to the mineral-rich fertility of her soils, the same land that produces high-protein hard wheat.

Pursuing the fertility factor to the individual farm, the wildlife men found examples to prove that when worn-out soils are restored wildlife returns. Gene Poirot, Missouri master farmer, observed jack rabbits began showing up after he started liming his 1800 acres near Golden City. The long-eared bunnies did their grazing in limed fields, ignoring the unlimed acres.

It was obvious to research men, however, that fertility alone was not enough. They could point to rich soils in northern Missouri, in Iowa and Illinois, and in the cotton-country of the Missouri bootheel, where the land is so intensively farmed there is practically no permanent cover—and very little wild game. So they set out to discover how more cover could be produced on the modern farm, in coordination with the farmer's main business of growing crops and livestock for profit. From their experiments and demonstrations in a dozen leading states has arisen the new practical science of farm game management.

Take the highly efficient farming establishment of Morton Tuttle near Prairie Home, Missouri, for example. Producer of hybrid seed corn and other certified seed crops, Shorthorn cattle, registered Hampshire sheep, fed lambs, and fat hogs by the carload, Tuttle has been named a Master Farmer of Missouri. He also has been awarded a medal by the State Conservation Commission because his 640-acre farm provides an excellent example of

how wildlife can thrive under a farming system that puts money in the bank account.

From the beginning, Tuttle kept wildlife in mind in his farm planning. Unlike many modern farmers, he has carefully preserved several miles of old Osage orange hedges which were planted as field dividers two generations ago. He likes them for their wildlife benefits, believes they contribute to a balance of nature which benefits his entire farm. He cites a study by the wildlife research unit of the state university which showed that fields bor-

dered by shrubbery fence rows have less insect damage to crops than fields with clean fences, due to the hundreds of songbirds that live in the hedges. He also believes he has less damage by mice, since small rodents like to winter and breed in grassy fence rows.

The wild things never get hungry on the Tuttle farm. Under his system of seed-crop farming, combine-shattered grain can be picked almost the year around by the quail, rabbits, squirrels, and other wildlife. This food is rich in vitamins and minerals because it is grown on fertile soil.

About 30 per cent of the Tuttle land is in timber, and the woodlots abound in squirrels. Last year the bushytails threatened plots of single-cross hybid corn in roasting ear stage. An SOS brought squirrel hunters from Prairie Home to the rescue. The Tuttle timber is grazed sparingly—some of it not at all—and den trees are carefully preserved.

Morton Tuttle's interest in wildlife is primarily esthetic; he never hunts and rarely fishes. Sons, Bill, 23, and Roy, 18, like to fish in the ponds but are only occasional hunters. The oldest son, Joe, who as a Navy pilot died in battle action against the Japs, was a crack shot but preferred to practice his marksmanship on crows and other pests rather than game. It fits into the Tuttle tradition of gracious living, however, to be able to invite friends to fish the ponds, or hunt quail over the rolling acres.

Many farmers are also sportsmen, and such is William B. Weakley of Clarksville, Missouri. Owner of 800 acres of rich Pike County land, Bill Weakley decided he was spending too much time and money running around over several states looking for places to hunt quail and work his pedigreed bird dogs. Under guidance of the State Conservation Commission he has started a program to produce more quail on his own place.

To begin with, Weakley is making all fence rows wider. Plows and mowers are stopped within 15 feet of the fence on either side. This leaves a strip of cover 30 feet wide—wide enough to be worth while from the standpoint of quail. To produce a cover more quickly, a mixture of sweet clover and lespedeza serecia is being seeded along all fence rows, waterways, and draws. Serecia is a perennial legume that produces a rank, woody growth about two feet high and stands as a dense tangle all winter. Quail use it for resting and roosting, and feed on its abundant seed.

New ponds will supply water on parts of the Weakley farm where water previously was lacking, and as a third step, one-acre food plots of Kaffir are being planted annually in a dozen places. Located next to bushy draws or timber patches, these food patches serve a dual purpose. They insure food in winter when blizzards strike—a critical time for game birds—and also tend to concentrate the coveys where hunters and dogs can quickly find them.

The needs of wildlife are not different from those of other living creatures. They must eat, drink, find shelter and a place to rear young. These needs have been expressed by conservationists in a three-word slogan—"Food, cover and water."

Food may be plentiful, but it also must be nutritious, and that is where fertility comes in. On

the average Midwestern farm where grain is produced, lack of food is rarely a problem for game birds. If food is scarce, fence-row and field-edge seedings of Korean lespedeza or lespedeza serecia will help, as will food-patch plantings in the Weakley fashion.

Cover requirements vary greatly with different kinds of wildlife. It is well known that bobwhite quail thrive best in a broken cover pattern, where woods, bushy thickets, pastures and cultivated fields are closely intermingled. This is no doubt due to the fact that quail need one kind of cover for nesting, another for roosting, a third kind for feeding, and still another for shelter and for protection from predators. Some species, like squirrels and raccoons, must find dens in hollow trees. Foxes and groundhogs, among others, make dens in the ground. When a Cooper's hawk strikes, quail like to dive into a handy thicket. Pheasants prefer dense weeds or tall grass for escape cover. All need

When winter comes the bobwhite joins his friends and relatives in a covey for mutual protection from the elements. They must have food and cover to survive the winter. They work for the farmer during the summer and he owes them a winter's keep, not a load of buckshot.

places to hide.

Water needs also vary. Some species, like wild ducks, muskrats, and bullfrogs, make their homes in aquatic surroundings and are equipped to take their food from the water. Others need water only to drink. Under normal conditions, quail and pheasants may get all they require from the dew. When dew fails in drouths, however, whole coveys may perish unless there are water holes.

Naturally, no wildlife plan can be drawn to fit every farm. On one farm the improvements may be built around a brook or creek. Another may be suited for marsh development with duck shooting and fur farming. On almost any Midwestern farm, however, there are opportunities for increasing small game, including rabbits, quail, pheasants, and squirrels if timber is present. These are the big four of American small game. In working out your own wildlife plan, the following practices probably can be adapted:

Conserve the soil. Prevent erosion and boost fertility by following practices recommended by soil conservation technicians in your community. Bigger crops and high land values will pay the bill; wildlife will benefit incidentally, but nonetheless positively. Develop fence row game refuges. These take very little land out of production and are a haven for all wildlife. Bill Weakley's combination of sweet clover and lespedeza serecia is a good start. Shrubbery can be hastened by plantings every hundred yards of native species such as wild grape, blackberry, wild plum, hawthorne, mulberry, wild rose, sumac, and sassafras. Plants can be obtained in most states from the department of forestry or conservation. Some commercial nurseries also handle this kind of stock.

Use living fences where practical. Multiflora rose seems destined to replace the discredited Osage orange hedges of the Midwest prairies. Introduced by the Soil Conservation Service, this Asiatic member of the rose family has emerged from its testing period in experimental fence plantings from Delaware to Missouri. Spaced in a single row with plants one to two feet apart, it produces an effective livestock barrier in three to five years and stands only eight feet high at full growth. It doesn't spread into adjacent fields, or sap adjacent crops; thus, it is exonerated of the three major crimes of Osage orange. Covered in late spring with clusters of white flowers, and in fall and winter with red berries, multiflora rose makes an attractive field border. Used for contour fences, it eliminates the problem of stretching wire around curves.

If you live in a soil conservation district, you probably can get multiflora rose stock from the Soil Conservation Service.

Multiflora rose hedges can be planted largely by mechanical means, by first back-farrowing, then bed-farrowing. After the plants are placed by hand, the roots can be covered with a plow and packed in with the tractor wheel. This is a method developed by Missouri game technicians.

Songbirds literally fill multiflora rose hedges with their nests. In winter pheasants, quail, and rabbits will take shelter under the thorny tangle and feed upon the red fruits. A wildlife biologist, F. D. Edminsteer, found that New York fields with hedges supported 60 per cent more pheasants than those without hedges.

Construct ponds. If you are a livestock farmer, you need water in every pasture. Build ponds at least eight feet deep so they will hold through dry seasons and can be turned into good fishing holes. Fence the pond, piping the water through the dam to a tank outside the fence. This insures clean water for livestock, and the enclosed area can be planted to trees and shrubs valuable for wildlife.

Fence out raw gullies and eroded areas. Relieved of grazing pressure and planted with trees, these scars of past land mis-use will heal and become havens for wild game. Use multiflora fences.

Keep livestock and fire out of your woodlands. This is sound farm forestry, and also turns your woodlots into wildlife areas. Fire and overgrazing destroy young sprouts and seedlings that are the timber crop of the future. They also destroy wild berry bushes, wild legumes, and other ground cover that makes woods attractive to game.

Don't burn fields. Spring burning of fallow fields, weed patches, and fence rows also burns young rabbits and birds that can't escape the flames. Nests are destroyed and adult birds and animals deprived of living quarters. The weeds that are burned would have added humus to the soil.

Preserve den trees. In harvesting timber, save those old, hollow trees where squirrels and raccoon live. Pile the slash but do not burn it. Cottontail rabbits will use the brush piles in winter and provide good shooting.

Provide travel lanes. Tie woodlots, ponds, and other cover together with hedges or brushy fence rows. Wild creatures need sheltered paths by which they can travel between nesting grounds, feeding grounds and water holes.

Take a conservative harvest. When hunting, be sure to leave enough game for next year's breeding stock, and make certain that your sportsmen guests do the same.

Under such a program of farm wildlife management, only in rare instances, if at all, will restocking be necessary or even helpful. This is because wildlife, unlike tame livestock, is highly mobile, and outside of urban and industrial areas, it would be difficult to find a section of land in the Midwest that does not have at least a breeding stock of small game and furbearers. "If you provide new homes for wildlife," according to I. T. Bode, director of the Missouri Conservation Commission, "nature herself will do the stocking, faster and better than man could do it." This is nature's effort to maintain her balance. When there is more food and cover available, wildlife will multiply and take advantage of it and the farmer who provided the better living conditions is repaid by better insect control and more wild game for his table.

Tennyson has said that nature is "red in tooth and claw," which is only another way of saying that nature must maintain a balance. The big fish eat the little fish and lay eggs and produce little fish which the big fish eat. Insects prey on plants, birds prey on the insects, and before man came into the scene, to throw nature out of balance, every form of wildlife maintained itself in proportionate numbers. Through the ages the plants, the insects, the water fowl and the fish and the living things that crawled and flew preyed on each other and kept up the cycle of life.

WILD RABBIT

NEST OF THE HARVEST MOUSE

GEESE RETURNING HOME

"*Mangez les* girls," says Brigham's French Canadian herdsman, Cesaire LaCoste,
as he converses with the cows in his own mixed language at feeding time.

# New England
# Dairy Farmer

WHEN Frank Trotter bought a young Jersey bull from the Brigham Farm in Vermont, E. S. Brigham and his herdsman, Cesaire LaCoste, gave him a bonus. In addition to a bull which should raise his herd average from the present 7,000 pounds of milk, LaCoste told him in his pleasant French-Canadian accent, "If you will follow our feeding program, you should be able to boost up your milk production by a thousand pounds per cow a year."

"I believe them," Trotter says with conviction, "in fact, I think that it's a conservative estimate of what their feeding will do. And I'm going to follow it.

"Look what they've done!" Trotter, who grass-farms 80 acres and milks 33 cows near Orleans, Indiana, will tell you with enthusiasm. "The national average production is around 6,400 pounds per cow —for all breeds. The national average for butterfat is around 240 pounds. But here's a man with a milking string of 125 Jersey cows with a 20-year average of 10,254 pounds of milk and 548 of fat! And that record is made on twice-a-day milking, in ordinary stanchions, up in Vermont where they have only five or six months of pasture. But when they do have pasture it is tops and they can fill a whole field full of cows that have produced over 100,000 pounds of milk."

Both Elbert Brigham and the herdsman, Cesaire LaCoste, who has been with him for more than a score of years, have strong and very different personalities which have worked wonderfully well together to produce this herd which is one of the greatest in the world. Brigham is 75 years old, tall, erect, with the sharp, dry directness that only generations of New England can produce—a successful Yankee. His personality is serious, his views are conservative, his politics Republican. Across his still spare waist hangs a Phi Beta Kappa key from Middlebury College. His approach to dairying is scientific.

LaCoste, on the other hand, is a man of intuition and feeling. In the barn where he and the men under him speak mainly in French, he converses with the cows in his own mixed language, "*Mangez les* girls," he will say as he puts their feed before them. "*Bonne veille,* girl," he says softly as he strokes the back of the old Quomage cow. Or he may speak sharply, *"Tiens-toi tranquille,"* to a cow who is misbehaving. Between him and his cows there is a rare kind of rapport: if one is puny they agonize together until she is better; if one is nervous he knows it and removes the cause. But it's a different story if she is like the one Frank Trotter saw as he walked through the barns with LaCoste. This one, an elderly Ton of Gold cow—a cow which has produced 2,000 pounds of butterfat in four successive years—had a good-sized knot on her tail. Trotter felt of it and asked LaCoste why he didn't have it removed. LaCoste shrugged. "If it doesn't bother her, and it doesn't bother me, why should it bother you?"

These are the men who threw in—for free—their feeding program when Trotter visited the farm. "If I could feed my cows like this, and I mean to some day," Trotter says, "I *know* they'd give another thousand pounds." Here is the winter schedule as Trotter carefully copied it in his notebook:

*6:30 a.m.*—When the milking is almost done, the mangers are swept clean and 10 pounds of corn or grass silage is fed with one-third of the day's grain ration on top of the silage. The grain is fed at the ratio of one pound of grain to three of milk produced. The cows must clean up their food quickly. At the Brigham farm a broom is one of the most

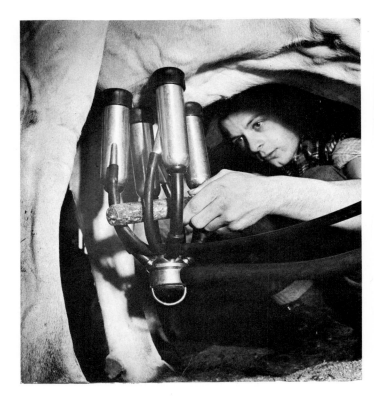

Attention to detail pays off at the Brigham Farm. Milking is not a chore, but a time for proving that good feeding and management makes production records.

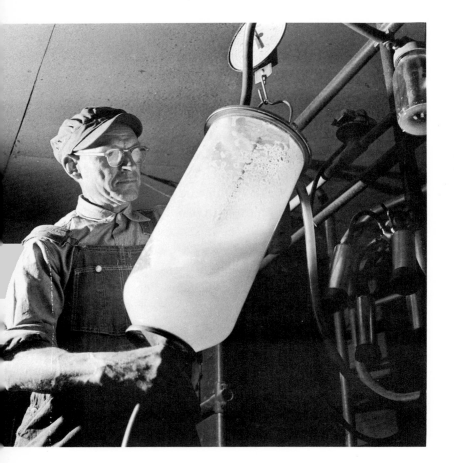

used tools in feeding. When the cows have eaten to the point where some of them are standing with their heads stretched out and cocked to one side, their black tongues looping out to scoop in the last of the silage and grain within reach, the men walk through the barn with their brooms sweeping the feed away from the slow eaters to their hungrier neighbors. "We don't want to leave food in front of them for too long," LaCoste says, "it will destroy their appetite."

*8:30 a.m.*—Dry timothy and clover hay is fed and the cows are curried.

*10:00 a.m.*—The cows go outdoors for an hour and the men sweep down the two big barns and sprinkle 100 pounds of superphosphate on the floor.

*11:00 a.m.*—10 pounds of corn silage and the next third of the grain ration are fed. "Now for awhile the cows must be quiet and make milk," LaCoste says.

*5:30 p.m.*—With night milking well along, the mangers are swept clean and 20 pounds or more of grass silage is fed with the last third of the grain on top followed by about five pounds of alfalfa hay.

The basis for this feeding program at Brigham Farm can be stated quite simply, *space in a cow's digestive apparatus is too valuable to be occupied by anything but the best of roughage and grain.*

Of course, that idea is not exactly new. Every dairyman worth his salt knows it, just as he knows the time-tested breeding and management practices used at Brigham Farm. The catch is that at Brigham Farm these good practices are followed religiously. A short time ago in a round-table discussion several leading dairymen from all over the country were asked this question, "How is the grain mixture changed when you have poor quality hay?" Several ideas were discussed such as raising the protein percentage. Brigham's reply was classic, "We do not feed poor hay."

He might have added that the ensilage, pasture, and grain which the cows eat is not poor quality either. Year after year the very best roughage and grain have been produced and bought to make the most of the precious space in the cow's stomachs. A Lincolnesque Yankee, Philip Spooner, is in charge of crop production and is responsible for their fine quality.

The Canadian border is only 14 miles from Brigham Farm and the winters are long and tough. Alfalfa has a hard time surviving. Usually it freezes out in two winters, though Brigham proudly showed Trotter a good stand of Ranger alfalfa that was five seasons old. Some of this damage has been alleviated at Brigham's by tiling, annual fertilizing with 500 pounds of 5-10-10, and heavy seeding. Even so there are years when spring will make a false start—the mild air and sparkling sunshine will trick the legumes into waking up and starting their growth—and then freezing, killing weather will set in again. When that happens, Brigham is ready with a top dressing of 150 pounds of ammonium nitrate to give the nitrogen the legumes would have provided.

To give alfalfa the best possible chance, it is seeded at the rate of three pounds to the acre to which Philip Spooner, the crop production man, adds five pounds of brome grass, four pounds timothy, four pounds red clover and a pound of ladino. A few fields meant only for hay are seeded with eight pounds of alfalfa and six pounds of brome. LaCoste is not enthusiastic about brome as a hay crop, however, considering it too coarse by the time it can be cut in the unfavorable June weather. He prefers timothy, which grows easily and well in Vermont. The trouble with timothy is that it doesn't yield as much.

The climate usually works out a choice of two kinds of hay, the fields which were recently seeded to the shotgun mixture produce alfalfa-clover-brome, and the fields seeded more than two years yield clover-brome-timothy.

The 500 tons of hay put up every year at Brigham Farm are divided now into two cuttings, but Brigham is thinking of taking a leaf from the European book on hay—taking hay crops off earlier and more often. Whenever the farm has European visitors, he says, they comment on the coarse, stemmy quality of the hay, explaining that back home they cut their hay fields repeatedly. Now that Brigham Farm has four new hay-driers, its owner feels he may try the same thing.

In thrifty New England manure is money and it's banked at Brigham Farm. Each gutter has a trap door in it through which manure is dropped to the cellar below.

179

In pre-drier years, putting up first-cutting hay was something. Underneath that heavy soil is a hardpan subsoil, and without the tiling (which Brigham believes pays at least 6 per cent a year) the ground in many places would support a colony of frogs. Humidity is high in a New England June, and even if a streak of rainless weather comes along, curing is a lengthy affair. Almost always Spooner had to resort to the old down-East custom of cocks and caps (hay forked into small stacks and covered with heavy cloth)—probably the world's most expensive system of putting up hay.

The driers, four of which were built for $2,000 by the regular hands at what Brigham calls "a good knitting job," are rapidly paying for themselves. They must dry hay put up in bales—baling is necessary because of the scattered barn space—and they do it successfully, drying bales stacked up to five deep and containing as much as 40 per cent moisture. A mobile oil heater with a capacity of 750,000 BTU's an hour supplements the fans.

"The cows eat that silage just like you would eat up ice cream," LaCoste told Trotter as they watched a cream-colored Jersey tucking it away. They have seven silos that are filled each year with 900 tons of grass silage and two large silos that hold 400 tons of corn silage which LaCoste claims haven't been completely empty in ten years.

This great feeling for silage came as a blow to Trotter who owns a silo but hasn't filled it for two years. He has pointed out to critics that since he quit feeding silage his cows have gained 1000 pounds in milk production. When pressed, however, he will admit that during these same two years he has conducted an extensive culling program and has been feeding better quality hay than he used to. After seeing how Brigham Farm feeds silage, he has drained the rain water out of his silo and plans to fill it with grass silage this summer.

Brigham Farm puts up two kinds of hay, two kinds of grass silage, and corn silage because a cow must eat a vast amount of roughage to produce an average of 36-plus pounds of milk every day and they intend to provide a tempting variety for her. "The cow is just like people," Cesaire LaCoste explains, "It takes some variety to keep her eating good so we try to feed her two kinds of hay and two kinds of silage every day."

There are other reasons for both corn and grass silage. Corn silage helps keep the cow's weight up and is fine for supplementary feeding in late sum-

Back in Indiana, the Trotters have put Brigham Farm feeding techniques to work and are aiming for their own high production records.

mer; grass silage has a desirable laxative tendency. "Comparing grass with corn," Brigham says, "we consider them of equal feeding value."

Twenty-five acres of corn, harvested with a field chopper as soon as the ears are dented, supplies the silage. The following spring the corn ground is seeded to oats and the standard grass mixture. Oat yields average 60-80 bushels per acre and a couple of times have reached the 100-bushel mark.

Grass silage for the milking herd is put up with around 200 pounds of beet pulp to the ton as a preservative as well as a production booster. The exact amount of preservative depends somewhat on the moisture content of the grass when it is blown into the silo; the rule being the more moisture, the more preservative. Corn meal, hominy, ground oats and wheat have also been used as a preservative with some success, but the no-preservative method has been tried and given up because of the possibility of objectionable odors in the milk. Brigham, by the way, retails his own milk in St. Albans. The 5.4 per cent creamline is left intact, and for every one of the 300 regular customers, there is another who wants to be on the list.

It is typical of this New England farm, where extravagance is looked on with about as much enthusiasm as is sorghum syrup or oleomargarine, that a nourishing but less expensive silage is put up for the growing heifers. For them—and all over six months get silage—the beet pulp is omitted and a less expensive preservative, molasses, is added at around 50 pounds to the ton.

"In New Zealand there is a dairyman with a herd average of more than 500 pounds of fat, produced without a pound of grain," Brigham told Trotter. "Another dairyman there believes in pasture rotation with such fervor that he has devised a fence which moves automatically, timed with a clock. We are not quite as strong on pasture as they are, perhaps, but we *do* believe that the success of a farm goes back to the soil and the pasture you can raise on it."

Because of the soil fertility, the cows go out on grass earlier than one might expect. The first of May—only 10 days behind Trotter's southern Indiana herd, but two to three weeks earlier than Brigham's Vermont neighbors who do not fertilize their pastures—is the average date. Immediately, the daily average production goes up to five pounds per cow. "And if your cows don't do as well," Cesaire LaCoste told Trotter, "then they're no good

or your pasture is no good." Trotter went home, looked at his records, and was not sure whether to be relieved or ashamed—his cows had increased production 4.9 pounds when he put them on pasture.

The pasture seed mix is the standard one used for hay at Brigham Farm; in fact, with the exception of those few fields seeded to alfalfa and brome, the fields are used interchangeably for hay, pasture, or silage. Brome, LaCoste thinks, is better for pasture than for hay. Reed's canary is poor in Vermont, and sudan grass "is for hungry cows." Ladino is the best pasture of all, and a good field of it can always be counted on to increase milk flow. Like all the rest of the 297 cultivated acres, pasture land is fertilized with 500 pounds of 5-10-10 annually. Manure is applied at the rate of five tons to the acre, but only to crop land, not to pasture. The manure, incidentally, is dropped through trap doors in the gutters of the cow barn into a manure cellar. Here the pyramids of manure are held, in what is probably the most heavily ammoniated atmosphere outside of a nitrogen plant, until Spooner is ready to apply it to the fields.

Pastures are divided by electric fences into plots of 6 to 12 acres which hold 50 to 60 cows. "We let the cows decide when a pasture has been grazed enough," LaCoste told Trotter. "When the cows hang back and don't want to go into a pasture, then it's time for a change." Usually pasturing periods run about a week to ten days.

During May and June production stays up—the highest of the year. "But in July and August, then it goes down," LaCoste frowns. "The pastures are dry and the cows are hot and too lazy to get up from under the tree and eat. That's why our winter production averages better than summer." Some corn silage is saved for supplementary feeding during these hot months and hay is always kept in racks in the field. Brigham would like to irrigate a few acres, but the lack of water prevents him. Lake Champlain is only about two miles away but still too far for pumping, and the wells in the immediate neighborhood are not good enough.

In 1949, when the Brigham herd became the only 100-cow herd in the world to average more than 600 pounds of fat—the official record was 11,703 pounds of milk, and 616 pounds of fat from 104 cows—the cows received an average of 3,397 pounds of grain, a ratio of one pound of grain to each 3.3 pounds of milk. "I swear, these figures give me an inferiority complex," Trotter said, "our herd average is 7,000 pounds of milk per cow and the grain ratio is one pound of grain to every two and a half pounds of milk—that's a real body blow to the milk check."

The Brigham feed is not expensive, as feeds go. When prices fluctuate the formula is changed to take advantage of lower-priced feeds. Over the years the protein content has been gradually decreased. It now runs somewhere between 16 and 17 per cent. Here is the current formula, which retails at about five dollars per hundred in Vermont and slightly less in the Midwest:

        200 pounds oats
        200 pounds bran
        200 pounds hominy
        100 pounds distillers dried grains
        100 pounds corn gluten feed
        100 pounds linseed oil meal
        100 pounds soybean oil meal
            (increased to 200 if linseed isn't available)
         10 pounds salt
         10 pounds bone meal
         10 pounds lime

The average cow in the Brigham herd gets 10 pounds of grain a day, a little more in the winter, when she gets it in three servings, and a little less in the summer, when the noon feeding is skipped and the pasture is good. The first-calf heifer may get a slightly larger helping; as Cesaire LaCoste says, "After all, she has three jobs to do—grow herself, grow a calf, and make 10,000 pounds of milk and 500 pounds of fat."

In the winter the dry cows and heifers get the same ration, minus a little protein, as the milking herd, though about half the quantity. In the best pasture season they get no grain at all.

Calves are weaned at 24 hours, fed whole milk for two months, then one-fourth whole milk and three-fourths skim milk for another month. They are gradually switched to a grain formula with a powdered skim milk base. The calves seem to have inherited a fierce appetite along with their dam's ability to produce. When the milk bucket is put in front of them, they jam their heads into it and drink furiously until the last drop is gone then fling the bucket off to the side and suck the whitened edge of their grain boxes, as though they were completely starved, until they are fed grain.

The very finest timothy mixed hay is kept before the calves at all times. If the season is right they are turned out to pasture shortly after vaccination at 6 months.

The herd sires get a formula of 80 per cent ground oats, 10 per cent linseed oil meal, and 10 per cent bran, with added salt, bone meal and lime.

Very often when people hear of the Brigham Farm their first comment is, "Oh, sure, Brigham can run a perfect set-up and break all the records, but don't forget to mention that he was president of a large insurance company, with plenty of money to back him up."

As a matter of fact, one of the members of the board of directors of the insurance company made about the same comment, though more elegantly, when he said as a joke, "Mr. Brigham, I wish that I could afford to support a farm."

Elbert Brigham's reply was direct and to the point. "It might surprise you," he said, "to know that I make more money per hour for my farm work than I do as president of this company." It is true that the farm is one of the great pleasures of his life, for he was a farmer before he was an insurance executive and to run an unproductive, money-consuming hobby-farm would border on the indecent as far as he is concerned.

But the farm is no showplace. Most of the people who come to Brigham Farm are hard-working Jersey farmers, like Frank Trotter, interested in the only showy item of the place, the cows.

They are something to see. Trotter, who is a skeptic when it comes to big production records, was more than half convinced that there was a catch somewhere in this 11,000-pound business. He changed his mind as soon as he walked in the barn door. The cows he saw were Jerseys, sure enough, but unlike any he had in his own barn or any he had seen in the show ring, even. Trotter's cows were about the same size as the national average for Jerseys, 800-900 pounds. But these Brigham Jerseys were big, they averaged a good thousand pounds, and some weighed over 1,300. A bit taken aback, he asked LaCoste if the increased feed costs for such big cows were offset by their production.

LaCoste is never one to mince words. "Would you be willing," he asked, "to feed your cows more if they produced 11,000 pounds of milk apiece?"

Some of this size, of course, is due to breeding (one of the present herd sires, June Volunteer Confident, weighs a whopping 1,800 pounds). And some of it is due to management. But much of it is due to feeding. A Brigham heifer, for instance, weighs 600 pounds when she is bred at 15 months—100 pounds more than most heifers weigh at that age.

LaCoste is proud of the big cows he manages.

"Those dainty show Jerseys," says herdman LaCoste with scorn, "seven hundred pounds, maybe! I'd just as soon have a string of milking rabbits. Give me big cows like these and I'll make them produce."

"These dainty little show Jerseys," he says with some scorn, "seven hundred pounds, maybe! I'd just as soon have a string of milking rabbits." Neither LaCoste nor his employer has ever taken a Brigham Jersey inside a show ring.

There are no blue or purple ribbons in the barn, but they will be glad to show the production records which are the payoff in their breeding efforts. They are prouder of their 145 Ton of Gold cows, their 60 tested dams, and their 36 cows which have produced over 100,000 pounds of milk than they would be over a patchwork quilt of purple ribbons. And they are proudest of an old cow who, even in her best days, would have been waved out of a show ring on

the first go-round; she is J. Royal King's Quomage who, in 1951, became the Living Lifetime Production champion of the Jersey breed after producing 166,822 pounds of milk with 8,151 pounds of butterfat and who is still adding to her record. "Quomage, like all of our herd, made her record on twice-a-day milking under normal farm conditions," Elbert Brigham told Trotter. "We feel that the significance of our records lies in the fact that the entire herd—not just exceptional cows—was on test and contributed to the herd production record. We haven't pulled any cows off test when they faltered and we haven't stripped the leaves off the alfalfa to provide special feed for a comer."

# Conversation with a pig

I BELIEVE I have one of America's biggest libraries of books about pigs. Twelve years before I could afford a pig of my own, I was buying books about them. I'm still buying them. I have them in English, French, Danish and Swedish. I have books on pig economics, pig genetics, pig ailments, pig breeds, pig feeds. Some have been written by learned professors in agriculture. Some by students who will soon be learned professors. Some have been written by mysterious unnamed men of great intelligence in the government. And for all their scholarly differences, the books have this in common. They were written by pig specialists, not by pig farmers.

There is a big difference. A pig specialist has learned most of his pigology from books, and from other pig specialists. But there are certain lessons of inestimable worth which can be learned only by living with pigs themselves the whole day long, and then by sleeping with them. And by making their way of life so much a part of your own that an ordi-

nary civilian can smell the animal husbandry in your clothes a block away against the wind.

There is, for instance, the problem of how to lift a little pig without making him squeal to high heaven. The books don't seem to take any note of the matter, but that squeal can be disastrous at times. Let us say that your sow is resting comfortably after presenting you with a lusty family of twelve. The nervousness and the birthing pains are over, and she is stretched out at your feet giving forth that peculiar music of satisfaction which sounds for all the world like a contented motor. But you notice among the little pink devils fighting over her faucets two which are smaller and weaker than the rest. They try to get hold of a good mouthful, but always there is a big fellow nearby to root them away. You know that in a matter of hours those two little fellows will have said goodbye to the world if you don't do something for them. So you decide to temporarily remove a few of the bigger fellows and

The simple caress of a firm but gently masculine hand along a sow's breasts will often
soothe her feminine neurotics as magically as if she were human.

leave the field open for the needy. If they are going to go out of this world, at least you intend to see them go with a full belly.

But you have forgotten that a pig is a pig with all his cussedness fully developed even when he is an hour old. Chances are that when you grab one of those little battlers to take him away from his mother, he will squirm, screech and fight like a child in a tantrum. Immediately his mother's motor stops purring. She jumps to her feet and whirls around to find the trouble. And her concern for the pig which is being kidnapped may lead her to trample two of three others.

How, then, do you kidnap a suckling pig? Well, gently take him by one hind leg and carry him head downward. He'll never make a sound and neither will his mother. You'll never read that in a book.

Nor will you ever read that the simple caress of a firm but gently masculine hand along a sow's breasts will often soothe her feminine neurotics as magically as if she were human. Sometimes a sow will be so nervous from her ordeal of farrowing she will refuse to lie down to nurse. In such a state she may roam around her sty, wading through her family until you feel like rushing in and hogtieing her into the proper position for motherhood. But time after time, I have approached such a sow, whispered little words of endearment to her, rubbed her lovingly along her teat line, and in no time at all she would be down on her side with her family tugging furiously at her vest buttons and her motor singing as steadily as if it had never stopped.

Now I do not claim to have made any profound or mysterious discovery in learning this. I am well aware this is not new to men who have worked with pigs over the years. But these are days when many a farmer is getting acquainted with pigs for the first time. If he is a westerner, he may be hoping that pig raising may help solve his crop-surplus woes. If he is an easterner, he may be tired of trying to please the milk inspector. So there are probably more beginners in this pig business today than ever before, and most of them start by reading the books.

But no book ever mentioned that trick of the breast rub to me. Perhaps they think that one shouldn't discuss such a topic, in even farm society.

Of course, mind you, it doesn't always work. A sow may exercise the inalienable right of her sex and insist upon remaining unsullied by the hand of man. And if you haven't made love to her before this time, don't expect her to reciprocate now. It's good, hard-headed business to be good to your sows at all times. A sow which is a pet is apt to make the best mother of all. In our barn the other day I caught the hired hand sitting on the sow as he waited the arrival of her next piglet. He was scratching her ears and telling her it would soon be over. It's going to be a dark day on the farm when that sow finally loads into the butcher's truck, but in the meantime she's the best mother we have on the place.

It's a serious thing, this problem of crushing, and there is as yet no sure answer for the boys who raise pigs by the thousands with all the blandishments of modern science. The government surveys will tell you that about a fifth of all new-born piglets will never survive their first week of life because of this peril. The farrowing crate has a goodly number of proponents and on many sows undoubtedly does a job. But there is pretty good evidence that with other sows, such a prison may lead to fretting and loss of milk. The New Zealanders have designed something a little more complicated and more costly—a farrowing house with an interior which twists like the turnings of a great snail shell. In this intricate affair, the sow can lie on only one spot and only one position and there is every inducement for her progeny to keep clear of her when she decides to lie down.

But for the present, a good many pig men will continue to expect their sows to do a profitable job of farrowing in the traditional box stall without too much help from science or engineering genuises.

For such an unadorned maternity ward, there is one scriptural commandment which you must not forget: *Let there be light!*

At our farm, the piglets are taken away from the mother as soon as they have untied the cords and stepped clear of the cellophane package they came in. They are taken out of the farrowing pen and allowed to dry in a cardboard box placed under a heat lamp. As they dry they make the acquaintance of the brothers and sisters they will be fighting for the next six weeks. And there they stay until the last lone straggler leaves the hatch and the mother tells us that she is finished and there are no more to come. Then, with the sow resting in the position to receive them, we turn the bunch into the pen for the first important meal.

But the important part is the light. Even if the weather is so warm there is no danger of chilling, we still like that light because it is the place where the piglets will congregate when they are finished eating, and when they are beneath that light, there is no more danger of crushing. But if you leave the piglets with the sow as they come, and then try to get them to forsake her for the safety haven beneath a lamp later, you may have trouble on your hands.

Let them find that first necessary warmth beneath a light, and you have a far better chance of getting them to your safety corner later. But the books don't

tell you that.

Nor do they go to any trouble to tell a man how to transplant piglets from one sow to another. You have two sows, let us say, each nursing a litter. One is a little sow you once thought a runt. She has thirteen piglets now. Over in another pen you have a sow which has taken a dozen first prizes. But she has only a half dozen pigs. (The books don't tell you why things like this happen either. But they happen.) So you think, "Well, if nature has to be so stupid about this, I'll have to be a little smarter."

How are you going to do it? You know that while some sows are by nature so missionary minded that the latchstring is always out for anyone, the most of them will bite a strange piglet in two.

My method is my own, and I must confess that sometimes it doesn't work. But what I would do in the case of the two sows I have just mentioned, would be as follows: First, remove those six favored brats from the prize sow, and take them far enough away so that when they get hungry, their squealing won't make their mother jump out of her pen to find them. And I would leave them there till they *were* hungry and their mother more than anxious to have them back.

In the meantime, I would remove one of the 13 from the runt sow, one of the highest, and put him in with the six. I now proceed to do what I can to get the smell of the six onto that one. So I rub pigs together. And here again I forget all concept of decency and rub that strange pig with the six rear ends of the others. I rub him thoroughly and all over. I also do not forget to rub him well behind. The reason is obvious. When this strange pig is introduced to his new mother, she may still suspect. And she will smell where the smell is most certain.

In any event, you stay close by to see whether your new pig is allowed to graft himself in with the rest. And after you have successfully grafted the first one, don't be too quick about repeating the process. Let her get used to the extra pig. I am sure that sows can count. I had a Yorkshire once who gave me seven fine piglets and wouldn't lie down until every one of the seven was placed in the pen with her. Which should prove that whatever else you may have to say about a Yorkshire, it can count to seven.

In the matter of the so-called black teeth, the books are pretty definite. Take a pair of fine pliers and snip off those teeth both top and bottom or they may injure the sow. But any pig farmer has seen many a litter grow all the way from sausage size to weaning age complete with teeth and with no visible irritation resulting to the sow at all. At our farm, we ask the mother if the teeth are to be yanked or not. If they never seem to interrupt the music of her motor, we leave them in. At the first flinch, however, we take them out.

But I am wondering if those teeth ever give trouble when the sow has enough teats and ample milk. It always seems to be with the poor sow where teeth trouble occurs. Perhaps the pigs have to try too hard.

The books are equally explicit when it comes to the matter of weaning and early feeding. We are told all pigs should be kept warm because they do not have built-in thermostats such as those possessed by other young domestic animals. One would wonder why the little beggars, smart as they always seem to be, wouldn't climb on top of their mother and keep warm that way. Only once in a while, one is smart enough. The only sow I ever owned whose entire litter would do that was a Minnesota No. 1. With her, soon as dinner was over, each youngster climbed on that portion of his mother's bacon nearest his teat, and there he crouched with his wary nose pointed toward that precious morsel like Launcelot guarding the Grail.

The books will tell you that 75 degrees is the correct temperature for piglets at weaning. And if you are a man who can carry a thermometer around with his jack knife, I suppose that is a good enough rule. But a much simpler way is to watch the flies. If the flies come out of hiding to cluster about the warm spot you have made for your weanlings, you can be fairly sure that the pigs are comfortable. Or if you have one of those stables which have no flies—these are often found in the books—then it is a good idea to watch the pigs themselves. If they persist in huddling one on top of the other for warmth, and are fighting for the best positions, they are still too cold. But if they strew themselves over the floor with no attempt to find bedfellows, they are not too cold.

Don't underestimate the importance of keeping your orphan pigs warm. No matter how tempting a weaning formula you set before him, a cold pig will not sample it.

There are many other things which one will never learn from the pig specialist, but I would not have you think that I am decrying the worth of these gentlemen at all. As they continue to write their books, I continue to read them and to add them to my library of pigology. With all the new developments in feeding, breeding and housing one cannot afford to be without the scholarly advice and findings of these men. No, they certainly have their place and I am glad that I have been able to make the acquaintance of many of them. Perhaps if I had the acquaintance of a few more, I could have been a pig specialist, too.

# The
# SISTERS

IN THE Book of Chronicles you will find long lists of "mighty men of valor . . . seventeen thousand two hundred soldiers fit to go out for war and battle" and somewhere buried in the Chronicles will be a little notation that Maachah, the wife of Machir, bore a son and thus produced another host of names of the mighty men of valor. As one wonders about the unknown Maachah, and her so little celebrated life, so one might wonder about and discover the unchronicled lives of the farm women of our grandmother's and mother's and our own time. For them there were and are the ancient and timeless things, the actual creation of the things one needs to live, and from generation to generation on the farm this contact remains the same, although the ways of living are made easier and simpler and the isolation lessened.

Having been surrounded since childhood with many sisters and the moving cloud of skirts of all our mother's many sisters, this old and unnamed picture of five women on a farm brings back very vividly a portion of life which had something of that Arcadian glow given only to childhood in the country. Although the stern forbidding faces of these five women are as far removed as possible from the gay and generous natures of my aunts, yet there is a kinship between the stiff expectancy of all old family portraits that reminds us of our own fat family albums. My aunts, much younger than these sisters, lived on neighboring farms near Columbia, Missouri. I recall the sweet dusty smell of the yellow clover in the short stretch of public road between the farms, the hot white sunlight on the stones and the enormous Percherons huddled under a solitary tree switching each other's flies and stamping in the dust.

The orderly succession of days, the sun, the crushed odor of the weeds, the sense of peace, and the feeling of timelessness, gave us as children the notion that the Lord had created the earth and heaven for our benefit.

We stood still and the sun revolved around us. Disquieting evidences that life was not merely an endless pattern of cool dewy mornings, hot fried chicken and starry summer nights were all around us, but we were happy as it is only possible for children to be happy in a small given space of time.

On the dairy farm of my aunt and uncle, the day began at four in the morning, in darkness in the winter, in the first grey light in summer when the pond mists were still cold all over the low places in the pasture. My aunt got up then and served the first of five meals for the day, and for her I doubt the sunrise was always as beautiful and magical a thing as the poets say, especially when it turned the pond waters to a sullen and ominous red with a coming storm, but she would not have chosen another way of life. "Farming," she used to say in the days of the last depression, "is the *pleasantest* way of losing money I know."

I recall Aunt Edith's days as hours of continuous motion, moving from stove to table, from house to barn, from barn to chicken house. Or riding recklessly in the old model T Ford, bumping wildly over the pastures on some tour of inspection up by the woodlots, or to round up the cows and start them down the dusty rutted road toward the barns. Her dishwashing was the amazement of our childhood. She sloshed every glass and plate through hot soapy water with the speed and delicacy of an express train, landing them on the other side of the sink in an unbroken shower, and got them back on the shelf before they even seemed off the table. She raised chickens, took care of the milk separator (whose intricate mechanism seemed to us children as complicated as the stomachs of a cow), churned butter, fed the wood stove where huge pans of skimmed milk sat souring for the chickens, kept the kerosene lamps cleaned and filled, washed clothes, hauled water, cooked enormous meals whose dimensions had something of the open-handed recklessness with which she did most things.

At one time she kept 18 cats and a little pet skunk that came softly out at twilight, and in the winter the kitchen sills were feeding stations for an endless stream of redbirds, woodpeckers and brilliant, noisy jays.

I remember the sheep barns full of crying lambs, some of which always had to be bottle-fed, and the rows of pig houses in the pastures like large cocked hats or little houseless roofs on the close-cropped grass. Each cow in the herd was always named, and so were the pigs, giving the feeling somehow of a large, though changing, family. Names ranging from simple Annie and Bessie to Sapphira and Hebe, and all the Greek gods and goddesses, and a particularly large and handsome pig was called Agamemnon, which seemed fitting to his enormous size.

It is so easy to speak in sweeping generalities, to speak of the rhythms of nature, and the beauty of country life, and the wisdom that people gain from the earth. But there was also, particularly in the generation of these fine, good women (who seem to be both defiant and suspicious of the camera), a quality almost completely opposed to the large and generous world of nature in which they lived. A hardness and self-righteousness, a narrowness and darkness of outlook. They confused order with integrity, cleanliness with godliness, and set up standards by which each life might be molded and judged with all the exactness of a pound of butter or the recipe for a pie. To justify their own lives they said with the spinster of the "Baker's Wife," "If this erring woman is not punished, what good has virtue done the rest of us?"

It is easy to dwell too much on this other side too, the endless work, the bitterness and the loneliness, the occasional tragedy. One such was the suicide of the little woman we knew very well who lived alone on her big farm with beautiful heirlooms and her herd of cattle, and the finding of her hanging outside in the rain with a rope around her neck. I recall too the words of a farm woman saying, "I keep waiting for something. All my life I seem to have been waiting for something . . ." But somewhere in between the beauty and the barrenness is the truth, and everywhere are the memorable unwritten chronicles of women's lives, farm women whose days have unity and purpose and are identified with the earth, with the most basic things of the world, and who make a contribution far exceeding that of the "mighty men of valor," although their names are not often recorded and their lives are little known.

This old and unnamed picture of five women on a farm brings back vividly a portion of life which had something of that Arcadian glow given only to childhood in the country.

# The
# four
# faces
# of
# WINTER

# Winter Beauty

Winter brings its own special artistry to the farm. Fields that were lush with green in June turn rusty gold. The trees are brown and bare, but one sharp, cold dawn the first glance at the nearest pasture takes your breath away. The trees' bare arms are covered with lacy shawls of hoarfrost, draped by Nature during the long night.

# The Fury of Winter

Range cattle know winter's violence. They have no stout Midwest barn or even lean-to shelter against its driving storms, and no one brings them breakfast every morning. A blinding two-day snow may cut them off in a hilly pocket where they could starve to death. Only a flying farmer can spot a missing calf's location; and then he still may have no hope of reaching it.

# Winter Fun

How many times have you sat on a big steel corn scoop shovel and gone turning, twisting and whirling down a steep grade on an icy crust? Many farm kids now have proportioned-to-fit skis instead of barrel slats for hill skiing, but everybody still waits for the creek to freeze over for skating. Sometimes it snows too, covering the ice, and the stones and the air pockets catch your skates and send you sprawling. Most everybody nurses a bruise or skins a knee, but it's worth it.

196

# Winter is work, too

From the bleak hours of early milking to the long haul of winter feed, the farmer's work goes on, 12 months a year. The homely picture of a farmer's winter ease in front of the baseburner is a figment of the past.

Winter months mean maintenance work on the many tools of modern farming, fitting them for another year's grinding work. It means work on fences, in the woodlot, in the barn. It means careful planning and some hopeful guessing on the state of the farm market months ahead in the uncertain future.

# Yankee Farmer

THEY say it was a big wind that blew the May-flower off her course to Virginia, but there are those in the Vermont hills who will tell you it wasn't chance at all. The Yankee was made for the stubborn, granite hills of New England, and he has perched atop them and worked their sides ever since. The shift in the wind was a good thing, because Yankees would be very unhappy in Virginia. His stern and earnest soul weathers the blizzards that flail across the stone walls with a composure that suggests the Almighty knew what he was doing when he shifted the wind.

You can point your finger down about anywhere in the rural areas of the six northeastern states and find a Yankee. You could spotlight a Massachusetts orchardist, a sweetcorn man from Sandy River, a timberland man from the Connecticut Lakes, or one of those phenomenal potato barons of way-up Aroos-took County—and you'd find each time an altogether different person who typifies and explains the Yankee. They're all alike—and they're all different. Take 'em as they come, and they're New England. Of all of them, one of the most interesting, the most stubborn, the hardest-working, the one with his feet firmest, and probably the most forward-looking is the sturdy dairy farmer of Vermont, beset by innumerable "di-few-c'lties" and disappointments. Nobody has licked him yet, and everybody and everything has tried.

Take Frank Lawrence of Crow Hill, St. Johnsbury, Vermont. Surrounded by more geographic beauty than you'll find in ten other states, Frank has swung his scythe and carried his rocks to the wall since he was a boy, and at eighty is still swinging and still carrying. His Anglo-Saxon ancestors gave him the blue eyes for looking off from the green hills.

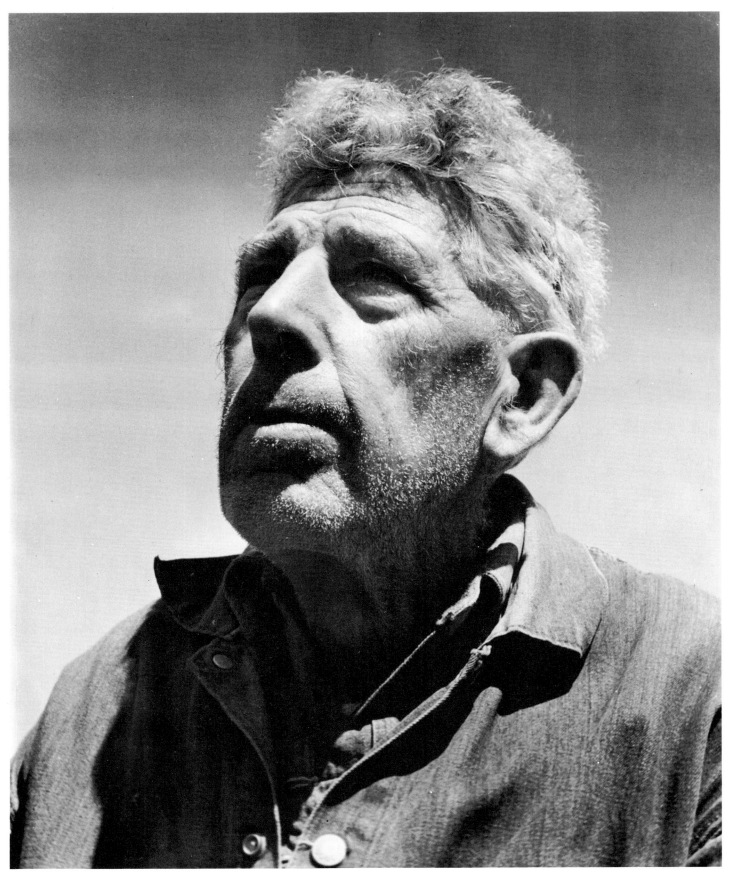

Down from the New England hills has come a legend of a tough and resourceful race of men who conquered an unsympathetic land. With sharp wits and an uncanny sense of values, they made the word Yankee a synonym for shrewd bargaining. But a Yankee is more; he's also like Frank Lawrence of Crow Hill, Vermont—a good farmer who can show most of us a lesson or two about making a living on a handful of rocky soil.

To fight rocks and hills for a living, a Yankee farmer needs a healthy breakfast to start the day.

These ancestors also gave us people who started things like Harvard, and dumped tea into Boston Harbor, and stood shoulder to shoulder in that hour of darkness and peril and need when the United States seemed like a good thing to originate.

Frank might also point out to you that early poll taxes in other states were paid by people who moved west to avoid being Yankees like him. Good-enough people, you know, but flighty. Couldn't settle down, had no gumption to tie to. Lit out when there was work to do. Frank would also explain about Yankees being stingy, close-lipped, nose-talkers, and "dry." *Some call it salty. Well, you never know when money will come in handy; sometimes it doesn't pay to volunteer information; what odds how you talk so long as you say something worth hearing; what harm in a remark that twinkles? You don't live by farming on the hills of Vermont all your life without having*

*some good qualities. A lot of people would be Yankees if they could stand up to the climate and still have something to eat when they put their feet under the table.*

So Frank Lawrence doesn't go to pieces when he has a horse to trade; he uses words the way he uses money; he probably doesn't think he's an individualist but he is; and he votes the straight Republican ticket because he never was in love with what he calls foolishness. You have to put a lot of basic things together to get at Frank's philosophy. Mostly it's just Frank, and he likes the way he is, and you can be somebody else as long as you don't bother him about it, and pay your own bills.

His background and his family, along with his tipped-up acres, are typical of others around him. When he was a lad he saw the old era of New England fade out gradually, until as a grown man he saw farming get about as low as the Winooski meadows. Now as an old man he reflects and sees a bright future for his state and his people—an awakening of the old spirit with new purpose, new methods, new blood. And, thank God, a proper amount of the traditions. Something old and something new—it's still Vermont and the sun gleams bright on the hills.

The Lawrence farm has been in the family since 1806. That's not the oldest, but it's about average for the early-cleared farms. Fishermen's sons were moving inland from the coast of Maine; folks were working up the rivers from Connecticut; New Hampshire was whetting her ax. Many a young man had hiked his new wife through the woods until they found a likely place to build. And Frank's great-grandfather thought his older brothers hadn't used him right, so he left them with their shipyard in Massachusetts and lifted his eyes to the hills. The house was like others raised in New England around the turn of the century—built mostly of sweat, with "weak heads and strong backs." They gathered the stone from the fields, clearing cropland as they built a house. They swung the broadax against the beams, and drew great upland logs to water mills for boards. They brought in nail-rods, and hammered out fastenings, perhaps a local smith was already there to do it for them. They sent back, maybe to Portland, for glazing—and the wagons toiled up through the notch. That wagon route would be the rail route when the rich country behind the mountains should be opened to the sea.

The farm was self-sufficient. It had to be. The price of things not produced was in terms of things they did produce. You could always work a day for somebody else, and labor was better than money then. The women had their share of it. They helped with the farm work, did the spinning and weaving, and made the food go through the long winter. They raised up sons, too, and a child of four or five was already assigned his woodbox and chicken chores. The pioneer days have been carefully treated by scores of New England authors who know a good tale when they hear one. But they were good days, and they set the pace for New England. When mere survival was taken care of those first farmers began sending out their produce. They sold stock, and now and then some garden stuff, and always there were loads of logs and boards moving toward those coastal cities. Cities are always learning but never heeding their sorriest lesson—that you can't harvest on paved streets. The barren predicament of sea-

board cities was Vermont's first farm asset, and the thundering milk trains that drive to Boston in the night are the continuing story of that first trade.

Goods seek the market, and if the Lawrences could sell, so could they buy. Up came peddlers and craftsmen—first on foot and then with wagons, and later to set up stores. There were tinsmiths and yard-goods packers, coming on business but welcome socially. Once a year the bootmaker would get around with his traveling shop, and he'd sit in the kitchen door in the sun and peg footwear for all the family. It took more than one veal hide to copper-toe the children all around. Sometimes a Yankee could dress up his values, and it wasn't always the trader who did the trading. Many a pack peddler came back hoping to recoup last year's sticking, and he didn't joke about Yankee ability at a sharp bargain when he had his goods laid out on the kitchen table. Those early settlers were not the ones to flip down a nickel and say, "Keep the change." A nickel was the price of an hour's labor in the woodlot. Many a farmer raised his family, and raised them well, and never saw $100 cash in a year. So you didn't become generous.

The agriculture pattern was good because it was diversified. Money came in dribbles, but it came from many sources and it came the year 'round. You had most all your living, and father always had something to sell. If income exceeds outgo, that's called profit, and the forebears showed a profit by spending less than they took in. Today, in New England, money is considered something to keep. The pattern failed, however, when farming developed into a business. Thrift and work couldn't keep undernourished farm land from failing up. As old folks, satisfied with little, died, their children left the farms deserted until every New England state had a deserted-farm problem.

The rudiments of almost all modern farm practices were understood and used by Yankee farmers a hundred years ago. Rotation was used, not scientifically, but because observation suggested it. Corn followed potatoes, not because of soil requirements but because potatoes killed back the sod and the corn piece would be fairly free of grass. Plowing under green crops was common. New England soil tends to be heavier, the humus goes deeper, and working in vegetation kept the ground from packing down. Modern farmers speak of aeration, but great-grandfather was satisfied to do it because it seemed to make things grow better. But as the years went

Gigantic dry lots provide milk for new populations in the West, but for more than 100 years the Vermont dairy farmer has fed the hungry cities along the eastern seaboard.

by the practice seemed lost without the reasons. Somewhere along the line the margin of profit dropped off and one field after another stayed in hay for years on end. New England soil needs lots of study, and that's the one thing the old-timers didn't give it.

In Vermont the tendency was to change over to straight dairying, buy what you couldn't raise, and cut the hay at all costs. Herds were bigger than the farms could support, and even in summer the farmers were buying feed when their own upland fields cut less than a ton to the acre.

With the industrialization of the region, along about 1875, textile and shoe factories attracted youth off the farms. The shorter day, the higher pay, and even the bright lights looked better than a day in the cornfield. Other factors joined to accelerate the decline. Frank Lawrence sees the picture about like this:

"Along about 50 years ago things around here were bobsledding downhill, and nobody dragging his feet. We were fitting the Yankee farmer to a shroud and didn't know it. It was along about Spanish War times—just when we might have been getting over the Civil War. You know, this section of the country lost a big part of its future in the Civil War—we've never gained back what we lost in boys and energy. Our farms poured volunteers into the army—some couldn't come home, some didn't. Those that did had hard sledding, and things were about to pick up when we hit another period.

"That was when the cities and the mills called, and some youngsters headed out into the west. In those days our farms stayed in the families, and if they had two boys, one of them worked out. Sometimes he'd save enough to pick up a farm, but often he just lit out and never came back. Those that decided to stay moved out farther onto the back roads, or higher up the hills, and Lord knows the meadow farms never budded gold pieces.

"But in Vermont we thought we found an answer, and that was when the milk business began to slap us around. The cities filled up with immigrants and our own children, and they all wanted milk. It was such a pretty set-up it made a lot of us scrap the old method of self-sufficiency, and we began being dairy farmers. We quit growing grain, and built bigger barns for cows. The prairie farmers shipped in our grain, and in a way we stopped being farmers and began operating factories where we took raw materials and turned out milk. We took in a lot of

money, but we paid out a lot to feed stores. What you keep is what counts, and we didn't count as much as you might think.

"Milk doesn't make a very pretty story. Hardly any of us are much more than feeders to big corporations that really run the business. Mostly they treat us all right, but I don't think anybody claims they do all they might. When the second World War came along and feed went crazy, some of those companies could have spent something and fought our battles for us—but nothing really successful came about, and times have been wicked. Anyway, it was this milk development that changed the whole farm picture for us, and only lately we began to fight back."

This fighting back has been in the manner of retrenchments. The Vermont farmers are working toward self-sufficiency again. They are growing grain, talking land conservation, working together in Farm Bureau, consumer and producer co-ops, herd improvement, even artificial breeding and advertising. Land rejuvenation interests men in manure loaders, pasture improvement, soil testing, new seeds, and long-term rotations. It is interesting to hear Vermonters talk about "salvage values" of cattle, when a few years back they met and talked nothing but milk, milk, milk.

But you don't get New England's picture from graphs and government reports. There is also the grand story of summer people and city folks who buy a farm and commute. The vacation and rustication aspect of New England rural areas has done a lot to the social and cultural life of the old farmer who still works the family acres. To most of the deserted farm stands have come real estate men, bringing cigar-smoking bankers and businessmen who can look in a back window and see what a few thousand dollars will do. Then these newcomers call the place their "farm," and truth-to-tell some of them have made the old-timers' eyes pop. They bring new tractors and flick-of-the-wrist implements, and paint the place up so the old farmer has to spruce a bit himself, and they buy blooded stock, and pay their taxes the same day the bill comes. They put wasteland into white pine plantings, campaign for better roads, take "showers" every morning, and lean over fences just for the thrill of being neighborly. At first they were queers, but they bought eggs and strawberry plants, hired somebody to lay in a "dreen," and paid for everything.

The old die-hards thought they held out all right,

but the newcomers called them characters and thought everything was wonderful. Then the "farmers'" daughters got invited to kitchen junkets by farmers' sons, and the tone of both parties went up a notch.

It's hard to put the finger on specific dates or persons in connection with the revival of good farming and the return of the New England hills to production. A generation ago the dissemination of modern agricultural information had slowgoing. County agents and home demonstration agents were upstarts with college training, and all they had were a flock of new ideas nobody had tried out. Frank Lawrence was one of the minority who took up with the new ideas. His son, Carl, now does the farming under his father's critical eye and he picks up any new idea that comes along. The Lawrences were among the loyal few who kept the county agents from unemployment.

"Potatoes this year, corn next" has gone into a long-range program under which the farmer looks ahead ten years to the barley from the lower field. Pastures are in grass longer, hay is baled in the fields for economical storage, silage is a studied conclusion to a careful plan. Superphosphate is a must in the barn manure trench, lime is bought by the ton, and almost anybody can spot magnesium deficiency when he sees it.

The grain growing brings great satisfaction. Farmers who never raised grain stand and smile at their fields. Experiment stations are at work on seeds. Rustless oats were once unknown, what with New England's fog and river damp. One summer in ten was long enough to grow corn—now you can wait until June, plant hybrids, and have a crop by mid-September. Neighborhoods join for the harvesting and threshing again—one man brings his reaper, another his power plant, and a third his threshing machine. Even combines, the pride of the golden prairies, are fairly common in New England now. Small fruits and orchards are going in; hundreds are already bearing. County agents have done a good job. People no longer put apple trees on their run-out fields and expect a crop. Apples grow on rich soil, need cultivation and mulch. Many a milk farmer has found that hay is worth more in apples than it is in milk, and they mulch the hillsides generously.

New England's growing season is a short burst, the glacial soil is unique, the moisture of the land

and air never fails completely, and the markets are close. These facts make it theoretically possible to compete with more favored farm regions. Indeed, some of these facts actually make New England the most favored of all, but other regions don't see it. "You don't talk about farming up here in this country the way you do in Iowa," says Carl Lawrence. Folks in New York's Cherry Hill Valley, the flat corn belt, the irrigated far west, and even the most-of-the-best country in the south look at New England and wonder why anybody tries to farm at all. A stranger riding across Vermont on Route 2, twisting in and out, up and down, seeing nothing but small side-hill fields, rocky pastures, and brief meadowlands would say, "No chance to farm here." They tell the story of the Vermont farmer who fell out of his cornfield three times in one morning.

You may have to spray thick lime-sulphur on the McIntosh trees all through a misty summer to lick the scab. But a real Yankee-grown McIntosh is the result, and nobody anywhere else has ever produced equal flavor. The buyers in New York and Boston know the difference. It isn't a long haul across the country to the market, either, but a man can hop in his truck after milking and be home again in time for supper.

Most important of all, in this awakening era, is the holdover of antique Yankee philosophizing. You don't put all your eggs in one "barskit," of course. The Lord will provide, but you do what you can in the meantime. Him as has gits. You can't put out what you don't have. And the gait of the steers tells who trained them. New England has small farms and small farmers, but life has always run deep and it is the little things that count.

Once again, the farms are sending out lumber. Pine, spruce, popple and fir has gone to pulp mills. More and more woodland products come from farms in small quantities, where back a few years they came from the wild lands and the big operations.

Yankee pastures were always a joke. Land that wasn't good for anything else went to pasture. Cows picked between the rocks, junipers, scrub-pines and bull-pines to find a living. Carl Lawrence feels the best indication of rejuvenation comes from the fact that farmers are working on these pastures. Sometimes this is just an application of bag fertilizer—because rocks are still the best crop. But some farms have planted the back pasture to Christmas trees or quick-growing pulp, and have put good tillable land into pasture. Then they rotate crops. build up the

soil, and finally get to a forage crop specially needed for summer feeding. A few years back winter rye was a rare sight, but now whole hills are as green when the snow goes as they ever were in mid-June. If things go well the rye is turned under in late May or June—but if it comes off wet it means a crop of grain, and another try next September for a green manure.

New England is supplied mainly by private utilities, and a few years back they grumbled at the cost of delivering power out in the country. But their corporate heads have been penetrated, and most of them are now very liberal toward farms. And why not? The farmer uses far more power than his apartment friend, and a well-equipped farm is almost as good a customer as a small mill. In fact, some farmers run mills—shook bolters, maybe, or cider presses. Mrs. Frank Lawrence probably speaks for every farm housewife. "It's a blessing! The men brag about lights in the barn, and come home every week or so with a new gadget, and nobody ever speaks about electricity in the house. I like electricity too. I used kerosene lamps for years, and slobbered over a scrub board in a wooden tub, and went for years at a time without taking the sad-irons off the stove. Now I enjoy life, and I think the best friend I have is the man who comes and reads the meter."

The up-and-coming Yankee farmer has a medium-tractor and what implements and tools his own place calls for. Hay loaders and side-delivery rakes are common. Buck-rakes and field balers are coming along fast. Tractor-driven potato diggers, orchard sprayers, and other mobile pieces are common.

"I've seen things make the cycle," says Frank Lawrence. "I recall when oxen gave way to horses, and now the tractors are taking over most of the work. And while we won't see oxen at work again, at least the cycle has gone around until our dairymen aren't ashamed to fatten some steers for heavy beef."

A lot of people think the New England winter plays a part in the shaping of Yankee character. Probably it does, but it isn't really a bad time. To an outsider it seems as if life for a Yankee farmer is made up of working all summer to live through the winter to work all summer again—and if you want to insist, that's about the size of it. Any discussion of winter's advantages become poetic rather than actual, and if there's anything a Yankee farmer detests it's getting poetical about winter.

Nature takes a rest through those snow-driven months, and man is just part of nature. There are things to do in the winter and they get done. There is also time to sit around and read, and if you have a shop with an airtight stove you can really enjoy yourself making things. You have next winter's wood to get out, and some long logs to haul before the snow gets too deep or the ground thaws again. The good housewife has a full cellar and a full attic. The Yankee farmer doesn't sit down every Christmas and make out a list of his advantages, and he doesn't like the north wind any better than anybody else. But he takes things as they come, and the most you'll get out of him is, "Oh, winter's all right."

Winter makes a good time, too, for going around to see things you want to look at. There used to be a time when a neighbor would wander in out of a storm and play a game of checkers, and then weeks would go by without company. But highways are kept open now and nobody is isolated above a few hours.

County agents keep thinking up new things to meet about. One night it's buckrakes, the next freezer techniques, then breeders' meetings, pomological societies, co-op meetings. When nothing else is going on the children have a 4-H gathering, or mother takes in the Stitch and Sew group. People on New

The town meeting is a New England tradition. The Yankee wants to run his own government, not by deputy but personally.

England farms, nowadays, think nothing of trips to the city, either, and when somebody agrees to stay home for chores the rest of the family may pack up and go to the Ice Follies in Boston.

A Vermont farmer can go to New York and explain the principle of building construction, but New Yorkers blink if you ask them to name four varieties of apples, potatoes, cows, or hens. Your Yankee farmer has opinions on UN matters as definitely as he does on the breed of sow he wants. The milk trains run into Boston at night, but they bring back morning papers the next day. Country weekly papers are mainly for local matters and don't strive to compete with dailies that can be printed a hundred miles away and delivered on time. The local editors are esteemed, and call each week to find if the cow had twins, if the peas are ripe, or if Aunt Abigail flew back from Chicago. Rural life is intimate and personal, and Yankee country papers rely on local treatment. The editor speaks his piece, but has no particular authority or power. The community spirit in New England is dominating, and the weekly paper serves chiefly to gratify this spirit. Some papers went all through the war without mentioning it except in local terms. That doesn't mean nobody was interested—it means New England weekly papers have a special function. Most Yankee farmers take a city daily paper to read the news, and a weekly paper to confirm what they have already heard about over the party-line 'phone.

It is hard for anyone not raised in the New England Town Meeting tradition to comprehend this attitude. The Yankee runs his own government, not by deputy nor theoretically, but personally. The Yankee would tell you, if anybody took the trouble to ask, that the United Nations won't work. Nice idea, he'd say, and too bad it can't be done. International diplomacy and the Brotherhood of Man make a nice snatch of song, but you don't erect a thing like that just by saying let's do it. The congregation of multitudes sounds like a good thing, but the Yankee knows that all civil values arise from the guarantee of personal things. You take something away from a man and he hates you. You give him something, and he joins right in. Town Meeting is where the Yankee farmer learned government, and he knows just how far you can go. It won't do any good to tell him he's wrong—he'll just tell you to wait and see. And perhaps that's as good an answer as any.

Longevity, too, is part of the Yankee theme. No-body is too old to plan ahead. They say Vermonters never die, but cease only by act of God—as when a bolt of lightning leaves them standing upright in the hayfield. One man of 90 had been postmaster since he was 45, and Washington suggested he retire. He wrote back that he'd never have taken the job except that he thought it was to be permanent. A woman of 76, when asked her occupation, said, "I take care of an old lady."

Something else that goes with being a Yankee is a certain inventive streak and skill with the hands. In Vermont and New Hampshire, where state departments have had a chance to collect activities, an amazing productivity has been observed. The people always made things, but you'd think this "arts and crafts" program was a revival to hear the publicity writers. Woodwork, needlework, baskets, painting, pottery, and old-time spinning and weaving lead the list. Farm folks have found income from this. The old fellow who used to whittle now finds he is a woodcarver, and his work is sold from a shop in Rockefeller Center at prices which don't offend him any to speak of. The experts speak of this as "developing new interests," and sometimes even as therapy. The Yankee will let you call it anything you want so long as your check is good. Roadside stands that sell products of the farm have amazing stocks—baby rabbits, maple products, samplers, cherry-wood bowls, butternut candy, new green peas, hooked rugs, duck eggs, and even films developed with overnight service.

Some of the old things in New England are gone. Some will never die. There are new methods, new ideas, new equipment, and sometimes new people. But New England started back on Plymouth Rock, and that was a long time ago. You can teach an old dog new tricks, and can even unlearn some of the old ones. But you've still got an old dog. The puppy ways are gone out of New England, and the faithful, steady, settled manners of the Yankee farmer are a basic asset no other farmland of the country can claim. It has been said before that being a Yankee is more than geography—it's a state of mind.

Old Frank Lawrence is looking ahead, and he says, "Best of all, our young people aren't all going to the cities. These youngsters are putting Yankee farming back on its feet."

But young Carl Lawrence, wisely, is looking back, and he says, "We young folks have learned an awful lot from people like Dad. He hasn't been around here 80 years without knowing something."

# MISTLETOE

UNLIKE THE Yule log which has given way to central heating, mistletoe is still a part of the lightheartedness of the Christmas season. And like most of our traditions it has an extensive background in custom and legend.

"Mistletan," which means "a different twig," was the name the ancients gave it. It was rightly called, for a plant whose roots never touched the ground and that died only when the host-tree died was a strange thing to the men of the time. That the plant grew so luxuriously between the earth and sky, firmly imbedded in the branches of the sacred oak, was reason enough for men to reverence it.

The English say that it is from a bird—the Missel Thrush—that mistletoe acquired its present name. In England and Europe this thrush carries the berries about spreading the plant like a small, winged Johnny Appleseed. Because the seeds, encased in a sticky pulp, cling to its bill and toes, "toe" was added to "missel" and a new word was coined.

In much earlier times, it is said, Jupiter took up residence in a mistletoe bush when he descended from Heaven; and Medea, the sorceress, used the juice from the plant to brew some of her best magic potions. The gathering of the plant was a part of the religious rites of the Druids of ancient Britain. The procedure involved two white bulls, never before harnessed, and white-robed priests who harvested the mistletoe with a gold hook.

Mistletoe was the "wonder drug" of the Age of Herbalism. Its reputation as a cure-all reached heights second only to Lydia Pinkham's Compound. Swedes wore rings of mistletoe and chewed the leaves to cure ulcer; the Germans hung sprigs in the doorway to ward off evil spirits; the French wore it as an amulet or brewed it into medicinal liquor, while the English were making a kind of wine of the berries.

Mistletoe also had the alleged virtue of producing fertility in plants, animals and human beings. Still supporting this theory are farmers in parts of Japan who sow minced mistletoe leaves with millet and other seeds believing that this will help produce a plentiful crop. Small twigs of the plant are fed to animals in England in an effort to make them more prolific.

Oliver Hereford went right to the heart of more modern interest in mistletoe many years ago when he penned the quatrain:

*It hath been writ that anye manne*
*May blameless kiss what mayde he canne*
*Nor anyone shall say hymn 'no'*
*Beneath the holye mistletoe.*

Just where along the line mistletoe acquired this magical property of licensing kissing is not known. According to a Scandinavian tale, Frigga, the goddess of marriage for whom Friday is named, was the first to declare the plant to be an emblem of love and to start the custom of kissing beneath its branches. To insure the magic of the ritual the youth took a berry from the branch and gave it to the lady—one for each favor bestowed. Thus the old saying, "A kiss for a berry, so long as a berry remains to be plucked." Stripped of its fruit, the magic of the mistletoe vanished.

Mistletoe gave its name "The Golden Bough" to the seventeen volumes that title a history of religion by Sir James Frazer. This history came to be written in a curious way. As a youth, Frazer heard a tale of the ancients in Italy that went like this:

"In olden times, when Diana was goddess of the hunt, there lived a tribe of fair-haired people near Aricia, Italy. The High Priest of the tribe lived on a hill overlooking the village. He spent his days, sword in hand, guarding a tree. To him were brought all the fruits and delicacies of the village, the best cuts of meat, the loveliest virgins, and the best catch of fish. Only one thing deterred the High Priest who guarded the sacred tree day and night. He was succeeded by whoever killed him."

Sir James Frazer, enchanted by this tale, set out to find the name of the tree. In doing so, he managed to write a history of religion that is regarded as one of the great pieces of literature.

But whatever mistletoe may be to custom and tradition, to the botanist it is a parasite, to the forester it is an enemy to be constantly combatted, and to the farmer it can be a cash crop.

There are more than 100 species in the American branch of the family, about eleven of them in North America. Texas is lucky, or unlucky, enough to have five of these. Botanically, the mistletoe growing in the United States varies enough from the European varieties to deserve a separate name, *Phoradendron* — meaning, appropriately enough, "tree thief." *Phoradendron flavenscens* is the tongue-twister assigned to the mistletoes which commonly grow east of the Mississippi River. These species are water tolerant, grow rapidly, berry out scantily, and while good for sale in the local and nearby markets at the holiday season, will not ship long distances successfully. *Phoradendron villosum* and *californicum* and their first cousins are the mistletoes whose leaves have less moisture and, therefore, ship well.

Most species of the mistletoe have abundant chlorophyll and can manufacture food. All the plant requires from its host are water and mineral nutrients. The dwarf mistletoe, however, is more nearly a completely parasitic plant with only scale-like leaves. It is particularly fond of the Ponderosa Pine and causes much damage in Southwestern forest areas each year. However much the forester may value the mistletoe at Christmas time as a subterfuge to kiss a pretty girl, his year-round professional view of it is as a plant which saps, dwarfs, and sometimes kills the trees it feeds upon.

Mistletoe doesn't rely entirely on the birds for a hand with its propagation. The berries when ripe explode with great force, catapulting the seed as far as 60 feet from the plant. There it sticks to a handy limb of another pine and, in time, sends down a rootlet which penetrates the tree's bark making contact between the parasite and the tree's water conducting system. The tree then becomes just another unwilling host.

Cutting infected trees seems to be one of the few practical methods of controlling mistletoes, but complete eradication is difficult, unless the infected area is clear cut. With some forest areas producing 10,000 board feet per acre, this way of breaking the mistletoe-hold causes hesitation even when labor is available.

To the farmer who sees mistletoe as a potential crop, the question is not how to kill it, but how to cultivate it.

"We can grow mistletoe with ease here in Florida," says R. E. Pinnell who, with his sons, has a wholesale florist firm in Tampa. "But the plant is worth little for sale to the trade because it mildews and spoils rapidly after cutting. Mistletoe leaves take up moisture from the air as well as from the host, and if it's grown in areas where there is a great deal of rainfall it becomes heavy with water and withstands shipping poorly. That's why we go to the farms and ranches in West Texas for all of the mistletoe we now sell," he says. "Mistletoe grown in the arid and semi-arid regions of the Southwest—Texas, Oklahoma, New Mexico and Arizona—is a good all-around plant for market. It doesn't have a high-moisture content, it berries out at the proper time, and holds up well under cutting and shipping."

*The Druids, or the Conversion of ye Britons to Christianity*

Mistletoe is really an ideal crop, Pinnell believes, because it isn't necessary, in most cases, even to take care of the propagation of the plant. "Years ago we tried planting mistletoe—which can be done easily," he says, "in an area where there was little growing at the time. This was done simply by dropping a fully ripe seed into the fork of branches, or placing it under the bark of the trees. The results were quite satisfactory, but an unnecessary expense because Mother Nature, assisted by the birds, did a better job and sent no bill."

Mistletoe starts to berry out in late summer; the berries at that time are small and green in color. They turn ivory-colored in November. By the middle of November the berries are usually fully ripe and waxy looking with a sticky pulp inside, and the plant is ready for market.

Harvesting is done with trucks and hooks attached to poles. The pickers drive under the trees on the ranches from which the mistletoe is bought, pull the bunches of mistletoe off with the hooks. As a general rule the entire bunch comes off at a slight tug.

As the clumps of greenery are brought in by the pickers, they must be culled, sorted, graded and broken up. The stems are snapped off the main body of the plant and the stalky stems with no berries are thrown out as are those with yellowed leaves and unripe berries.

But withered, or freshly cut, the charm of mistletoe will be on hand, come Christmas, to pucker the lips of the young and even shake the resolution of old bachelors.

Serene and detached.

# How to make Old-fashioned Country Ham

**M**OST people prefer the knife-and-fork approach to hogs, and that's logical, for the test of the hog is in the flavor. And pork fanciers generally consider the ham the sweetest meat on the hog.

But those who like fine hams maintain that not all ham is ham, and a real ham is about as hard to find as a hen's egg in a haymow. By "real" ham he means the smoked, dry-cured country ham of his childhood days on the farm.

There are still country hams to be had, however, for a few people have preserved the ancient skill of curing pork, and some of them have turned their knowledge into a profitable business.

The difference between hams, according to the ham connoisseurs, is largely the difference between the people who cure them. A good green ham is an item of great potential, but it can be rendered worthless by the unskilled hand. The cure is the thing.

To the Virginian, a ham by any other name does not taste as sweet. And the New England Yankee is convinced that ham is ham only when it has been smoked in a New England smokehouse. Kentucky has its ham, too, as famous in some circles as its horses and bluegrass.

The Henrys check ham quality by running an ice pick to the bone. They can tell how good it is by the odor on the pick.

Down in Kentucky there are a few dedicated souls who have found that there is a good farm business in offering old-fashioned, country-cured hams to travelers whose nostrils still yearn for the rich, lingering, smokehouse odors of childhood.

The largest of these country-ham producers is Old Hickory Farm, which occupies a river-bottom setting not far from Ghent, Kentucky, on the Ohio River. The old brick house was built more than 100 years ago by John Anthony Gex; and what he knew about curing hams, which is said to have been considerable, he passed on to his descendants. Today the big ham business which centers around Old Hickory is run by the Gex family, and a great-granddaughter, Mrs. Ellis Henry, who, with her husband, has established a branch smokehouse down in Pee Wee Valley, not far from Louisville.

It was really Ellis Henry and not his wife who started sharing this Kentucky family's favorite meat with other people. "After the '37 flood," he says, "we lived up on the farm for several years. I had never tasted country ham until I came here from

Pennsylvania, and I was sure a lot of other people hadn't either. I didn't see how they could help but like it if they were exposed to it. In 1938 I bought 50 green hams from a Louisville packing house, cured them at home and sold them. I borrowed $200 to get started. Since then we've been increasing the volume a little each year."

The Henrys make no secret of how they cure their famous hams. They'll reveal the procedure, step by step, without fear of competition. "Not many people want to go into this business," Henry says. "The risk is too great. If something goes wrong you can lose a lot of hams and it doesn't take a professor to figure out that you can't afford to lose many."

There is nothing about the Old Hickory curing process that isn't common knowledge to a lot of old-timers. "We cure hams today just the same as they were cured 100 years ago," they say. "Country hams were the common thing then. Today they're a delicacy, a treat, and that's what brings the customers back year after year. We've sold hams here to people from California and Texas and Canada and Mexico, and every year a lot of them write back and reorder by mail."

Following a ham from hog to skillet would reveal the following steps in the curing process:

1. *Get a good ham.* Henry says the best hams come from corn-fed hogs. If they're fed right the meat is firm and not soft. "Make no mistake about that," he says, "even the peanut-fed hogs which supply the famous Virginia hams are finished on corn." He likes a large ham, and has it specially trimmed to leave four fingers of meat below the shank bone. The meat should be fresh. The sooner it can be cured after the body heat leaves the animal the better. It's best to start the curing 24 hours after butchering. Hams from hogs which have hung in storage for a few weeks often spoil during curing for some little-known reason. The hide is left on a country ham during curing.

2. *Thoroughly rub the ham with coarse salt.* Frank Howard, the Henrys' ham foreman, figures that in his 64 years he has "rubbed" more hams than any other man in the state of Kentucky. This old colored man is an artist with a ham. "I started helping my mother cure meat when I was 10 years old," he says, "and by the time I was 14, people heard that I knew how to handle meat and I couldn't find time to do all the work they wanted me to do.

"The way we salt hams here is to spread coarse salt all over a table and start rubbing it into a ham.

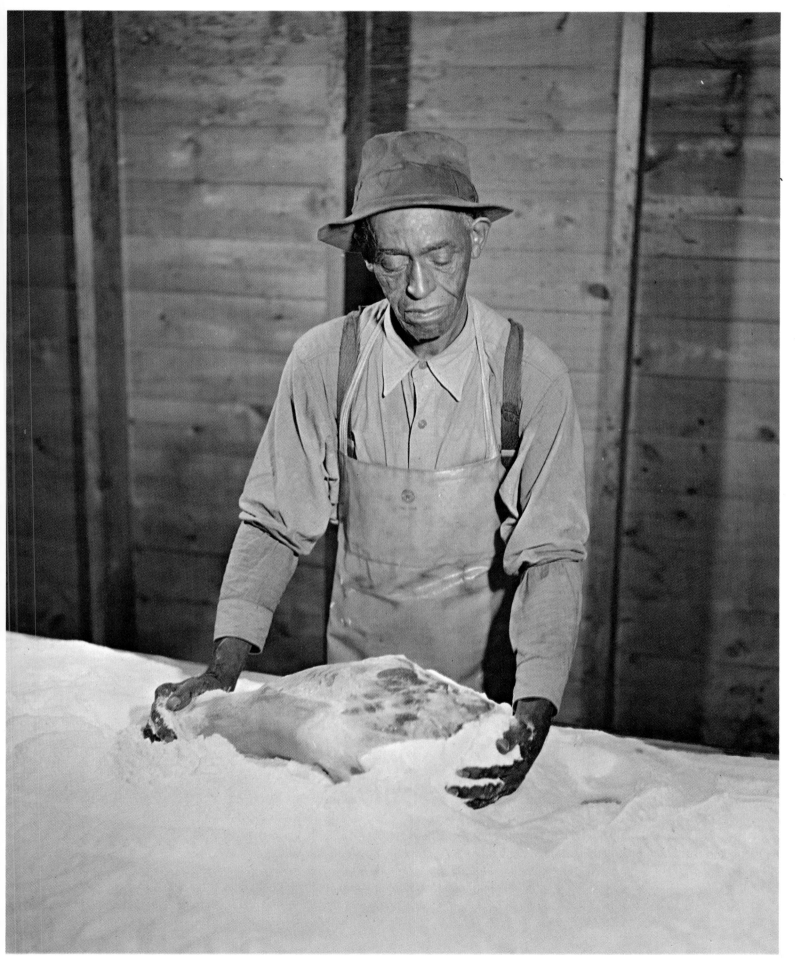

Frank Howard has been curing pork country style since he was 10 years old. "Nothing hard about it," he says, "you just gotta know how to salt 'em and how to smoke 'em."

# Simple Ham Curing Tips:

You have to work it 'specially good around the hock and the butt ends and you got to put plenty salt on. The salt draws the water out of a ham and helps make it keep."

3. *Pack the ham in salt.* In the Pee Wee Valley smokehouse, hams are cured in season at the rate of about 600 a week, and ricked on the floor in a pile four deep. The butt ends are turned to the outside of the rick and the whole pile is packed down in the coarse salt.

4. *Give it a second rubbing with salt.* After the ham has been salted down from five to seven days, depending on the weather, it is taken up, the salt is knocked off and it is immediately rubbed again in the same way it was rubbed the first time. Then it is packed down in salt once more. In humid or hot weather the hams take salt faster and should be treated sooner than in cold, dry weather. The Henrys have internal meat thermometers sticking in hams throughout the meat stack and keep a daily check on meat temperatures. The best temperature for curing is about 40 degrees. When the temperature drops below 32 degrees that day is discounted and an extra day is added to the curing time because hams won't absorb much salt at below-freezing temperatures. This second salt packing lasts from three weeks to about 40 days, depending again on the weather. "One day I look at them and say, to myself, 'They're done,'" Frank Howard says. "You don't get that out of the ham, you get it out of your head."

5. *Remove all the salt* with a brush and cold water.

6. *Hang them up for smoking.* Smoking does two things for a ham and both of them are vital to getting quality meat. Smoke adds flavor and helps the keeping qualities. Old Hickory hams are fittingly smoked with green hickory wood. The wood is allowed to smolder in wash tubs throughout the big smokehouses for three to five weeks. Every day the tubs are moved to get uniform smoke concentration. "You can use a lot of different woods," says John Hinkle, the old colored expert on smoking meat who works for the Henrys. "Sassafras, apple, hickory, wild cherry, corncobs—they're all good. What I'd like to smoke 'em with is hickory dust that comes off the belts in an axe handle factory. That dust is real

fine. You will fill a tub with it and start a fire in the middle with a few shavings and it never will flame up. That smoke just goes on and makes that ham better and better." When a ham is finished smoking it has a dark brown color and an odor that can only be described adequately as the odor of country-smoked ham.

7. *Wrap the smoked ham* in a couple of sheets of heavy paper and tie it into a cotton sack. Where country hams are still farm-cured for the home table, the farmer's wife usually hangs the hams in sugar sacks. The sacks which the Henrys have made especially for the purpose are about the same. "You have to wrap and tie them tight to keep flies from laying eggs in them," Mrs. Henry says. "Flies can ruin a ham."

8. *Hang the hams up in the sacks to age.* "They should age at least 'til the next September," Mrs. Henry says. "The best ones are those that have aged two years. All this time they're losing weight, which helps account for the high price of country hams. By the time the ham is two years old it may weigh 50 per cent less than it did green. As soon as frost hits the hams they're ready to eat. If they're not cured long enough they might be stringy and tough, and salty, and they wouldn't have the 'character' they should have."

The Henrys feel that sugar and such other preservatives as saltpeter are not necessary and, in fact, detract from the quality of the meat. "Country ham is characteristically a salty dish," Mrs. Henry says. "It's salt and smoke that make it real country ham."

But, like women's hats, there's no accounting for tastes in recipes for curing pork. Some people think pork should be cured with salt alone; others insist upon adding either sugar or saltpeter, and some like a combination of all three. In the South the dry cure is popular; in the North, where protection from subfreezing temperatures is important, the brine cure predominates. Hickory, oak, chestnut, apple, pecan, corncobs—each smokehouse fuel capable of imparting a distinctive flavor to pork has its quota of champions. All pork fanciers agree, however, on one point: The best-flavored pork is the pork that has been cured at home.

Here are some curing tips for other types of ham:

# Recipes for Old Time Hams:

### Virginia Ham (Smithfield)

Sprinkle the flesh surface of the ham with finely pulverized saltpeter, using from 4 to 6 ounces per 100 pounds of green ham. Immediately following this application of saltpeter, give them a rubbing with a liberal amount of fine table or flake salt and stack them in bulk, skin side down, in a cool place. Do not allow them to rest in the juice or brine coming from the ham. Allow three or four days to elapse and then give them another good rubbing of salt and let them cure one day for each pound of ham.

At the end of this curing period, wash the hams and when partially dry, give them a rubbing with black pepper. Place them in a smokehouse and smoke intermittently for about a month and then re-pepper them, place them in sacks and allow them to age for 10 to 12 months.

### Virginia Ham (Old Time)

The hams are given one long thorough rubbing of salt, the hock end is packed with salt, and an extra layer is spread over each ham as it is packed into a barrel and left to cure for seven weeks. The lid of the barrel should be set on 2″x4″'s or bricks placed in the bottom of the barrel to keep the hams out of the concentrated brine that comes from the ham. Oldtimers say that this must be done when the moon points down or the cure won't take. Moon up or down, at the end of seven weeks the hams are rubbed with a mixture made up of ½ pound black pepper, 1 quart of molasses, 1 pound brown sugar, 1 ounce saltpeter, and 1 ounce of red pepper and allowed to cure another two weeks. Put them in stockinettes and hang them in the meat house, with the hocks hanging down, where they should age from 30 days to eight months.

In other words, hang them "not for days, not for years," but—until they are eaten.

On each of the sacks containing an Old Hickory ham are printed some of Mrs. Henry's suggestions for cooking the meat, for, as she says, "It takes good cooking as well as a good ham to bring out a ham's real character."

She suggests that the cook begin by washing the ham thoroughly and soaking it overnight in cold water. It should then be cooked by boiling it skin side down in enough water to cover it. It should simmer for at least 25 minutes for each pound of ham. Add water as needed to keep the meat covered.

Take the cooked ham from its pot and remove the skin while the ham is warm. As a final touch the ham should be sprinkled with brown sugar and bread crumbs and baked in an oven until it is brown.

The baked ham is ready to eat, or for those who prefer, slices from it can be either broiled or fried. The ham, according to Mrs. Henry, should never be sliced before it is boiled. Cooking it whole traps the juices where they do the most good.

There's a knack to slicing a ham. Always begin from the small end and slant the knife at about 45 degrees and cut to the bone. Mrs. Henry says ham should be sliced about an eighth of an inch thick.

But there is no hurry about cooking a country-cured ham. Properly salted and smoked it will keep through any kind of weather. Cured hams, as any country boy knows, will mold, but this is no catastrophe. The mold can be brushed off, and does not harm the flavor.

People who cure their own hams have some definite ideas on what a country ham is not: It is not tough and stringy; it is not flabby, oily meat; it is not too salty, because it has been aged properly; it is not cured with one of the prepared ham cures that can be purchased in tin boxes; it is not the kind of ham you buy at the super-market.

And, suh, it is not bad eating!

# winter's night feast:
# Popcorn!

TIME was when popcorn enjoyed a calm, if not quiet, private life in the home. It came out on winter evenings popped with butter, or at Christmas time when it was strung to adorn the tree, and moulded into balls with sugar syrup.

Popcorn is a celebrity now, and has no private life. Its cultivation, processing, and peddling are big business. One movie vice president reported triumphantly that the profits to his company from the popcorn sales were larger than those made on the pictures themselves. Popcorn cultivation has moved from the three-row strip in the kitchen garden to broad fields that supply an industry.

The Indians developed popcorn as they did maize, or hog corn, and were popping it when Columbus arrived. For four hundred years after the white man was introduced to popcorn he modestly refrained from exploiting it in any way. Before the hybrid people started to improve the strains, such varieties as Queen's Golden, Golden Tom Thumb, Little Giant, Mapledale, and Baby Rice were the favorites. The ears were minute, some no larger than a big thumb, and the grains were small, but the flavor was marvelous and it was tender and fluffy.

Popcorn was first mentioned in seed catalogs in the early 1880's. The seed people played up a "Squirrel Tooth" variety with pointed kernels and a larger ear than the common garden type.

Those of us who were small boys in that period remember the way this vicious corn chewed up the fingers when we shelled it; but it was worth it. In the early 1920's, a large yellow-kernel type, now commonly known as the South American, was be-coming popular and it is from this variety that most of the hybrids have been developed.

Any soil that will grow good dent field corn will also grow good popcorn. Fertilizer recommendations for the two crops are identical. It may be even more important in the case of popcorn to practice good rotation to aid in controlling weeds, corn insect pests, and diseases.

Popcorn will respond to a better prepared seedbed than dent corn but it can be planted in wet ground that would rot ordinary corn. The rate of planting is somewhat heavier than for dent corn because the stalk and ear are smaller and require less moisture and plant food. The rate is 4 to 5 kernels to the hill, or about 12 inches apart in the row if drilled. This amounts to 5 or 6 pounds of seed per acre for the South American variety. Most implement dealers supply the smaller plates for planting, or blank plates can be drilled. Cultivation is the same as for dent corn, but in the earlier stages more care is required to discourage weeds. The popcorn plants, being smaller and more delicate, are easily discouraged in competition with weeds.

For home use popcorn with the correct moisture content may be kept indefinitely in optimum popping condition by sealing in air-tight jars. If the corn is too dry when sealed it may be reconditioned. Add 1 tablespoonful of water to a quart jar three-fourths full of popcorn and shake well morning and night for two days. If still too dry the process may be repeated. Popcorn that has once reached the proper popping condition ordinarily will maintain

A man needs a healthy supply of hot-buttered popcorn to play his sharpest game of dominoes.

approximately correct moisture content through the winter months under Midwest conditions. It need not be sealed if stored in a garage or other unheated building.

There are many methods of popping corn. Types of poppers range from the small wire hand popper held over a glowing fire to the large commercial electrically heated units. Any cooking utensil, such as a frying pan or sauce pan (covered) may be successfully used, especially if some fat or oil is added. Regardless of the type used, it is important that the popper be at the right temperature. This varies from 375 to 400 degrees, for best results. If the corn is popped too slowly, some of the moisture will escape before popping begins and maximum expansion will not be obtained. The reverse can

also happen if the popper is too hot because the kernels scorch and do not become uniformly heated. A constant stirring during popping is recommended to keep the kernels from scorching on one side. Popcorn may be popped dry or with corn oil, lard, bacon fat, butter, or commercial seasoning. If salt is added to the popper, of a very fine grain such as used by popcorn stands, it is much more satisfactory than ordinary table salt. The fine salt seems to penetrate the popping kernels and give a better flavor.

A long time ago superstitious people believed there was a little devil in each grain of popcorn. Heating him up made him mad and caused him pain and his explosive efforts to get out of his hot box resulted in the popped grain.

# Father's "right-hand man"

**M**Y FATHER and I had a job. The year was 1905, and I was five years old. The job, to me the most satisfactory in the world, was to light the street lamps each evening just before sundown for a section of our small town located in southeastern Massachusetts. Our route consisted of about three miles of winding country road, along which were spaced lamp posts holding four-sided glass lanterns, the front panel of which opened. You know, the kind you hunt for in antique shops, or occasionally see in a dooryard wired for an electric light. But back in 1905 each lantern held a small kerosene lamp which Father cared for as meticulously as any lighthouse keeper. Perched high upon the seat of an old express wagon, he trimmed the wick and filled each lamp with just enough oil to burn until daylight. Then on the next afternoon, we repeated the process.

What made the job so satisfying was the fact that I drove the horse. I had already been exposed to that fever for which there is no cure, the love of

horses, and I had a bad case. I groomed and fussed around the old black horse most of the day, deriving from it a pleasure only another afflicted with this particular mania can understand. I knew each piece of harness and every buckle, and could manage most of them if someone lifted the harness onto the horse for me. So you see, because the lamps had to be tended each day, it meant that I could harness and drive my beloved horse every day, come gales, rain, snow, or fine weather. There never seemed to be any question of my going. I tagged along with Father most of the time, and he called me his "Right-hand Man."

Mother dressed me for the weather and I was comfortable and happy.

Many vivid memories of those drives remain with me. April, and the chill evening breeze carrying the good smell of wet earth; the welcome fragrance of fresh, green grass as our wagon wheels turned into a grassy wheel-rut leading to a lamppost. The ear-splitting din of the peepers as the road dipped down toward the swamp at the foot of our hill, then the sudden silence as the noise of our wagon startled them; and as we drew away, the first brave peep, followed by the swelling chorus. Summer, and the roadsides white with elderberry bloom whose fragrance lay heavy on the soft, warm air, haunting, and almost intolerably sweet; the horse's hoofs padding softly in the deep, warm sand of the road as we jogged along. Autumn, with gusty rains splattering against our rubber coats, and the dead leaves driving along ahead of chill winds. We had to start out quite early to make the rounds before dark.

Each season held new excitement and adventure, but best of all was winter. In winter our familiar countryside changed almost daily. One day the badly-rutted roads would be iron hard, smoke would rise straight up from chimneys, and no one would be outside the farmhouses. Then again ponds would appear in fields where no ponds had been before, and miraculously, the breeze which rippled them would be from the south. Likely as not the ponds would be mirrors of ice on the next afternoon, with the neighboring youngsters trying out their skates. Then came snow, and stone walls and fences disappeared, leaving a sweeping expanse of glistening white, whose surface was artfully crimped and scalloped by a fanciful but sharp north wind. We had to use the express wagon even in the snow because it was high and brought us within easy reach of the lamps, so that the fat black horse had to exert himself, and throw his head down and pull.

One winter afternoon is as vivid in my memory as if it were yesterday. There had been a considerable amount of snow followed by rain, and then it had frozen. The result was a world of ice. Fields and roads alike were glassy-smooth. Dark limbs of trees were sheathed in ice. I remember sitting high up on the wagon seat watching the horse's newly-sharpened shoes prick into the glare ice of the road. As we drove along, the afternoon sun flooded the fields with a pink-and-gold light which the ice reflected from unexpected places. Jewels blazed and blinked at us from corners of buildings and pasture fences. It was a dazzling afternoon.

Upon our return, Father unharnessed and rubbed down the steaming horse, while I bustled around, bedding him, and fetching his grain and hay. The cold had been very severe, so Father sent me scurrying ahead into the house, where Mother took my aching fingers into her two warm hands and rubbed them until the numbness went, and the blood came prickling back.

Oh the heavenly warmth of that lamplit kitchen! In the center of the room, under the hanging lamp, was the table, laden with food. Always in the middle of the table, and to me the best centerpiece ever contrived, was our dessert. Very often this was a huge layer cake, filled and frosted an inch deep with whipped cream from our Jersey cow. Mother could make hamburg steak and mashed potatoes and one or two vegetables from the cellar seem like a banquet. There would be sweet pickles, and dills, and home-made bread and butter, and then the cake. Lightning cake, she called it, because it went together lightning quick. It would have disappeared that quickly too if she had allowed it. One piece was our allowance. It was gone before you got a real good taste of it and it was futile to eye the plate after that. You would just be reminded that there was more meat and potatoes if you were still hungry. That usually settled it; at that point we were hungry only for more cake. Mother was a good cook and no effort was too great for her to make for her family. She always said, "Better to eat, than to pay a doctor's bill!"

Sometimes there would be stewed kidney beans with fat, brown baked potatoes, or split green peas and carrots cooked with a ham bone. There might be a New England boiled dinner, and afterward the inevitable red flannel hash which was way and above better than the boiled dinner itself. Saturday night always brought baked beans and brown bread. Mother's brown bread was not soggy, not dry, but a combination of moistness and crumbliness that drank up the butter, and melted in your mouth even faster than did the lightning cake.

Winter desserts consisted of great slabs of fluffy gingerbread, eaten warm with applesauce; Indian pudding with whey that floated around it; baked apples with heavy cream; and sometimes brown bread pudding, made from leftover brown bread, and served with sauce made with elderberry wine, sugar and eggs. There was a lavendar-colored froth on top; the sauce itself was the color of purple grapes. Let the gods have ambrosia, I'll take mother's wine sauce.

On very rare and special occasions, perhaps once and never more than twice each winter, we had molasses tops. This was a wonderful treat. Molasses tops were the main course, the dessert, in fact the whole meal. You just ate until you either laid down your fork or burst. They were made of dough similar to doughnuts, with a bit more baking powder and perhaps not quite so sweet. They were cut out like biscuits and fried in deep fat where they puffed up and became crispy and tender on the outside and quite hollow inside. These were heaped upon a huge platter. Meanwhile a saucepan of molasses was boiled to just the right consistency, so that when it was poured over the tops it wasn't runny, and it didn't candy, just in-between. Mother knew when it was just right. A dish of molasses tops with their candy-like coating would dispel the gloom of the darkest winter day.

The next farm to ours was the Town Farm. The man who ran it was a short, round, lovable Dane with pink cheeks, and crisp, crinkly hair. He looked like a Norse sailor, and had, in fact, followed the sea most of his life. He and his missus had raised a large family of children who were all married and in homes of their own. So Cappy, as he was called, and Mrs. Cappy were alone again, and under their capable supervision the Town Farm prospered. Cappy, no doubt, was a good man in an emergency at sea, but one thing he didn't care to cope with was a frisky horse between the shafts of a cutter. So in winter, when the young horse which they kept became fractious from standing too long in the barn without exercise, Cappy came trudging cross-lots to our house to ask my father to exercise his horse for him. To Father this was a labor of love, or perhaps it would be nearer the truth to say that it was I who loved it, and to Father it was just a neighborly good deed. But I know that he enjoyed it too, for he was a good hand with horses. So the next day we heard sleigh bells, and the pretty, high-stepping horse came prancing up to our door, the shiny red cutter gleaming against the white snow. Mother and I, dressed in our warmest clothes, climbed in beside Father, tucked the fur robe around us, and away we flew. A feeling of pride welled up in me to be riding in such style! Our own horse was old, and never could it be said that he flew over the ground. Furthermore, we owned no shiny cutter nor fur robe. As we sped along over the snow and I sat watching the horse's high-held head, with mane tossing in the breeze, I thought of fairy stories of princes and princesses, and it seemed to me that I was a real princess.

About the end of February or the first of March, when the seed catalogs began to arrive, we started our first chore in preparation for spring. This was setting the incubator. When the number of eggs, carefully saved in boxes and baskets and stored in a cool place, reached the right amount, we started

out; Father carried the baskets of clean, brown eggs covered with a cloth to keep them from becoming chilled; and I carried the lantern. Carefully we picked our way through the slushy snow to the brooder house. The incubator cellar was reached by a trap door in the brooder house floor. This door was rigged with a pulley and weight, so that a slight pull on a ring in the floor, and up it popped. The temperature down there was always mild, and the air which rushed up to meet us was moist and pleasantly odorous. To this snug underground room we journeyed twice a day to turn and cool the eggs, and tend the lamp which kept them warm. For nineteen days we performed our duties faithfully, pinch-hitting for about ten mother hens. On the twentieth day the eggs were not turned, because, as Father explained to me, on that day the chick itself maneuvers the egg into a position from which it can best extricate itself.

The tray on which the eggs were left at the last turning had an open strip, about two inches wide, near the incubator door. The door was fitted with a glass panel, and it was through this that I watched the miracle of birth. There, before my very eyes, an egg pipped bit by bit, the shell dropped away, and the hole grew larger and larger. Then, with strength unbelievable in such a little fellow, a wet baby chick pushed his way out, and lay panting and gasping from his struggle. After a few minutes' rest, he'd come scrambling over the other eggs toward the light, and down he'd go through the open strip in the tray. This landed him in the space below called the nursery, where he'd dry off and grow fluffy. Each one invariably made his way toward the light of the glass panel, and joined his fluffy friends below. By night the hatch was over, and the nursery full of lively, chirping chicks.

Upstairs in the brooder house we had their new home ready. Windows ran all along the south side; built out from these windows at the sill was a wooden platform about a yard wide, surrounded by a miniature wire fence. This platform was covered with dry sand, and a small door of the brooder opened upon it. It was like a sunny playground, and the chicks were like children racing around it and cutting capers. It was fun watching them! It seems to me that later generations of children have missed a lot of happy experiences. In those days almost every family hatched a few chicks.

By the time the chicks were hatched it was spring. The apricot tree beside the driveway was sheathed in pink and white blossoms before any leaves appeared, and sometimes it bloomed even before the snow was entirely gone. The fruit never hung on long enough to ripen but that tree earned its right to live by contributing the first breath-taking beauty of spring.

In our back yard were strips of grassland in which were planted peach and pear trees. The land in between was plowed, and here Father planted his garden, and I had mine. When these trees were in bloom, and straight rows of tiny young plants etched green lines across the brown rectangles, with everything raked and made ship-shape, it really presented a colorful picture. I was inordinately proud of my part in it.

Beyond the garden plot lay the apple orchard. There was a Red Astrachan, a Russet, a Northern Spy, and a Tolman Sweet. Those four stood together. Then beyond were a few Baldwins. What a flood of childhood memories comes rushing back at the thought of those old trees; like kind old friends who have made life richer for having known them. The Baldwins had low crotches which made comfortable laps in which to sit on hot summer afternoons and daydream. I spent hours there, building air castles. The Astrachan tree bore early, and I often carried a gnarly, prematurely-ripened drop around in my pocket, just to smell its spicy aroma. My favorite was the Northern Spy. Now there was a tree, with its wide, generous arms spreading low to the ground. And it bore its fruit, firm, tart, and juicy, right down on those low branches where a small girl could reach it. All through October when I'd come home from school, always hungry, I reached the back door by way of the Northern Spy tree. Show me a Northern Spy today, and I'm back under that old tree, sinking my teeth into crisp, fragrant apples. I remember the Russet, too. No earthly good until after Christmas; then they were excellent with a tender skin and rich, creamy flesh with an unforgettable flavor.

It was on one of the high limbs of the Russet tree that Father put my swing. With someone to push and run under, it carried me as high as the treetop. It tied my stomach up in knots, and sometimes made me quite sick and dizzy. Then Father would dig up a spadeful of earth and make me lean down close to it and take long, deep breaths. The clean smell of the cool, moist earth cured my sickness every time, I don't know how or why. It might be that my Father's strange cure had something more than my childish faith in its favor.

Many evenings I came out after supper and sat in the swing, enjoying the cool air, laden with the scent from the clover field. The golden sunlight lay on the house and barn, and the pasture fence held the usual king birds, who came there every evening to survey their world, even as I was doing.

The pasture was at its best in the spring. Close cropped by the cows, it felt like a carpet under bare feet, and it stretched on and on invitingly. There actually were about thirty acres of it, including pine groves, bogs, swamps, sand pits, and woods. Here in the early spring we gathered wild flowers. Father taught me their names long before I went to school. Some of the names he gave them were different from ones I later learned, but I thought his were prettier. He called anemones, snow drops; and the wild iris that blooms in the swamps in June, he called blue flags. We gathered great bunches of the golden marsh marigold, or cowslip. Then we carried a basket for the tender leaves and buds which we took home to be cooked. Their flavor was very similar to dandelions.

The edge of the pine grove was frosted with false Solomon's seal, and I knew the sunny slope where the first ladies slippers bloomed. There was a brook in which we gathered watercress, so early in spring my feet became numb in the icy water. The warm sunshine intensified the fragrance of the wild azalea bloom, and I gathered lambkill, adder's tongue, meadow rue, turtlehead, and many others.

All through my childhood I never tired of roaming the pasture land. From the time the red maple keyes colored the swamps in the spring, through the hot, hazy summer, 'til I gathered Christmas greens in the winter woods, I knew it intimately. Once in a densely-wooded section of our swamp I came upon some beautiful wild orchids. Pure white, the flowers were made up of a cluster of flowerets each with a beautifully-fringed lower lip. And, I remember coming suddenly upon a clearing aglow with the bright tangerine-colored squaw weed. I've seen an old tumbled-down wall covered with a mosaic of wild vines, a landscape gardener's envy; little wild plants among rocks, making a natural rock garden; and ferns growing in beautiful array beside an old cart path. Little things, perhaps, but a wise father pointed them out, and taught me to see and enjoy them, a store of lovely pictures to be reviewed and enjoyed again and again at will. They make an infallible insurance against a world which seems too much with us.

# nothin' sticks to your ribs like

# Corn dodgers

**P**HINIAS CANTRELL was born and bred in the South, where corn pone, corn squeezins, corn on the cob, and all manner of things made from corn are as mothers' milk. When Phinias found himself stranded in the North, through no fault of his own you may be sure, he spent most of his time looking for the kind of corn bread he had been raised on. From explaining so many times to damnyankees just what a good piece of corn bread tastes like, and how it is made, and how the meal is ground, he got to be quite an authority on the subject.

He'd give you a full-dress lecture at the drop of a hat. Just offer him a piece of Northern Bread, and off he'd go.

"This stuff ain't fit for man or beast," he'd say. "No more flavor than a piece of burlap. Now you take corn bread, there's something that will stick to your ribs. Corn bread is a body builder, and it tastes fine. Let me tell you how to make corn bread.

"To make good corn bread, the way we make it in the South, you have to have just the right kind of meal, meal ground on stone burrs. But let me start at the beginning.

"First, you get yourself some good corn. We always use yellow corn. It's sweeter to my way of thinking and the bread has a good yellow to it. If you can't get yellow meal, white will do, but it's milder in flavor. For the most part we make corn bread from freshly-ground meal that is still warm from the friction heat of the burr stones, as warm as the underneath side of a settin' hen, and buttermilk from the morning's churning.

"There was a time when we could get water-ground meal, which was better because the mill stones turned slow-like and didn't scorch the meal, like a motor-driven mill sometimes does. Another thing, the meal absorbs some of the dampness that was always around a water mill and this gave it a

# and hush puppies

little different flavor. But you had to watch any meal you had on hand to see that it didn't spoil from the dampness. Somehow we liked it better than the meal we get from today's mills that are run by engines."

Phinias has a mild contempt for the "factory" meal now sold in grocery stores. "It lays around on the shelf and loses its flavor," he says, "and it isn't the best when it is fresh. But if you can't get anything else, use it. Even that kind will make better bread than wheat flour.

"There's some city folks who don't know the difference between good corn bread and a mash you mix up for the pigs. They drive long distances and pay fancy prices for stone-ground corn meal because they think it's quaint. We don't think it's quaint; we just know good corn bread and we know you can't make the best corn bread unless you have the fresh meal out of a burr-stone mill."

To the Southerner the best corn bread is "Yellow Bread," which calls for fresh eggs and butter and tastes more like cake in comparison to the bland tasting "Shortenin' Bread," made famous by the popular song.

"To make the best-tasting Yaller Bread that can be found below the Mason-Dixon line," says Phinias, "you mix together two cups of corn meal, a teaspoon of salt and one teaspoon of soda. After the dry ingredients are well mixed, add two cups of sour milk and two eggs. Beat the eggs well before adding them. Melt one-fourth cup of butter and pour it into the batter and it will be just thin enough now to drop loosely from a spoon into a pan that has been greased and warmed. Stoke the fire until the oven is at 375 degrees, put the pan of batter in, and bake for half an hour.

"We fit the size of our recipe to the size of the family," continues Phinias. "The two-cup recipe will fill a pan 8 by 10 inches. When we were boys at home, we had corn bread three times a day. There would be a pan half as big as the top of the stove full of golden bread, baked to a fine crusty brown and cut in rows of even squares. I've not seen a pan of good corn bread of any size since I left home.

"My brother's wife, who is short on most everything else, makes a good meal bread the way she learned back in her home in Kentucky. They don't use any eggs and, for the most part, cook their bread in a skillet. They call this 'Shortenin' Bread' and some people, especially in Kentucky, think it's the best kind of corn bread.

"Shortenin' Bread is easier to make than Yaller Bread. There is one recipe that calls for wheat flour, which keeps the bread from crumbling, they say. Shortenin' Bread calls for a lot of melted lard or bacon drippings. This grease is to Shortenin' Bread what yeast is to a loaf of Northern Bread. Most all the good Shortenin' Bread experts use white meal.

"In making Shortenin' Bread, the first thing is to heat the oven to a hot 450 degrees for the 25 minutes baking time. Then measure out 4 cups of meal into a big iron skillet. Add a good-sized teaspoon of salt and stir in two cups of sour milk and a fourth cup of drippings. If you haven't a cow or can't get milk, water will do. Early settlers made a bread that wasn't much more than meal and water. It wasn't the best, but it was corn bread. Corn bread is like whiskey—there's no such thing as bad whiskey. Some is just better than others.

"Made either way and covered with beans, cooked sweet with jowl, and a glass of buttermilk or with mustard and dandelion greens picked in early spring, or kale made tender by the first frost, there is nothing better anywhere.

"Then there's Spoon Bread. That's the angel food cake of corn bread," says Phinias.

"Now the best recipe for Spoon Bread, like in politics and religion, is a matter of opinion. Spoon Bread takes a little more time and care than plain corn bread or griddle cakes. First, heat one quart of milk in a double boiler; drop into this an egg-sized lump of butter. Pour the hot liquid over two cups of corn meal to which you have added a little more than a teaspoon of salt. Stir until the meal and milk seem to be one; then add two egg yolks that have been beaten. Spoon Bread, which is more of a sponge cake than a bread, must be light and fluffy. Here is where the cook must use her sixth sense. Beat the

two egg whites to a stiff peak, then fold quickly into the warm mixture. Have a well-buttered, warmed earthenware dish ready, pour in the batter and bake in a hot oven (400 degrees) for 30 minutes or until the bread is firm in the middle. If it isn't done just right and isn't timed right, the bread turns out flat.

"For a man who likes his corn bread golden brown," says Phinias, "get a corn stick mold and make up a batch of corn bread batter, any kind of ordinary batter will do. The mold is usually made of cast iron and may or may not have a cover, which is hinged. The molds are in the shape of ears of corn, usually six in number. You pour the batter in one side and close the top and put it in the oven. The bread will rise and cook against the impressions to make a pretty piece of bread. It tastes like any corn bread, but is easier to butter and handy to eat.

"We always have something special with a mess of catfish," says Phinias. "We'd make a corn meal dumpling that we call Hush Puppies. For a long time Northerners didn't know about Hush Puppies, but once they ate them, they came back for more. Generally they are fried along with fish but always in deep, hot fat. To make Hush Puppies, sift together two cups of corn meal, two tablespoons of flour, one teaspoon of baking powder, and one-half teaspoon salt. Add a cup of buttermilk and blend in one beaten egg, spoon out and drop in deep, hot fat. It is important that the grease be very hot to keep the Puppies from becoming grease logged."

According to Phinias there is no limit to the good things one can make from corn meal. There are Corn Sticks and Hush Puppies, Corn Pones and Dodgers. Then there are Griddle Cakes or Meal Cakes. Griddle Cakes are made from a batter that is the same as that for corn bread, but thinner, and fried on a smoking hot skillet until they are brown and lacy on the edges.

Corn Pones are made much like Griddle Cakes, but without soda and they are baked instead of fried. These flat cakes are made by mixing together a cup and a half of corn meal, one-half teaspoon of salt and enough sour milk, about one and one-fourth cups, to make a thin batter. Drop the batter off a large spoon onto a slightly-greased skillet or heavy baking pan, cover, and bake in a moderate oven until brown.

The Dodger can be baked, steamed in a pot like a dumpling, or fried in a greased skillet. To make them, mix a dough of a cup of salted meal, two tablespoons of melted drippings, and a small amount of cold water. Roll the dough in your hands into sticks about three or four inches long and the thickness of a broom handle, and drop into the top of a pot filled with boiling turnip greens. Let them steam for twenty minutes and serve with the potlikker.

Phinias can grow lyrical when he describes the eating qualities of corn bread. He drools as he tells you, "Take a slab of Yaller Bread, split it down the middle, and sop it in the skillet after you've fried a slice of country ham. You've got something there, suh, that's too good for a king. Corn bread, any kind of corn bread, makes everything better. Chicken gravy, ham gravy, beans, maple syrup, sorghum, black strap, dunk it in your coffee, eat it straight, or with butter and jelly, no matter how you fix it, corn bread is the top eatin' treat of the universe."

As a sort of bonus which goes with his lecture on corn bread, Phinias usually adds a bit of philosophy. "Generally," he says, "the simplest things in life give the greatest pleasure. Corn bread is one of them. It's cheap, easy to make, and it's mighty filling. Most of our pioneering was done on corn bread, and if the South hadn't run out of corn we wouldn't have lost the War. You can't go wrong if you stick to corn bread, because it will stick to you."

# The Coyote Hunter

HERB STODDARD claims he hunts for a living and ranches for a hobby. Herb contradicts himself, for he has made a very comfortable living for his family with his cattle since those days in 1914 when he trailed down from Miles City to the piece of range he has occupied ever since on the edge of the Bad Lands of the Rosebud Indian Reservation in South Dakota.

Yet, in a very important way, this old cowboy has made a living from hunting. Coursing his hounds has been for him an essential part of the good life.

The first time I saw Herb was at a cattle sale one day at Martin, South Dakota. The tight little sale barn was jammed from ringside to rafters with consignors and buyers. Martin is on the Pine Ridge Indian Reservation and the crowd was well sprinkled with stolid Sioux bucks attired in their monotonously-drab jackets and trousers topped off by battered, broad-brimmed hats. The balance of the crowd was made up of white farmers and ranchers, some in overalls, others in various degrees of Western attire. Among these, one in particular stood out like a rugged old Longhorn among a bunch of modern show steers. I had noticed him joshing with the auctioneer before the sale started and later, whenever there was a lull in the chant, I could hear his deep, clear voice booming out a row or two behind me.

He was tall. There were few in the crowd who could top his rugged, well-proportioned frame. He seemed agile as a cat as he moved about and as he gesticulated in his conversation; yet it was apparent that leathery face had felt the bite of at least sixty winters. His cowboy boots, stockman's trousers and Western jacket fit him with the ease that goes with long and pleasant association. His keen, grey eyes peered from beneath the brim of the largest and blackest Stetson in the place, and a black neckerchief, knotted on the side cowboy style, shielded his throat. Here was a flesh-and-blood character who might have stepped right out of one of Charlie Russell's canvases of life on the open range.

Eventually I was able to maneuver myself alongside this cowboy, and immediately I found the subject closest to his heart was hunting and hounds. Soon I had an invitation to come to the Stoddard ranch.

Herb is no ordinary hunter. He has the customary collection of guns to be found in any ranch house, the inevitable .30-.30 carbine and a few shotguns. But the weapon of his choice is a dog rather than a gun. And the dog of his choice is the greyhound.

His quarry is the coyote, though jack rabbits, badgers, or a deer in season will do when the tricky wild dogs are scarce. There is a $7.50 bounty on coyotes in South Dakota, which Herb aims to collect; but he's not a bounty hunter. With him, hunting is pure sport.

"Coyotes aren't a real pest out here, anyway," he said that first night as we planned the morrow's hunting. "If you killed off the coyotes, the jack rabbits and gophers would darn soon ruin the range. The coyote's the best mouser that ever lived. Every time I catch one I cut him open to see what he's been eating—that's the only way to learn to hunt; find out what the critters eat, then you'll know where to catch them—and I've found as many as 14 of those little bobtail mice in one stomach.

"Even the professional exterminators don't really aim to kill off all the coyotes. They'd be pushing themselves out of reach of the biscuits if they did. Exterminating the coyote is like enforcing Prohibition. Nobody's really interested in making it work;

When hunting far afield, Herb uses his Jeep. A specially-built box on the back holds six to eight dogs. They can be released as soon as game is sighted by means of a latch controlled from the driver's seat.

if they were, the coyote would long ago have become as rare around these parts as the grey wolf."

We went to bed that night with the wind howling around the ranch house. We were hoping it promised some snow before morning. "Hunting's best when there's snow on the ground," Herb had said. "It makes it easy to pick up a trail; and cold weather makes the coyotes get out and hunt more themselves. Right now they have so much fat on them and such a heavy coat of hair they only need a mouse a day to keep them going, and they spend most of the time just lying around. If you try to hunt in warm weather you'll be liable to get disgusted like another gobbler (gobbler is Herb's term for any human male) who came out here and finally decided this isn't even good 'next year' country."

Sleep ended the next morning with a clanking from the basement as Herb shook the furnace and got a good fire going so Mom would be comfortable while we were off on the hunt. Sleep had ended, but not the night. It was still black as a buzzard's wing outside as we downed stacks of Mom's pancakes floating in honey. Speaking with all the experience of a long-suffering hunter's wife, she urged this visitor to "fill up because it might be a long time till you get back for dinner."

When Herb hunts on his own range he usually goes on horseback with a half-dozen or so of his greyhounds crowding around the heels of his mare. But this morning he used his Jeep as he always does when he has company along, or goes farther afield.

"Wait here," he said, as I found myself smack up against the gate to one of the dog runs. In a minute or so he was back with the Jeep and as he swung around broadside to the pen I could see, in the headlight beams, the lithe forms of the dogs leaping over one another and up against the netting.

The Jeep is equipped with a specially-designed box which Herb built to carry the dogs. This box has an opening along the top of both sides just wide enough for the hounds to stick their heads through and the entire left side is hinged at the bottom so it can drop open to let the dogs in and out. The latch on this door is controlled from the driver's seat by means of a rope. When Herb sights his game and maneuvers the Jeep into position he pulls the rope, the dogs leap out and the chase is on.

I climbed in beside Herb, and two gates and ten minutes later, just as the first yellow streaks of dawn had broken over the eastern hills enough to make it possible to distinguish the brindles from the reds in the pack, we stopped on the edge of the badlands to let the dogs out for a breather before beginning our serious hunting.

If I hadn't suspected it before, it was very apparent by this time that while a man might be able to call Herb Stoddard a cur—if he smiled right—he'd better make no such remark about one of Herb's dogs.

As he gazed off across the spectacular wastes at our feet, he mused, "Dogs that can catch a coyote down through there are quite a set of hounds. But these can do it."

The Stoddard hounds are of Australian stock, coming from a strain imported by John Pesek, of Ravenna, Nebraska. Pesek, a wrestler, went to Australia a few years back to match headlocks and half-Nelsons with the Aussie matmen. When he came home he brought with him a greyhound called Pacific Dream reputed to have cost him $12,000. Most of the dogs Stoddard courses today are grandsons and granddaughters of Pacific Dream.

Herb has been running dogs for more than 40 years. In that time he has handled close to 500 hounds. He is satisfied that the Australian greyhound has no equal as a coursing dog.

At a safe distance, the quarry catches his breath.

"I started out training bird dogs—pointers," he said, "but there's no sport in that any more. The season's so short nowadays you can't make a good dog. It used to be you could hunt all year and a dog had a chance to learn something.

"In running coyotes I've used wolfhounds, staghounds, greyhounds and all kinds of crosses. The Australian greyhound can run faster and fight better than any of them. He has a much better coat of hair than the English greyhound and better feet. When he fights he goes right for the throat.

"I had some dogs once with a lot of staghound in them. When they'd get a coyote they'd go for his belly and they'd take an awful beating before they finally had him whipped.

"They'd never stay with a critter after they'd killed it, either. They'd get one over the hill and out of sight somewhere, kill it and leave it and you'd never find it. These dogs stay right there until you get to them.

"Here Jill! Come on Jerry!" he sang out. "Let's go, fellows!" and the dogs were back in the Jeep.

As we started across the range, the long shadow of the Jeep moving ahead of us, Herb put on his glasses. "I never had any use for these things," he said, "till they told me I needed them to see the coyotes; then I really ran to get them." His store teeth went into his shirt pocket. "When I get tense," he explained, "I bite something fierce. It's hard on those teeth." The decks were cleared for action.

Our hopes for snow had not been fulfilled, though there had been a hard frost during the night and snowbanks from a heavy storm some weeks earlier still lay in the draws and below the ridge of the hills. Our first maneuver was to circle the scattered remains of some calves which earlier in the year had tasted the forbidden delights of a poisonous weed. "There's nothing like a coyote to clean up carrion," Herb said. "Even when there's nothing left but the hide and bones they'll come back to gnaw a little. Thought we might see some signs here." But no signs were evident, so we headed out on the open range.

The dogs were eagerly watching the passing scene as the Jeep bounced over well-worn cow trails, bucked through prairie dog towns and crawled in and out of breaks a man afoot would have had a hard time navigating. "It takes a good driver to hit all the bumps," Herb bragged as his practiced eyes searched the landscape.

We turned toward the horse herd because, as Herb pointed out, coyotes like to stay close to horses or cattle to use them as their sentinels. This bunch, however, was innocent of fronting for coyotes.

We came up to a fence. Jeeps can't jump, but a barbwire fence is no obstacle to a man with pliers and hammers. Before I had a chance to settle myself in the driver's seat, Herb had the wires down. I drove across; he restapled them and we were on our way again in no more time than it takes to open a gate.

By this time the sun was well up and we'd had nary a sign of coyotes. "If we don't see one soon we'll turn the dogs on a jack rabbit," Herb said.

"Ordinarily, I carry my gun along and shoot rabbits for dog food. It's hard on the hounds to run rabbits on this hard ground. The best rabbit chasing is when the grass is long and the ground is soft. Just last week Gyp broke her toe running a rabbit across a piece of wheat stubble. That's why I left her home this morning. When the ground gets hard a rabbit can run much faster. Why I've seen—"

At that moment a long-eared jack rabbit looking half as big as an antelope jumped up no more than ten yards off the right front wheel. Herb gunned the Jeep, cut it hard to the right to start the dogs in the right direction and pulled the rope. Without a sound the hounds exploded from the box. Jerry, a big brindle, hit the ground first, with Jill, a little red bitch, right at his loin. Running for his life, the rabbit found a cow trail warmed just enough by the morning sun to make it slick going for the hounds but perfect for his fur-shod feet. He was pulling away from the dogs as the trail began to curve in a direction that would give the hounds the edge, so he left it and headed for a snowbank, an old trick for a wise rabbit whose strategy is to scamper lightly across the snow in which the hounds will flounder.

But nature failed him. Days of alternate freezing and thawing had crusted the snow hard enough to carry a man and as the dogs raced over it they were gaining with every leap. Jill was a length ahead of the pack now. The action was beautiful. Leveled out for all they were worth the dogs seemed to fly rather than run; their feet barely touched the ground. Seemingly, their motion was completely effortless. Suddenly, Jill gave that little extra push. With fangs bared she grabbed the rabbit in the hip; another dog slashed at his throat and the race was over, little more than a minute after it had started.

"They're still a little soft," said Herb. "I guess I've been feeding them a little heavy and they haven't run enough yet this fall."

As the hounds caught their wind, Herb talked about his dogs. The hounds are 18 months old before he starts hunting them. By the time they are four years old they have started to slip. There isn't too much to choose between the male and the female so far as hunting is concerned, though Herb thinks the bitch may be a little smarter and she's always hunting, doesn't have the distractions which sometimes bother the male.

In selecting his hounds he looks for a short-coupled individual with a good, straight hind leg. It should have catlike feet which give it the appearance of almost standing on tiptoe. By the time the hound is ready for serious running it should be well muscled over the kidney. A pointed nose seems to indicate speed. Herb says he wouldn't think of raising pups out of a dog with poor feet; and a crooked-legged dog will cut itself to pieces running in the badlands. The English greyhounds, he feels, are inclined to have tender feet and a poor coat of hair.

When it comes time to train the youngsters, Herb always likes to start them with older dogs. The most important lesson is the one the man must learn himself: "If you teach one little thing to a dog in a day you've done darn well," he said. "Next day you have to go back and start all over and then add one thing more. It's the same in training a horse."

He always rides horseback when he is starting a green bunch. He has better control over them and they have every opportunity to become acquainted with the environment in which they will be hunting for the rest of their lives. It helps to get them to use their nose and develops their trailing ability, qualities notoriously rare in greyhounds which hunt by sight.

"Some of the young hounds in this pack I started to train without an old dog along," Herb said. "I sure got disgusted with them that first morning. I started out in the pasture north of the house and the first thing they saw was a hawk, so they took after him. Then, pretty soon I saw a coyote—and they just sat there and looked up at me.

"I rode on a little farther and came up on a flat and there were two coyotes and an eagle. The pups took after the eagle. Next thing we came to was a prairie dog town and they had a picnic chasing prairie dogs.

"Finally, we came up on another flat and there were two coyote pups. That brindle bitch spotted them and took out after one of them and all of a sudden the whole bunch came alive and they ran him down and caught him. After that they had a rough idea of what they were born for."

The hounds were rested now. At Herb's signal they leaped back into the box, we threw the rabbit in the back and were off for more hunting, Herb talking continually, his informative lectures spiced with salty cracks every so often. "I grew so tall 'cause I stayed green so long," he said. It was apparent his shade of green was the same as a C-note when he drove right smack to the spot—in the midst of a huge piece of range without tree or landmark—where two weeks earlier he had seen an instrument off a weather balloon. "I was chasing a coyote when I saw it and didn't have time to pick it up," he said as he stored it under the dog box. "We'll take it along and send it back where it belongs."

By now the shadows were as short as they ever get on a December day and the prospects of catching a coyote were getting as short as the shadows.

"Skinny's Springs is just over the next hill," said Herb, "we'll go on down there and if we don't see anything we'll go home and see what Mom's dinner is like."

At that instant we caught a split-second glimpse of a couple of coyotes silhouetted against the cloudless sky as they turned tail and disappeared over the brow of the hill two hundred yards in front of us.

"I knew there were two families raised here last spring. Those must be some of the pups," Herb said under his breath as he stamped down on the accelerator and we took off like the well-known scared ape. But when we topped the rise there were no coyotes to be seen. Further, at the foot of the hill before us was a rough draw, one of the very few of the kind that Jeep had to go around rather than across. By the time we got to the other side it was apparent our quarry had left the country.

But that was the end of any thought of dinner. Herb had tasted something more exquisite than meat and potatoes and he wasn't about to quit now.

"A coyote always wheels and runs with the wind if he can, so you can't sneak up on him," he said as he hauled the Jeep to leeward. For the next two hours it seemed like we combed every break and draw in Washabaugh and Millette Counties. St. Peter's was the only gate we didn't negotiate and at times we even came perilously close to it as the Jeep twisted and plunged up, down, around and across terrain a self-respecting mule would have hesitated to set foot on. In a dozen spots where there were no gates Herb went into action with his pliers.

And all the while I learned about coyotes. "They're smart," Herb said, "one of the smartest things in the wild. That's why it's such sport to hunt them this way. Those gobblers who hunt them by plane have just about cleaned them all off the level land. Even though they return to the breaks later, the coyotes breed and make their dens on the level land. In weather like this a coyote will come over a hill and lie in a draw with the wind coming down the draw so he can see everything below him and the wind will warn him of what's coming up behind.

"They're so darn smart they even seem to change color or blend into the land where they live. In the badlands they almost look like a grey wolf; here in the red grass they get a kind of reddish tinge; and over on that gumbo land they get almost black.

"I had some hounds once that had a lot of stag in them. There was an old coyote around here that knew just how fast those dogs could run. Every time I'd turn loose on him he'd put out just enough to stay a little ahead of them. He'd breeze along and look behind to see what they were doing and then all of a sudden he'd drop over the wall into the badlands and that would be the end of it.

"I finally fooled that old son-of-a-gun, though. I got some real fast greyhounds one day and by the time he'd wised up to the switch they had him.

"And fight! Pound for pound nothing has more fight than a coyote. They talk about bobcats, but a bobcat's easy to stop. A coyote fights to the last breath. Some gobblers claim they've heard them cry like a baby when they're caught. I haven't. I've never heard one whine. They just stand there and take it.

"How fast can a coyote run? Some of these fellows get a couple of drinks in them and come up with all kinds of silly estimates. I've heard some of

The dogs sprawl on the snowbank and lick the snow to cool off after a run. It doesn't take much to overheat a greyhound.

'em say they've clocked 'em with a pickup going 50 and 60 miles an hour. But that's the trouble with a pickup, half the time the hind wheels are off the ground. I'd say they go maybe 30 to 35 miles an hour.

"Over a short distance a good greyhound will outrun 'em at a ratio of about 7 to 5. My hounds have never been outrun though a coyote can out-endurance them if he gets a few breaks. Every second a hound hesitates the coyote gains ten yards.

"I'd hate to see the day when they're all gone. They're as much a part of the West as this land. That's why I never hunt any later in the spring than March. The bitches are all heavy with pups by then and you have to give them a chance.

"I came on a fellow once who was digging out a den. 'How much do you get for those pups?' I asked him.

" 'Three dollars,' he said.

" 'How many do you have?' I asked.

" 'Six.'

" 'I'll give you eighteen dollars to let 'em go,' I said, but he'd already killed them."

We were a good many miles from home by this time. We hadn't found a trace of our quarry. The shadows were beginning to lengthen again as the landscape took on that rosy hue that sets in so early on a winter afternoon. With undisguised reluctance Herb gave up the chase and we headed back to the ranch.

By the time we got back to the ranch and the dogs were put up we realized it had been more than a few hours since breakfast. Again Mrs. Stoddard's patience came to the fore. We had barely crawled out of our jackets and boots when a dinner fit for any hunters appeared on the table. "You get used to living in suspense when you've been married over forty years to a man like this," she said. "When he goes hunting, time doesn't mean a thing. I wasn't expecting you very early, anyhow." Herb devoutly made the Sign of the Cross and said grace and the feast was on.

Just before dark we made one more brief and unsuccessful foray in a big pasture close to head-quarters, fed the rabbit to the dogs and called it a day.

The next morning it was up and out in the dark again as Herb told about the cowhand who used to work for him and spread the word after he left, " 'Stoddards' is a good place to work but a heck of a place to sleep. My boots used to still be warm when I'd put them on in the morning.' "

We loaded the same pack of hounds we had used the day before into the Jeep, leaving Gyp, the hound with the broken toe, and a couple of young dogs at home.

Skinny's Springs was our immediate objective and as soon as we were through the first gate we turned the dogs out and let them loosen up.

We saw no more coyotes that second morning than we had the first. Shortly past noon we pulled into Norris, "a town with houses on both sides of the street," as Herb described it, though the street is no more than a hundred yards long and the houses are rapidly-deteriorating specimens of early Twentieth Century Americana. There we picked up the makings of a lunch as Herb joshed with the Indians who make up the bulk of the town's population.

Late afternoon found us down on a piece of summer pasture belonging to Herb's friend, Shorty Hannum, an ex-jockey and "a darn good cowman."

"Wouldn't it beat you?" asked Herb. "That's the way it goes every time. Two weeks ago I went out with my son-in-law and we caught four coyotes in one morning. Here we've hunted almost two days and haven't caught a thing."

That must have been the password, for at that moment a big, rusty coyote dashed across our path. Herb didn't even have to turn the Jeep. He just jerked the rope and the hounds were off and running. The coyote headed for a break a good half-mile or more away across the range, his ears back, his tail down and his hind feet throwing dirt at the hounds as he streaked along. Golly, he was fast! But not fast enough. He was still fifty yards from the break when the little red bitch lunged and grabbed his hip. As he turned to strike back, Pat, one of the brindles, got his throat. That was it.

We drove up with the Jeep, picked up the carcass and slid it beneath the dog box. Tomorrow Herb would skin it and add the pelt to his growing collection in the trees behind the ranch house. He had twelve already in about a month of hunting. With a little luck and less competition from the flyboys he might even get close to the record of 88 he caught back in 1942.

The sun was a big red semi-circle now, sinking behind one of Shorty's windmills. A few big, fluffy clouds had picked up the rose and saffron tints of its dying moments. The air was growing colder with another promise of snow and the only sound that could be heard was the distant bellowing of a bunch of newly-weaned calves.

# The Calico Cat

MOST farmers have cats whether they like them or not. Cats have a habit of adopting the farmer or staying with the farm when it changes hands. A farm in the spring would seem to be lacking something without a mother cat prowling around the out-buildings followed by a brood of sore-eyed kittens with their tails pointing to heaven.

As a rat killer the cat cannot compare with a barn owl or a black snake and certainly not with a good shot of Antu or Red Squill, but a good hunting cat that will take the offensive against a tough, fighting rat is of real value around the farm.

In their natural state, cats live mainly on rodents, birds, bugs and fish. Since they teamed up with man, they have acquired a taste for vegetables and dairy foods. Besides their regular food, cats nibble a little grass as a tonic, and eat, smell, roll in, and generally go on a tear if they can get catnip. They also love valerian and marum but hate wild rue, which has been used as a cat repellent by fastening sprigs of it to the dove cote or tying bits of it under a hen's wings.

Some people seem to feel that the cat should be able to forage for himself and that feeding him will take away his sharpness as a hunter. This does not work out so well in practice, however, since you want the cat to kill far more mice and rats than it needs for food, and furthermore, you want your hunter in good physical condition to tangle with rats. As an old English proverb put it:

> "Who will not feed the cats
> Must feed the mice and rats."

Two meals a day, morning and evening, are recommended for the cat. The diet may be half vegetables and half meat. There is some disagreement among the experts on the advisability of feeding starchy foods like boiled potatoes, but cats love them and seem to thrive on them to a ripe old age. Most cats like cooked green vegetables and some like raw carrots, raw fruit, and will gnaw onion until the tears run. Cats relish the cooked entrails and lungs of chickens and other animals and the gristly ears of sheep, pigs, and cattle. In spite of their strong hatred of water some cats will fish for themselves by scooping the fish out of the water and some will dive in after the fish. All of them like fish and clams, oysters and other shell fish. Cats love milk, cheese and butter and most farm cats know the milking schedule and are on hand to get a handout or a few squirts from the teat. Cats love to gnaw on bones and will pick one clean but they should not be fed chicken bones since these break into sharp fragments. Even though cats, unlike dogs, chew their food, they will swallow the sharp chicken bones which may pierce their intestines. The two-meal schedule should be increased for mother cats if they are to develop and nurse their kittens.

Cats are subject to a number of diseases such as distemper, worms, fits, gastritis, cat typhoid, inflamed eyes and a variety of skin diseases. They are susceptible to rabies and can transmit this disease to other animals and to man.

There are many stories of female cats mating with such oddly assorted animals as rabbits, lynx, racoons and skunk, but none of these alleged mismatings have ever been authenticated. The female comes into heat two or three times a year in the north and four times in warmer climates. There seems to be considerable variation in the heat periods since some owners of Siamese cats report that their heat periods come as often as once a month.

With her odor and her love call the female lets everyone in the neighborhood, including all the toms, know of her desires. She will remain in heat from three days to two weeks. During this period she is extremely promiscuous and will entertain every tom in the county.

During this process of many matings, it is quite possible for the individual kittens of a single litter to be fathered by different males. When her heat period ends the toms spend another 24 noisy hours on the premises and then disperse. The period of gestation lasts from 55 to 69 days, with most cats giving birth at 62 days. Zoologists say this wide spread in the gestation is caused by past mating with wild cats, which have a different length of gestation.

The expectant mother doesn't seem to realize she is changing shape and will try to go through narrow openings that she was once able to use and may kill her young and even herself.

The cat will produce four to eight kittens in a litter, but prolific animals have been known to throw as many as twelve.

Cats are very sensitive to vibrations and there are many tales of cats who have reacted to an earthquake long before humans could feel the tremors. They are described as showing sudden fright, hair on end, ears flattened and eyes shining, mewing and raving. Much this same reaction has been noted in dogs, horses and other animals.

Cats may not have nine lives, but scientists have observed that they do have the faculty of landing on their feet from any position when falling, which helps prolong the one life they have. They have been known to survive a fall of four stories, but can make the twist when dropped from as low as six inches.

The Chinese were realistic about cats. They ate them. They also used them as time pieces. By looking into the cat's eyes and noting the size of the pupil they judged the time of day. Thus:

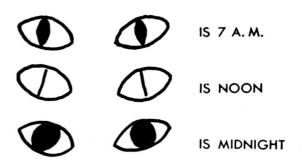

IS 7 A. M.

IS NOON

IS MIDNIGHT

Both males and females can be altered to do away with the annoyance of their constant reproduction. Male cats should be castrated between four and eight months of age and females spayed between two and six months. The operation, which can be done by an experienced veterinarian, is not serious at this age, but is dangerous if delayed until maturity. This operation improves the hunting abilities of the male cats, but the females that have been spayed seem to lose their zest for the sport.

Old Robbie puts up with a lot from a farmhouseful of cats. But once in a while a look flashes in his eye and then a kitten takes off in a hurry.

# Hawkeye Hatchetman

## Bob Garst's bold ideas make kindling out of old farm theories

Roswell Garst of Coon Rapids, Iowa, has spent a good part of his life jolting people out of their old ideas. He's a past master at puncturing old farming theories and some new ones as well. He has leveled his booming voice at his own friends and neighbors, at college professors, agronomists, bankers and the Department of Agriculture in Washington, and Premier Khrushchev of the Union of Soviet Socialist Republics. He has been no respecter of rank or dignity.

Starting with a new kind of corn seed called "hybrid" that Henry Wallace developed in the 30's, Garst and a neighboring farmer, Charles Thomas, have proved that professional plant management in developing specialized seeds could raise the corn yield of the county, the state, and eventually the country. Their firm, Garst & Thomas, produce Pioneer Hybrid Seed Corn and Hybrid Grain Sorghums for the Southwestern Corn Belt and have at Coon Rapids the largest individual hybrid corn plant and the only plant in the country for the head drying of hybrid grain sorghum seeds.

People who meet Roswell Garst for the first time take his bold imagination and enthusiasm for that of a super-salesman rather than a highly successful farmer from Iowa. But he is both. His ideas demonstrate the inventive mind and the ability to be articulate about the new high-production approach to farming that separates the modern farmer from his hard-working but circumscribed grandfather.

When the experiments of Paul Gerlaugh at the Wooster, Ohio, Experiment Station in 1947 showed that feeder cattle did practically as well on a corn and cobmeal mixture as they did on straight corn, Garst, who had a mountain of corncobs from the seed corn business, took this idea and ran with it.

Taking a cue from Drs. Wise Burroughs and Lorraine Gall who were working at the Reynoldsburg, Ohio, laboratory of the Ohio Experiment Station, Garst asked himself: "Why can't I feed a little extra protein to steers and encourage the bacteria in the rumen? Then perhaps the whole corn crop can be used." Garst's formula, which used molasses and urea to increase the output of the steers' protein factory, was used to fatten thousands of steers on corncobs. The formula was as follows:

    14 pounds ground corncobs
    3 pounds ground shelled corn
    1 pound soybean meal
    3 pounds of molasses—urea mixture
        (90% molasses—10% urea)

Steamed bonemeal and salt was fed free choice. Garst aimed to feed three percent of the steer's live weight daily in terms of the total formula. The cattle were weighed every two weeks and gained a pound-and-three-quarters a day. Their cost per pound of gain was less than one-half the average cost per pound of gain when cattle were fed a normal ration of corn, protein and hay. When sold, the steers were within a few cents of the top of the market.

As urea-feeding was developed during the next few years, Garst continued to be one of the active private experimenters with the new protein trigger. Things he learned helped other farmers find cheaper ways to produce good beef, and shook up college recommendations on the use of shelled corn for feeding cattle for market. He held field days at his farm to show farmers from Iowa and neighboring states how his corncob diet really worked in feeding cattle.

Garst's ideas on soils and fertility follow the same

Roswell Garst, right, converts mountains of corn cobs turned out by his hybrid seed company each year into a cattle feed that costs him half as much per pound of gain as normal feed.

Disking the seedbed with Aldrin and broadcasting with Atrazine keeps the corn rows practically weed and bug-free, without further work after planting, says Garst. Only 4-man-days time handled the job of getting in the 80 acres of corn.

unorthodox and provocative pattern. "If you are in a good farming area, forget about the old four-year rotations and plowed-down clover," says Garst. "Nitrogen is the key to all of our agricultural production. The way to get the quickest and most efficient use of the stuff is in the synthetic form."

To prove his theory, Garst tells how he paid for half the price of a farm from its produce the first year after buying it. He bought a farm, the Whaley place as it is known, in the rough country south of Coon Rapids, for $65 an acre. That was all it was worth, too—steep hills, worn-out, gullied, on the verge of abandonment. He piled 300 pounds of ammonia nitrate to the acre and put about 100 pounds of 13-39-0 to it at planting time, filled in the gullies with a bulldozer and in the wettest, worst spring Iowa had seen for a good many years, he planted corn on every inch a Caterpillar could traverse.

The Whaley place produced 65 bushels of corn to the acre the first year. Then the following year it again was given the heavy fertilizer treatment and more corn, and as Garst said, "That crop paid for the labor and fertilizer, so I could afford to put it in grass, give it a heavy nitrogen application and use it for what it's suited to, grazing cattle."

One of the verbal bombs that Garst has burst in ag college classrooms and at meetings of farm leaders is the firm conviction that a ton of lowly corncobs is worth more than a ton of clover hay. Here's the way he makes his point. "For easy figuring," says Garst, "let's use dozen units. Take a farmer who in addition to his corn operation has 12 cows and calves, 12 acres of pasture, 12 acres of hay. I see no use in putting up any hay. What he had better do is pasture the whole 24 acres with 18 head instead of his previous 12 head. Then he can grind corncobs and feed the ground cobs with a supplement about like we use or about like Purdue Cattle Supplement A, instead of using hay. (A 1000 lb. mix of Purdue Cattle Supplement A consists of 643.1 lb. soybean oil meal; 285.8 lb. molasses feed (45% molasses); 51.4 lb. bone meal; 17.2 lb. salt; 2.5 lb. vitamin A concentrate.) The advantages are many—

1. It is no easy job to make hay in humid climate;
2. He has six more calves for sale every fall;
3. It's lots easier to feed the cobs in the winter than hay;
4. The world needs meat.

"The 12 acres he would have used for hay would have yielded 24 tons. That's only the cobs from 4,000 bushels of corn. The haymow provides ample

242

"Our automation in feeding has gotten ahead of our field technique. We can feed a bushel of corn in seconds; now we must turn our attention to production. My goal: 'a bushel a minute.' We're coming close this year."

storage space for more than that amount of cobs and it's certainly easier for a farmer to grind 24 tons of cobs than it is to put up 24 tons of hay.

"Furthermore, Beeson of the Purdue Station reports that calves fed clover hay over the winter averaged only .75 lb. gain per day. If he figures hay at $25 per ton, the cost per pound of gain was 28c. If the ground cobs cost $5 per ton, and Purdue Cattle Supplement A $90 per ton, calves fed this ration put on 1.6 lbs. per day at a cost of 12½c per lb.

"In the face of these figures it is simply ridiculous to put up hay in the Corn Belt where cobs are available. The cobs are responsible for furnishing the roughage in such a feeding operation with a high protein supplement and are definitely more valuable than the hay."

In his search for making farming a big-production operation, Garst has used liquid fertilizers to avoid the handling problems of dry fertilizer and his present aim in corn production is "a bushel of corn a minute." He says, "Our automation in feeding has gotten ahead of our field technique. We can feed a bushel of corn in seconds; now we must turn our attention to production.

"This season, 1961, we will be making our first attempt at really low labor costs per acre of corn produced. We took a field where we cut silage last year and did not plow it. First we chiseled in approximately 120 lbs. of actual nitrogen in liquid form. Then we disked the field, applying liquid Aldrin on the front side of the disk. We always carry tanks on each side of the tractor for this purpose and it eliminates one trip through the field.

"Then we planted the field with an 8-row planter and as we harrowed the corn in, we broadcast Atrazine on the backside of the harrow. Actually, it took us four man days to get the corn crop in on 80 acres of land—one man day for each 20 acres—about a third of an hour per acre.

"The corn has not been cultivated but the Atrazine has kept it practically weed free and it looks like a very grand crop.

"We will cut it for silage again this year because of its convenient location for that purpose. However, if we harvested it with a four-row combine, I think we might well have raised a bushel of corn in one minute's time."

This is the Garst kind of big thinking in the cornfield. Like many another successful American farmer he has the right to feel that he should receive a good price for his corn and his meat. He's earned it by his thinking and his day-by-day management.

243

# Long Necks
## and Powerful Arms

There is no more cropland in use now in the United States than there was in 1920. But crop production per acre has risen so sharply with mechanization that the farmer whose production supported eight people at home and abroad in 1920 now feeds 23 singlehandedly.

Machinery is only one reason, although an important one. Fertilizer is another. And neither would be as effective as they are, without the improved varieties of crops and livestock which the geneticists have put at the farmer's disposal.

# The Constant Enemy

Weeds, pests, floods and wind cut down more of the farmer's crop each year than acreage allotments ever have. The farmer uses modern farming techniques, new chemicals and infinite patience to fight a constant enemy.

The seed is the beginning of the crop, but to germinate and put out vigorous growth, the seed and the young plant must escape or overcome hundreds of diseases and compete with dozens of weeds. Some of the diseases will be on the seed covering itself and some in the soil from which it must draw its nourishment. As with every living thing, the seed and the young plant depends for its survival on its inherited vigor and resistance to disease. The modern farmer bolsters this mysterious will to live with chemical protection.

His animals as well as his plants need help in fighting pests. The job is not easy. It is difficult to poison a pest which neither eats nor drinks. For example, the heel fly doesn't, for it has no mouth. In its grub stage it has a mouth and a voracious appetite, but at this point in its life cycle it spends its time inside the cattle which it infests. Known to farmers as the cattle grub, warble or wolf, it burrows beneath the hide, destroys meat tissues, and leaves the animal by cutting a neat hole which damages the leather. The cattle grub is only one of hundreds of pests the farmer fights.

# Plant pests

This Striped Blister Beetle has a beautiful paint job but he is bad news to truck farmers and gardeners.

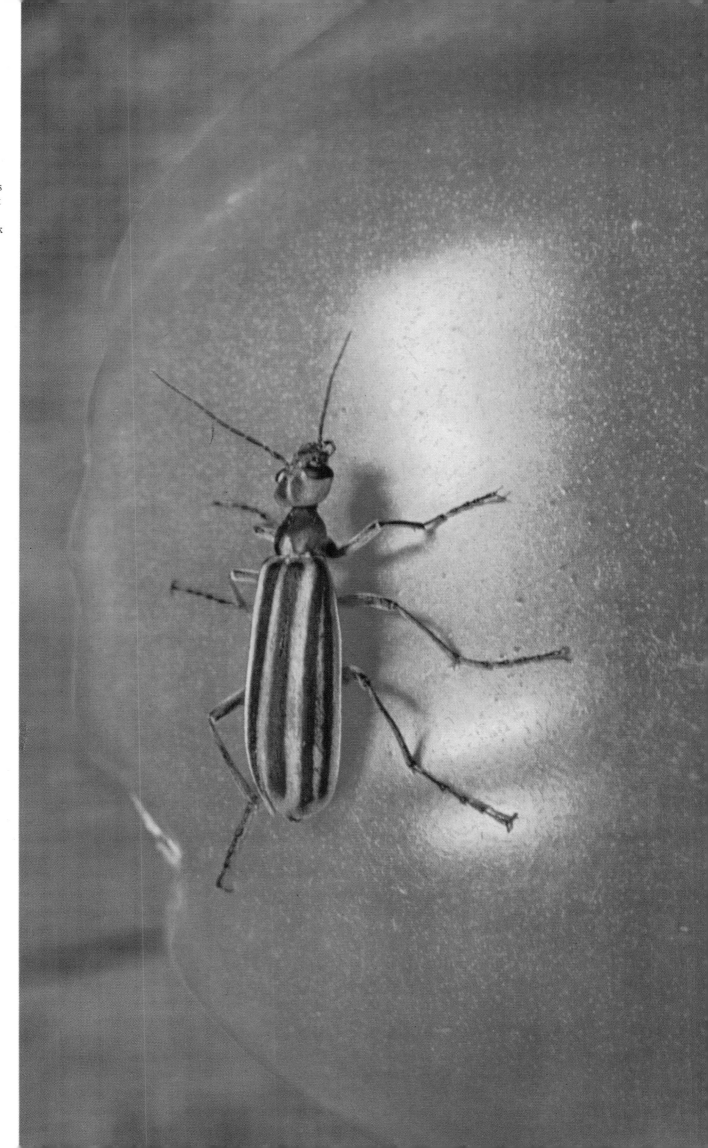

# Corn bugs

The enemy line-up against corn includes the wire worm, which eats the seed, the sprout, and the roots of corn. . . .

chinchbugs which migrate from small grain to corn on foot, and which may be stopped with a chemical barrier. . . .

newly-hatched corn-borers which can best be attacked with granular insecticides, and . . .

the fall army worm which migrates each year from the south as a moth.

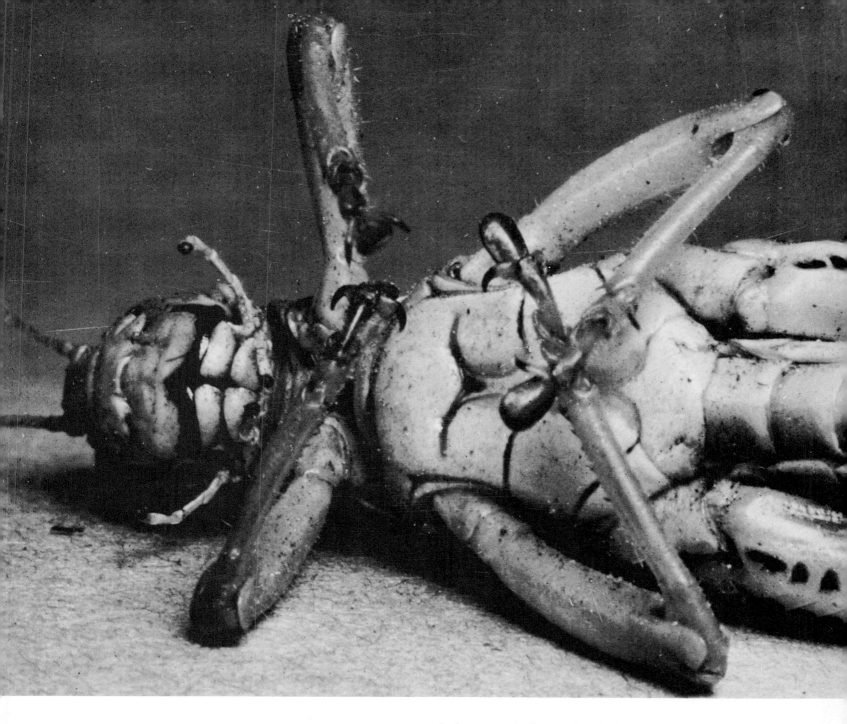

# Grasshoppers, locusts

## and crickets

Orthopterans is the word zoologists use to describe insects which have mouths for biting. Grasshoppers, locusts and crickets are the farmer's enemies on this battlefield. In the bleak year of 1848, the entire Mormon settlement in Utah faced starvation because hordes of crickets moved across the pioneer farms and gardens, leaving not so much as a blade of grass behind them. At the height of the devastation, after the Mormons had failed to stop the plague with flails, water-filled ditches and fire barriers, they were saved by the miracle of the seagulls. Huge flocks of gulls, thousands of the gray-and-white birds, flew in from the islands of Great Salt Lake and gorged themselves on the crickets until the avalanche of insects had been destroyed. Today, the miracle of modern chemistry has supplied us with weapons which would stop such an attack at the first sign of crop damage.

# Dust and wind

The forces of nature are gradually coming under the thumb of man. We have figured out ingenious ways of combatting frost; we have built structures to control floods; we have forced reluctant clouds to give up their rain, and we're learning how to stop lightning before it hits the earth.

One force which has us stumped is the wind. Across the Dust Belt, the danger of blowing top soil is still a very real threat. The 300-mile strip of farmland reaching from Canada to Mexico, east of the Rocky Mountains, has been tilled intensively and farmers in the Great Plains, with the bitter memories of the 30's, have their senses alerted to detect the first signs of a new major dust storm.

Science is helping by providing new ways to supplement the time-tested trash mulching, grass farming and windbreak methods of stopping soil erosion before it starts.

# Increasing Milk Production by Horn Elevation

THE history of horn elevating may be divided, roughly, into three periods. The earliest reference in historical writings comes in Holy Scripture where God commanded the lifting up of ceremonial horns, as a result of which Hemen (whose name is apt) sired 14 sons and three daughters. This period offers small information to the dairy farmer and technician, and is interesting only cursorially.

The second period extends from about 75 B. C. to the landing of the Pilgrims, which was in 1620 at Plymouth, Massachusetts. The third period brings us up to date, and includes the election of James K. Polk. It was not until 1939 that elevating horns of dairy cattle was considered a factor in dairy improvement. Research at Lisbon University establishes the affinity between milk production and horn elevation.

### Accidental Polling

Opportunity to investigate horn elevating came when a scrub Ayershire, in the barn of Telesphore Plourde, Peppermint Corner, Maine, knocked off her horns trying to get out of the barn. Mr. Plourde called on members of the University staff who cornered the cow in upper Oxford County and replaced the lost horns. Mr. Plourde observed and mentioned that the angle of adjustment was about $13\frac{1}{2}$ degrees in excess of the original angle, but aside from giving the heifer a slightly startled appearance the general aspect was not inferior to the former stance.

### Lactation Commences

This cow, whose name was Lulu, came in heat the following Monday, and was bred artificially to Rufus High Barclay's Petunia's Lad II. She threw triplet bull calves, and freshened with 21.6 to 21.7 pounds per milking, at 6-hour intervals. At the time the University staff did not find this noteworthy, but they became interested when Mr. Plourde stated that the heifer's mother had never given more than a quart of milk a

Opposite page, Edmund Trollop, young Harvard graduate and Acting Dean of Dairying at Lisbon University, stands before an illustrated case history of horn elevation.

day, was always bred with difficulty, and his wife had frequently complained that it took 37 gallons of her milk to make one small pat of inferior butter.

## Was Elevation a Factor?

This astonishing improvement, in a single generation, was immediately of interest, and students at the University made frequent research excursions to the Plourde dairy. Careful studies revealed that the new elevation of Lulu's horns was the only accountable factor in the increased milk production.

## Diet Studies

Lulu was given successively reductive nutriments, varying from complete concentrates to complete roughages, with intermediate admixtures of computed values, but her production figure remained constant. (See Table I)

### TABLE I

|  | Amount | Results |
|---|---|---|
| Mixture A | 2 quarts | Good |
| B | " | " |
| C | " | " |
| D | " | " |
| E | " | " |
| F | " | " |

Other factors, such as pasturage, water, milking time, and temperature, were likewise found to be nil. When horn elevation was deduced to be the causative factor, experiments were conducted to determine which angle of horn attachment would produce the greatest desired effect.

## Various Angles

Table II shows the remarkable increase in milk production over a seven-month period as the horns of Lulu were successively raised from their second position to that ultimately considered the maximum.

### Table II

| Angle of Lift | Pounds Produced |
|---|---|
| 32 degrees | 76 |
| 78 " | 128 |
| 82 " | 156 |
| 101 " | 167 |
| 127 " | 202 |
| 156 " | 313 |
| 180 " | 582 |

At the completion of the seventh elevation Lulu's horns were sticking straight up in the air, were a bright green in color, and Lulu was dead. It could be assumed that overproduction had sapped every vestige of vitality, and the conclusion was drawn that elevating the horns above 82 degrees was likely to produce an abnormal strain on the alveoli.

## Subject Renewed

In 1954 the study was revived. In that year a total of 130 cows in this area were given horn elevations, with a casualty rate of only 17%. Results tend to show that a corrected elevation of between 10 and 35 degrees, measured from a perpendicular to a line from the base of the left horn to the tip

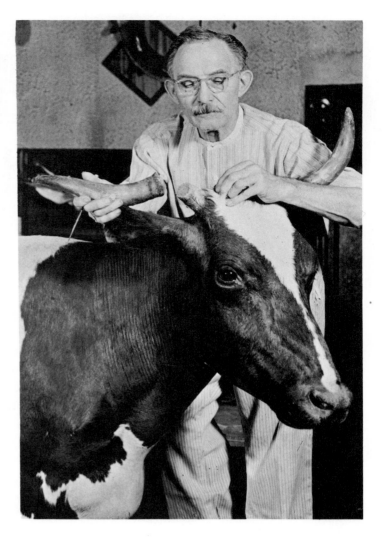

Dr. Adams Smedley at Maine's Lisbon University demonstrates the proper method of changing the angle of deviation of a Guernsey's right horn.

of the right horn, will double milk production within a period of three weeks. The right horn was chosen as the basis of operation, because rarely do both horns have an identical declination, and it was essential to unify the initiatory fundamentals.

## Casualty Rate Reduced

No cow was found to have the correct angle from birth, although two cows were all right in one horn. It was believed only coincidence that in these two cases the right horn was the one at a proper angle. The casualty rate of 17% was eliminated almost at the second interval of adjustment, as operators found the horn is more safely removed by giving it a sharp rap with a baseball bat.

## Interim Conclusions

Although observation tends to support the theory that all cows will produce more milk if their horns are set at the correct angle for the particular breed and the quantity of milk desired, experiments have not progressed far enough to establish that as an unalterable rule. Further research is probably needed. Since milk production has been the object of this study, no horn elevations were attempted on bulls.

# The Dance
## that lasted 100 years

Reactionaries in early America who protested against "the abomination of permitting a man who was neither your lover nor your husband to encircle your waist with his arms, and slightly press the contours of your waist," were powerless to discourage the pastime of dancing.

From colonial copies of English court dances emerged one dance which has held its popularity even into our own time. Today's square dance is a free-wheeling American version of the Quadrille, a modification of the French contredanse for four couples which was introduced in London in 1815. As the Quadrille moved west and south in this country, it merged with the dances pioneer settlers brought from the Spanish colonies and other countries. Dancers added a little bit here, changed a little there, developing the styles which are now traditional in various regions of America.

In recent years, city kids have discovered something that rural people already knew about the square dance. It's a lot easier to meet a pretty, new girl in the crowd!

# *Acknowledgments*

ARTICLES: *The Signs of Spring*, Samuel Gottscho. *A Bill for Horace's Bull*, Alfred S. Campbell. *Spring Weeds You Can Eat*, Grant Cannon. *The Good Shepherd*, Charles Koch. *The Good Life of the Gilfilens*, Chester Charles. *Green Mountain Sap*, Margaret Christowe. *Witch Way to Water*, B. T. Sandefur. *Dry Land Spongers*, Art Conrad. *The Innovator*, Charles Koch. *Feeling for Turtles*, Charles Webb. *Summer Romance*, Rosemary Bader. *The Old Swimming Hole*, Frederic Knoop. *The New Pioneers*, Ralph McGinnis. *Pickling Time*, Mary Catherine Lloyd. *Cooperation in Plum Valley*, George Laycock and Dorothy Douglas. *The Friendly Meal*, James D. Frye. *The Bad Year*, Louis Bromfield—Harper & Brothers. *She's Sort of an Antique*, Chester Charles. *The Standardbred*, Charles Koch. *Texas Cattle Man*, Grant Cannon. *Forest Pool*, Sigurd Olson—Alfred A. Knopf, Inc. *Home Made Bread*, Alden Stahr. *The Eye of the Farmer*, Charles Koch. *Jim, the Wonder Dog*, Ralph McGinnis. *The Dilemma of the Grain Farmer*, Charles Koch. *Judd McKnight*, Frank Farmer. *The Blind Farmer*, Grant Cannon. *The Farm's Wildlife*, Charles Callison. *New England Dairy Farmer*, Janice Turner and Grant Cannon. *Conversation with a Pig*, H. Gordon Green. *The Sisters*, Josephine Johnson. *How to Make Old Fashioned Country Ham*, Thomas P. Ziegler and Grant Cannon. *Yankee Farmer*, Haydn Pearson and John Gould. *Mistletoe*, Joann Bell Pierce. *Winter's Night Feast: Popcorn*, Deane E. Schneider. *Father's Right Hand Man*, Gladys Bryant Taylor. *Corn Dodgers and Hush Puppies*, Eleanor Cullen. *The Coyote Hunter*, Charles Koch. *Hawkeye Hatchetman*, Frederic Knoop. *Horn Elevation*, John Gould.

ILLUSTRATIONS: Jacket, F. Knoop.  End Papers, J. Munroe.  6, 7, G. Heilman.  8, S. Gottscho.  9, K. Ruohomaa, Black Star.  10, S. Gottscho.  12, 13, J. Munroe.  15, F. Knoop.  16, C. Harper.  17, F. Knoop.  18, 21, 24, 25, K. Pazovski.  27, 28, 29, 30, 31, 32, B. Goodman.  34, R. Pinney—H. Armstrong Roberts.  35, R. Pinney.  37, J. Titchen, Photo-library.  39, 40, R. Pinney.  43, F. Knoop.  45, A. Conrad.  46, A. Tritschler.  47. A. Conrad.  48, F. Knoop.  50, F. Knoop—J. Munroe.  53, 55, F. Knoop.  56, 57, B. Snyder.  59, B. O'Brien.  61, A. Bruehl.  63, Harold M. Lambert Studio.  64, 66, 67, 68, 69, 71, 72, R. Goodman.  74, F. Knoop.  76, K. Pazovski.  78, J. Munroe.  79, Soil Conservation Service.  81, J. Munroe.  83, 84, F. Knoop.  86, J. Munroe.  90, Knell, U.S.D.A.  93, F. Knoop.  95, H. Gehr.  97, 98, 99, J. Munroe.  100, 102, 103, F. Knoop.  104, 105, 106, J. Munroe.  107, U. S. Trotting Assn.  108, 109, J. Munroe.  110, 111, 112, F. Knoop.  113, Standard Oil.  114, 115, 116, 117, 118, 119, F. Knoop.  120, T. Lake.  123, F. Knoop.  124, C. LaTour.  126, 127, F. M. Demarest.  128, U.S.D.A.  129, 130, 131, 132, 133, R. Goodman.  135, B. Taylor.  136, C. Mitchell.  138, Mrs. S. Van Arsdale.  140, F. Knoop.  145, G. Heilman.  146, C. Koch.  148, J. Munroe.  149, Farmers' Union Grain Terminal Assn.  151, 154, 155, 156, 157, 159, 161, 162, 163, 164, 167, J. Munroe.  170, Soil Conservation Service.  171, A. Monner.  172, 173, Wisconsin Conservation Dept.  175, R. Austing and D. Koehler.  176, 178, 179, 180, 183, 184, J. Munroe.  185, R. McGinnis.  186, E. Pikar.  188, Y. Somerset.  191, W. Whitesell.  193, E. Peterson.  195, R. Riner, Jr.  196, 197, J. Clark.  198, J. Munroe.  199, Caterpillar Tractor Co.  200, R. Mathers.  202, 203, B. Cowherd.  205, U.S.D.A.  207, 208, K. Ruohomaa, Black Star.  210, J. Munroe.  213, K. Ruohomaa, Black Star.  214, W. Sanders, Black Star.  215. L. Williams.  221, J. Munroe.  222, B. O'Brien.  229, F. Knoop.  230, 232, K. Pazovski.  233, U.S.D.A.  235, K. Pazovski.  237, 239, F. Knoop.  241, 242, 243, 244, 245, F. Knoop.  247, J. H. Gerard.  248, S. Kyd.  249, Hercules Powder Co.  250, 251, U.S.D.A.  252, J. Munroe.  253, Museum of Science and Industry—Chicago.  254, Brown Brothers.  255, F. Knoop.

Editorial assistants, members of the staff of *The Farm Quarterly*; production James Rosenthal, Jack McCain; color lithography consultant, Murray Monse.